A|STATE

You will never forget The City.

But The City will forget you.

CREDITS

Original Concept: Malcolm Craig
Additional Concepts: Rab Robertson & John Wilson
Writing: Malcolm Craig
Additional Writing: Iain McAllister
Editing: Iain McAllister
Typesetting: Paul Bourne & Malcolm Craig
System Design: Malcolm Craig
Cover & Interior Art: Paul Bourne
Graphic Design: Paul Bourne
Proofreading: Rab Robertson
Additional System Revision & Advice: John Kahane, Iain McAllister & Matthew Seaborn
CGS Website Design: Paul Bourne & John Wilson
Business Management: John Wilson
Playtesting: Tam Connelly, Alex Duchart, Gareth Fortheringham, Baz Johnston, Chris Jones, Ally Leishman, Stuart McKelvie, Andy MacVicar, Brian Pickles & Fraser Thornton.

Thanks to: Matthew Barrowcliffe, Chris Baylis, Ferry Bazelmans, Brett Bernstein, Conpulsion, Simon Cox (cyberpunk.co.uk), Matt Drake, DrakCon, David Innes, Ed Handley, Berin Kinsman (unclebear.com), Guy McLimore, Jens Meyer, China Mieville, Jay Forster, Liam O'Connor (Black Lion Games, Edinburgh), Janet Pashley, Greg Porter, Simon Proctor, Ron van der Velden, James Wallis (for invaluable help and advice right at the very start), Mike (Asylum Books & Games, Aberdeen), Dylan (Impact Games, Liverpool), Angus Abranson, Gregor Hutton, Leanne Fulton, John & Irene Craig, Mary MacMillan, Jim Fallone, Conpulsion, DrakCon, Gaelcon, UberCon, WarpCon, BiMonSciFiCon, all the members of the Contested Ground Studios forum and mailing list, all the members of the Digital Publishers Group (digitalrpg.org) and all those people who've given us help, advice, encouragement, discouragement, criticism, abuse, wise words and general support: you know who you are and you know we're grateful.

Published by:
Contested Ground Studios
74 Mungalhead Road
Falkirk
Scotland
FK2 7JG
www.contestedground.co.uk
mail to: info@contestedground.co.uk

Disclaimer

a/state is a game for mature gamers. Remember, it's only a game. The views expressed in some parts of this book do not necessarily represent the view of the staff of Contested Ground Studios. This is a work of fiction and should be treated as such. Contested Ground Studios take no responsibility for physical or mental damage as a result of reading or using this book in other ways. In other words, if you hit your friend over the head with this, then it's not our fault. If anything in a/state disturbs or upsets you, then it's probably best that you stop reading now. If you choose to continue, then on your head be it. Although, as we said, it's only a game and should be treated as such. If you're a concerned parent who's reading this, aghast at what your child has been looking at, then maybe you should pay closer attention to what your child is purchasing, rather than blaming us for publishing what is, admittedly, a fairly darkly themed game.

Support your friendly local games shop!

contents

contents

Welcome to The City...

"The City is here to test us. It is part of His Great Plan. The Almighty, in His aspect as The Great Architect, has created this domain for us. Only the true believers will gain admittance to His Eternal City in the Heavens. Everyone else? They're all just damned to an eternity in the slums and wastes of The Great Demolisher. And it serves them right."

Father Jurich Karsten, Third Church of God The Architect

the preface

Welcome to The City. A sepiatone world lit by guttering gas lamps and the flickering filaments of electric bulbs. A closed world, isolated and alone. Stinking canals radiate out through The City, thick with effluent and the detritus of millions of lives. Dank alleys wind between corroding concrete towerblocks, wide boulevards swarm with peddlers, traders, sellers, buyers, thieves and victims. The City is full of dark places where the lights of knowledge, morality and justice fail to glow.

Welcome to The City. A world of contrasts and contradictions. The citizens live their lives in a tangle of technological obscurity. In crumbling brick tenements, they crowd round dim televisions, sedated by the media output. In the factories, workshops, mills and yards, they toil and strain with rusting, decaying machinery. Above them all, the macrocorps stand like gods, islands of glittering advancement in a sea of black oil, flaking iron and reeking gas.

Welcome to The City. A world of pain, fear, longing and hatred. Where the basest human emotions rise to the surface, where men will cripple each other for a dull shilling. Yet light, life, love and hope manage to raise their voices, occasionally heard above the clamour of darkness. Through all the evil and wreckage, some still manage to retain a sense of decency and honour.

Welcome to The City. A world of superstition, folk tales, wild religion and rampant rumour. The Shift and The Bombardment are apocalyptic legends from the far past, feeding the nightmares and fantasies of current generations. Some pray to God for salvation, others pray to a cold, empty universe. In hidden places, black rites are carried out, for reasons as varied and obscure as The City itself. Folk heroes and villains stalk the streets: Ticktock Man, The Leaper, Iron Lady, all contributing to the second city, the city carried on the tongues and in the minds of its citizens.

Welcome to The City. A world of strangers and beings who do not belong. The Shifted, strange entities, whispered about in pubs and taverns, lest the very mention of their name summon them from the dark. The Ubel, twitching and creaking through the backstreets in their bloodstained rags, chittering incomprehensibly. Lugner, whispering maddening dreams in the night. Drache, as insubstantial as mist, clouds of unreason. Hager, assassins and kidnappers, looming figures cast in black cloth and pale flesh. The Simils, pitied and reviled in equal measure, clanking golems of iron, brass and stone.

Welcome to The City.
You will never forget The City.
But The City will forget you.

Welcome to a/state, the role-playing game of gothic horror SF. Within these pages, you'll find masses of detailed information on The City, the people who inhabit it, the organisations who attempt to control it and the technology they use. A simple but detailed game system allows you to generate interesting characters for hundreds of hours of fascinating gaming in The City.

a/state is divided into eight chapters, as follows:

The Preface
The bit you're reading right now.

The Precepts
An introduction to The City, its past, its present and possible future. You'll find essays, lectures and stories giving information on many aspects of city life, from the stinking canals to sports and entertainment.

The Place
33 areas of The City described in detail, with highlighted locations and important local personalities.

The Power
Who controls life in The City? Macrocorporations, religions, criminal syndicates and many others all try to influence the lives of the citizens. From the seeming altruism of the Three Canals Metropolitan Area Authority to the fractured infighting of the Mortal God Church, everyone fights their own corner and scrabbles for the reigns of power.

The Procedure
The basic rules system for play in the The City. Covering task resolution, man to man combat and vehicle combat.

The Players
The people who make the game really live. Presented here are rules for creating unique characters for play in a/state.

The Product
From clunky, primitive sparklock pistols to tiny nanoscale dingins, all the variety of technology available is featured here.

The Prescription
A brutal murder in Folly Hills leads the players into a web of intrigue, double dealing and deceit. An introductory a/state adventure for any number of players.

An education

Heckle was strung out by the ravagers during the assault on the Virus House. It was never expected that he survive, least of all with some fragment of personality intact. Yet, survive he did. Not as anyone would remember him. None who witnessed the concrete scream of the Virus House would ever really be the same. The shudderlines and eyehacks saw to that, reducing Brigade troopers to dust and drooling husks. Heckle scraped a living in Dreamingspires, rooting amongst the rubbish left by a society of scavengers. The Risers and Tunnel Scurts left him well alone, aware on an almost primal level that there was something wrong with him.

•

"What a massively serendipitous circumstance, eh?"
"Granted, yes. But there still remains the essential question of how to retrieve the information."
The first speaker turned towards the second, fixing her with a stare of peculiar quality. His face was rough and chalky, as if hewn from some crumbling sedimentary stone. The lighting in the room did nothing to improve his disquieting appearance. All uplighters and harsh bulbs, throwing their luminance towards the ceiling in angry cones. The woman backed away and dropped herself onto a low green couch with an audible thud, grimacing as she hit the unyielding surface.
"Ah, yes. Should have warned you, the frame is not terribly well padded. Sorry about that."
"I'm sure I'll survive. Bruised buttocks are not the worst I'll have suffered." She glanced about the room, it's bare concrete walls decorated with warble-prints and artfully applied layers of rust. One of the prints chose that moment to start humming up and down the scale, a low intensity ululation that set her teeth on edge within seconds.
"Anyway, I'm also pretty certain that you didn't call me here to exchange pleasantries, hmmm?"
"True, true. You were, shall we say, involved with Heckle, yes?" A quizzical eyebrow arched up across the white chalk cliff of a forehead.
"Involved? You might say that. Possibly."
"But you were his psychologist after the Virus House?"
"As well you know, Scorn. As well you know. Why go through this pretence, what do you want? Just spit it out, man."
"Really, Madame, there's no need to adopt such a hectoring tone. You forget yourself. Come on, you're the only one who ever broke through to Heckle, got anything out of him. You managed..."

"I managed to get ten words out of him. Words that have been pored over. It was nonsense. Heckle was totally insane. More to the point, it was your fault that he was let go. Bloody stupid move if you ask me."
"But we're not asking you for your opinion, Miss Volkersam, we are most certainly not asking for your opinion."
The seated woman stiffened her shoulders and made to rise.
"Now, now, dear lady. Don't take offence, we'd just like you to speak to Heckle again. Quietly."
"So, as discussed, you know where he is. He won't want to talk. Would you, after what he went through? I mean, God, who knows?"
The chalk faced man strolled over to the window which took up the entire north wall of the room. Through the smog and haze, The City stretched on, seemingly limitless. The rings and lines of the canals glittered with the lights of small craft. Brick smokestacks exhaled vertical rivers of brown particulates, the swollen disks of aerostats bumbled through the thickening gloom.
"There." The man pointed, indicated somewhere far removed from their current position. "Out there. Dreamingspires."
"You. Have. Got. To. Be. Fucking. Joking. Really? Dreamingspires? Are you quite, quite mad? Absolutely no way."
"Yes, Dreamingspires. Don't worry, you'll have protection."
"Protection?" the word screeched from her mouth as if propelled by a blast of compressed air "I wouldn't go in there with the bloody Brigade. God, man! They tear you apart. You remember that incident with that flowghost, Murayam or whatever he was called. Hirplakker lost gun platforms in there. Bloody gun platforms!"
"Calm down, Miss Volkersam! There is no need to get hysterical. We've managed to obtain top class assistance for you. Top class." His voice petered out slightly with the last statement. "I'd like you to meet Miss Card, she comes highly recommended by our friends in, shall we say, lower society."

•

A tall figure entered into the room, quietly, cautiously. A woman, shaven headed and wide eyed, walking warily, as if expecting an inquisition at any moment. She took up position behind the couch, her faded black culottes rippling gently and her heavy, ancient, threadbare frock coat striking an incongruous chord, giving the appearance of a somewhat shabby and down at heel assassin.
"Miss Volkersam, I'd like you to meet Miss Card. She'll be your companion when visiting Mr Heckle." The seated woman rose and turned towards the newcomer, who raised a faint, questioning eyebrow.
"Miss Card, nice to meet you."
"Probably not, I'd imagine. But you can keep your illusions if it makes you feel any better." A sharp cough sounded from

the window area.

"Ladies, you're both professionals, let's keep things civil here."

"Civil? CIVIL? Scorn, I really think this is pushing it. You appear to have hired some form of streetscum in one of your twisted games and...."

"I really don't like being called scum, if it's all the same to you. Just 'cos I come from Mire End, don't give you the right to have a go." Something dropped into her hand from the sleeve of her shabby coat; a long grey object which glittered faintly. Volkersam spun to face Scorn.

"You've taken on a bloody ghostfighter, haven't you? Fuck, Scorn, you really better know what you're up to."

"Miss Card comes highly recommended by some friends of mine. Honestly, appearances can be deceptive. Miss Card is a highly skilled individual, but I'd urge you not to find out in a hurry. I'd really prefer if this project didn't start out on a mutually antagonistic basis. For a start, you're going to have to travel to Dreamingspires on your own, I'm afraid we can't provide transport at this time. Not after previous incidents, anyway."

●

The canal thronged. Alive with the hum of commerce. An artery choked by the very things which kept it alive. The city slowly died because of its very existence. On a squalid rooftop, Volkersam and Card paid tuppence to ride a fast zipline across the canal to a rude landing stage. The journey from Luminosity Tower had been made in silence and an air of mutual distrust. Water taxis clustered around, swaying at the end of their tethers, the owners shouting at the end of theirs. Huge lead acid batteries spat and crackled as water slopped over their terminals. Combustion engines, reeking of the fish oil they burnt barked and stuttered. The canalside heaved with people.

●

"Look, Miss Volkersam, I know you don't trust me. I know you don't like what I am. I know..."

"Does this monologue have a point, or do you just like the sound of your own voice?"

"I'm just trying to establish..."

"Don't. Don't try to establish anything. I'm not interested in having a relationship with your class or kind." The remark was accompanied with a hard stare. A stare which was matched by numerous bystanders who overheard these loud and uncautious remarks. A long arm extended in a whiplash movement, catching Volkersam just below the ribcage, doubling her over, rich food spewing onto the greasy flagstones. The crowd laughed, jeered, gestured. Taxi pilots hurled sug-

gestions like missiles, invective fell like rain. Taken by her collar, Volkersam was dragged into an alley, buildings on either side leaned towards each other in the manner of conspirators plotting dark schemes, iron staircases dripped orange water into spreading puddles of rust.

"Holy.....shit...."

"Look you, I just saved your neck there. You think that was hard, you talk like that again in a crowd and I'll leave you to them. They can smell you, from up there, clean, well fed, pampered. You talk like that, you get nailed and sold to a deathdealer. Down here, you're just another resource, you're food."

"Scum, thieves..." a hacking cough and dribbles of vomit concluded the remarks.

"Nah. Down here, your kind are the thieves. You lot hold on to the good stuff, resources. Dribble it out like a soup kitchen, feeding us scraps. You use these people, these are people who slave in your factories, without them you're nothing. Show some respect and keep your fucking mouth shut. My contract says keep you alive, doesn't say anything about not hurting you bad to keep you from getting yourself killed, see?" Card held a flat, grey, long knife in front of Volkersams face. Blunt ended and broad, its surface glittered gently in the wan light. As the blade tapered down to its edge, a trick of the light made it seem as if you could almost see through it.

"See this? It's a llive, killed five people to get the money for this. From your kind! Not saying they didn't deserve it, probably did, who knows. Took lots of money to get this, 'cos you people keep things back. Keep the people down."

"It's alive?"

"No, it's a llive. El el eye vee ee."

"Oh."

"Right. Now let's go."

●

Shift change was always busy on the railways. Transit Militia in shaggy grey greatcoats patrolled the platforms and staircases, checking tickets, swinging their billy clubs, waiting for an opportunity to start something, waiting for someone to run. Workers in darned, sweat-stained clothes jostled one another as the train approached, a single yellow eye coming down the tracks. Fat blue sparks illuminated the railway line, jolting down from the overhead lines. As a single consciousness, the waiting passengers eased back, wary of the iron creature coming to rest in the station. Drizzle turned to steam as it hit metal plates hot from the exertions of the giant motor. Militiamen swung their clubs, cracked heads as the crowd surged forward for the doors. Passengers trying to leave the carriages were pushed back by the horde and chaos ensued until the Militia cleared space, clubbing and yelling.

Clutching Volkersam by the hand and strategically prodding, poking and punching, Card cleared a lane to the carriage door. The interior was already crammed with unwashed bodies, voices were being raised and those with seats eyed with unconcealed disdain. The two women found themselves wedged into a corner, hemmed in by a scrawny figure coated in brick dust and a fat woman clutching a package of reeking fish.

Vokersam shuddered, "This is bloody awful!"

"Keep your voice down, you daft bint! You determined to get us killed?"

"No, but..."

"Then shut it. And for your own sake, get your ticket ready. The Militia don't take kindly to fare dodgers."

"The what?"

"Transit Militia. Keep control on the railways. Dodge the fare, you get a beating. You run, you get shot. They hate fare dodgers, they do."

"Isn't that a bit brutal?"

"Don't make me laugh, you think your lot would do any less? I've seen how you guys handle industrial disputes, don't come it."

With a jolt which caused more than a few people to fall to the floor, the train lurched off once more. Inside the swaying, bouncing carriages, the atmosphere was stifling, thick with a cocktail of smells; oil, sweat, fish and hot iron. Young men with greased hair and shabby frock coats eyed up a gaggle of young girls on their way home from the factories. Their eyes lit upon Card and Volkersam, resting for a moment before catching Card's unblinking stare and hurriedly looking away. Nervous laughs. A Militiaman rattled the connecting door from the next carriage and shoved his way in, demanding tickets. With an audible groan, the passengers started to produced the tokens from their pockets, bags and bundles, handing them to the officer without meeting his eyes. The pair of sparklocks on his belt swayed and jangled against a greasy bunch of keys as he pushed his way through the heaving mass.

•

The window squeaked as Volkersam cleared away the moisture and dirt with the edge of her sleeve. The train rattled along its brick arches, the tenements on either side occasionally giving way to offer a view of the wider city. Lights blinked under the evening haze, soot, rain and smoke mingling noxiously. The overhead speaking tube running through the carriage barked angrily "14th and Hoken. 14th and Hoken, all change, all change." The train ground into the station, hemmed in on one side by three decrepit, sagging concrete towerblocks and on the other side by a rubbish filled capillary canal.

"Where are we now?"

"Southern tip of the Three Canals Metropolitan Area, the TCMA, got to travel north-west to get to Dreamingspires. Best to get a canal taxi. Afford it?"

"Yes, I have funds. Who are those guys over there?"

"Provosts, local police force. Rough bunch, corrupt as hell."

The passengers spilled out of the station down a broad flight of brick stairs, mingling with the crowds already on the street. The crumbling towerblocks loomed above, black with soot, crusted with lichen and moss, filthy with age. A bass howl came from overhead and a yellow shape streaked by, skimming the roofs, causing pedestrians to duck and run. Volkersam glanced at the rapidly retreating shape "Mikefighter. NYG, I'd say."

"Say again?"

"Nakamura-Yebisu Group, one of their Weapons Division mikefighters."

"Oh, know a lot about that kind of thing do you?"

"A bit, worked with a lot of military types, you pick up a thing or two here and there."

"Ah."

•

The pair blended in with the crowd, heading back down the trainlines in the direction of Ring Canal 1. Alleys sprouted off from the main boulevard like so many veins in a corpse. Dark figures lurked in some, others contained small groups conducting clandestine business deals, others housed whole families, crouching under tattered tarpaulins. Down the alleys were visible the brick arches of the railway line, shops, dwellings and huddling places visible beneath their curved roofs. Rickshaw pullers barged through the crowds, tooting their horns and yelling at obstructive pedestrians. Swearing followed their progress, their passengers found themselves coated in spittle, targets of the masses envious of someone able to afford not to walk. Through it all, the Provosts strode, their dark blue coats billowing out behind them, peaked caps soaked with the dirty rain. Citizens avoided their eyes, darting only furtive looks at those who were nominally their protectors. They stopped to hassle a Collectivist who was distributing pamphlets, haranguing a small crowd which had gathered about the upturned box on which he stood. The lead Provost kicked the box out from under him and stamped on his face.

"Fuck off out of here trash. Get back to the Republic where you belong!"

The Collectivist attempted to stand but was booted back to the ground by another Provost. The crowd followed their lead, a dull roar emerging from their throats as they kicked and punched the poor unfortunate.

"Does that kind of thing happen round here a lot?"

"Kind of, most people don't like the Collectivists. They run the Red Canal Collectivist Republic, just across the canal from the TCMA. Have some strange notions about stuff, TCMA don't like them as a rule."

"I see."

"No, you probably don't. The RCCR is strong, lots of military gear. But the TCMA is better off, generally."

"So why don't they like them?"

"Jealousy? Envy? People always think the buildings on the other side of the canal are better kept, that kind of thing. Mind you, they didn't do themselves any favours with the Cox Lane Incident a few years ago."

"Ah, was it one of those kind of incidents?"

"Depends what you mean. Someone got their info all fouled up and sent a squadron of warcrawls into Cox Lane on the TCMA side of the Red Canal. The things practically demolished the place, killed lots of folk, kids included. People round here have never really forgiven them. Can't say as I blame them, all in all."

"I always thought the RCCR and the TCMA were just silly little administrations controlling a few burghs here and there?"

"Yeah, that's what a lot of you folk think. That's what you're afraid of, they're more powerful than most give 'em credit for. It was your kind that kick-started the RCCR in the first place, giving 'em weapons, warcrawls and stuff. Now they're self-sufficient and you boys don't like it one little bit."

"Uh huh. Right."

•

Ahead, scores of canal taxis, barges and boats clamoured for business. Oars smacked into flesh, engines revved and coughed, fights broke out as a patron sat helplessly, wishing only to be on his way. A group of Provosts lounged by a tea stall, puffing on their slim, blown glass nebelweed pipes and gulping down hot mugs of thick, black spiced tea. Overhead, cablecars stuttered along their rusted lines, swaying to and fro in the wind. A dandified young man, clad in a threadbare green suit and a rather incongruous red top hat approached Card and Volkersam.

"Good day to you ladies, perchance are you looking for transport hereabouts?"

Card faced him and flexed her hands, shaking her sleeves drying her palms on her lapels.

"So what'f we are? No biz of yours."

"Oh, sorry. I was just concerned that two lovely ladies such as yourself may be in need of guidance in these rough parts."

"Well, yes, we'd like to go to Dre..." There was a sharp crack and one of Card's booted feet caught Volkersam square on the shin, eliciting a sharp, but mercifully brief, scream.

"We're going up the Red, know any one that can take us there?"

"Why certainly. I myself have the finest and fastest skiff in these parts. I'd be more than happy to transport you for a small consideration."

"We're going a long way. May need you for a long spell."

"If you have the appropriate monies, dear lady, then I am at your disposal"

Volkersam glared up from rubbing her shin, her eyes burning through her rain tangled hair.

•

The tiered ochre banks of the Red Canal whipped past, giant steps created by quarrying of the carefully constructed walls to provide stone for building. On the left lay the Red Canal Collectivist Republic, on the right the Three Canals Metropolitan Area, glaring at each other in mutual suspicion. The occasional RCCR warcrawl could be seen on the banks, its guns not quite trained on the buildings across the water. Blue and grey flags fluttered wetly from the stubby masts fixed to the warcrawl's turret. Heavily laden iron barges moved sluggishly up and down the canal, their cargoes hidden from sight under tarpaulins. The valuable ones were easy to spot: escorted by gunskiffs, armed troopers standing watch in the decks. The only bright spots along this section of the canal were the huge murals painted onto the canalside buildings by the RCCR: stern, stylised faces stared out relentlessly, cartoon warcrawls crushed enemies beneath their tracks, proud komrades strove to create their collectivist utopia. All designed to wind up the TCMA folk and maybe convince a few to cross the canal and join their ranks.

•

Up the canal lay Dreamingspires, refuge for the dispossessed, the impoverished, the insane. Some said the Fulgurators Guild had built Dreamingspires hundreds of years ago as a model burgh, a shining example to the rest of The City. Then money, or will or enthusiasm ran out. Now the half-completed towerblocks stood as mute reminders of the pride and folly of the Guild, their concrete worn and pitted with time. Fungal encrustations scarred the surfaces and burrowed into the walls. As Dreamingspires drew closer, they could see the towers rising out of the mist, apparently caught in some gigantic web. These were the cables, ropes and ziplines that the inhabitants slung between their decaying homes. A smell began to drift down on the wind.

•

Drawing a rag over his face, the taxi driver hunkered down over his motor and remained silent. The skiff crawled towards the bank, tying up at a partially submerged jetty just down from the outflow of a stinking, diseased stream. Volkersam gagged. Card stood and surveyed the scene.

"That's the Gross Burn. Probably don't want to go near that if I were you. Pretty nasty. You finished?"

Volkersam stood and wiped spew from her mouth, leaving silvery trails on the sleeve of her coat. The taxi driver looked distinctly unamused by the entire proceedings.

"You, wait for us here."

"You must be kidding lady, it's not worth my life to stay here."

"Look, just hang about off the bank then, idiot. We'll shout for you when we need you. There's good money in this for you.""Fair nuff."

Card turned to Volkersam who was by now wobbling along the sunken jetty, slimy water slapping at her boots.

"Hey! Wait a sec!"

"What? I thought we needed to push on?"

"Er...let me go first, probably wisest. And don't insult anyone, don't look at anyone, don't pick anything up, don't do anything at all."

"What, are you afraid I might upset someone?"

"You really still don't get it, do you? It's not a matter of upsetting someone, it's that you don't belong here. You're kind just don't understand that this is about as low as you can get. What do they have to lose by killing you and taking your stuff? Nothing. They can only gain. Now wait for me."

●

For Volkersam, Dreamingspires was a place of unimaginable horror. Nothing in her life had prepared her for this. People scrabbled in the dirt, questing for food, bits of metal, anything usable, scrawny dogs slunk about, drinking from the varicoloured pools on the ground. Everyone was dressed, at best, in rags. Deformed or mutilated children were everywhere, some missing limbs, eyes, digits or suffering from some more subtle deformity. The adults were little better, all scarred, wasted and riddled with disease. They stared with blank eyes at the two women as they marched between the towering buildings. Up close, the blocks looked as if they would topple over at any moment. Rusty ribs of iron jutted out at odd angles, massive fragments of concrete lay scattered at their bases. It was astounding that people chose to live among such destruction and decay. Truly astounding.

●

They found Heckle. Eventually. After many threats, bribes and pained negotiations, they were directed to the basement of one of the most decrepit and wasted towers. The darkness was lit by faint shafts of light, the floor more like a series of holes joined together by thin pieces of concrete than an actual floor. Moans came from around the walls, from huddled figures. The smell was truly sickening. Corrupting flesh and putrefying human waste. In a far corner, crouched under a filthy tarpaulin, was Heckle. He lay on a pallet, staring up at the tarpaulin, his emaciated frame clad only in a thin loincloth. In the cold atmosphere of the basement, they could see his skin puckered and tightened as his body sought to retain some heat. Once a tall, proud soldier. One of the elite, a leader of men. Heckle had been loved by those under his command and respected by those above him. Hence, he was chosen to assault the Virus House. His men would have followed him into the arms of The Shifted, had he asked. They would have followed him to annihilation at the city limits, had he only said. Now, he lay in his own filth, amongst the wreckage of The City. Volkersam squatted down and spoke softly.

"Major? Major Heckle? It's me, Adina. You remember me, don't you?" The wasted head rotated round and the blank eyes fixed on Volkersam. No flicker of intelligence or personality showed in those eyes, nothing at all.

"Major Heckle, we need to ask you a few things, important things. I've come here to bring you back."

The mouth opened to reveal the jagged stumps of rotten teeth and the empty space where his tongue should have been. Card took a momentary step back and Volkersam rocked on her heels.

"Heckle, we can fix you, sort you out. Everything will be better again." Was that a hint of a smile on the ravaged face? He looked towards Card. For a split second there was a flash in those eyes. A signal from one fighter to another, a common understanding between those who face the horrors of combat. Then nothing. Card nodded and drew her Ilive, stepping towards the prone figure. Volkersam whirled round, standing as she turned.

"NO! Card! You can't, we must keep him alive!"

The knife silently moved through an arc, ending the argument.

●

The taxi puttered back down the Red Canal, two figures sitting in the stern, one being propped up by the other. The driver glanced back and fiddled with his red top hat.

"Where to, lady?"

Card glanced up and lowered her eyebrows.

"Mire End. Take us to Mire End. For now."

"That's a long way, lady. Cost you."

"Don't worry, I can pay."

She turned back to the emaciated figure clad in a woman's coat. The figure stared blankly at the surface of the canal as it swished by. Card tightened her arm around the figure, drawing it close like a child.

"You're safe now. They can't get you. We'll keep you safe."

Heckle turned and looked into her eyes. He smiled.

"I tell you one thing, there's something not right about this place. I've seen things, done things and turned my back on things that, well, I forget. But, there's something deep, something really, really wrong with The City. I don't care for all these academics and speculators who study The Shifted and mutter on endlessly about lost science. There's something out there that we're not getting told. Someone is hiding something, something really big. Why do we all accept that we can't leave this place? Because we're told we can't. Who tells us? Rumour, folklore, stories. Old wives tales. Something's happening, something bad."

Nina Locke, Stringer, Sideband Media.

the precepts

tales of the city

Centuries of industry and human activity have created a pall that hangs over The City. Some pilots say they have seen the stars. Eight giant mercantile structures dominate The City. Yet in many ways, they fail abjectly in their goals. So numerous are the inhabitants, so fractured the layout of this giant sprawl, that domination is impossible. Yet they fight, and scheme and plot and affect the lives of millions. The citizens struggle to get by. Fear and desperation are the defining attributes of society. Some sell their souls to the corporate monoliths, others get by on their own, and others seek solace in the blissful ignorance of religion, whilst the unfortunate are driven beyond the edge of insanity.

The unremittingly heavy nature of The City crushes even the most hardened soul. The oppressive presence of the millions of gargoyles, spires, arches, buttresses and walls would drain the life out of the most optimistic of people. Stone, brick and concrete are the bones of The City. The Canals are the blood. The corrupted, unfathomably complex network which makes up the Dataflow the nervous system. Despair, madness and suicide are commonplace, just normal facets of life in the crushing urban maze. A good night's sleep is a luxury enjoyed by only the rich or the dead. The Sound is everywhere, the constant hum of traffic, of industry and of all human activity. Silence must be bought, and then only at the highest of prices.

The variety of technology is remarkable. Some live in claustrophobic brick-built tenements, lit by gas piped in from ancient landfills, flickering blue flames in the dark. Others repose in utter luxury atop a granite spire, served by armies of semi-aware drones or fully aware slaves. The greatest division of technology can be seen in that defining icon of The City: the gun. Backstreet gangers, guffers and underworlders kill each other with oily cartridge pistols and smoking sparklocks while the macrocorporate security shoot back with magnetic repeaters. Some men's wealth can be judged by how hitech a firearm they carry. A sad and inescapable fact.

Nearly one thousand years ago, as far as anyone can tell, two legends came in to being. Why and how these cataclysmic events happened remains unknown. But learned men are sure they happened, and since then things have been different in The City. Philosophers, scientists and poets argue that The City once had a name. In the present it is simply called The City, for there is nowhere else other than the blasted Outlands.

One event came to be known as The Shift, rumoured to be a change so great that the very fabric of The City was transformed forever. Places and people were altered, new beings sprang, fully formed, into existence. Then, so the tellers of tales would have it, The City was subjected to a rain of fire: The Bombardment. Infernos fell from the sky and laid waste to whole tracts of land. More important than the destruction of the physical was the destruction of knowledge that The Bombardment caused. Datacores were wiped, libraries reduced to ashes and the memories of the survivors scarred. Few remnants of life before The Shift and The Bombardment remain. A few structures of vast size and strength remain to remind the inhabitants of the past. For centuries people have lived in limbo, the only history that of the past hundred decades. The people also discovered that invisible forces prevented them from leaving their wasted home. Survivors trying to reach the Outlands disappeared in a storm of vapour and a titanic thunderclap. To the present day, no one leaves The City.

Folklore has it that the Outlands were once fertile and green, now they are a blasted land of desert, rock and desiccated forests. The City itself is a place of dark alleys, ponderous architecture and stinking canals. In the centuries following The Shift and The Bombardment, the survivors sought to band together and make some sort of life for themselves. Not only did they have to deal with the destruction of their technology; they had to deal with the creatures which became known as The Shifted: beings which seemed to have come from nowhere. It appears these entities are just as angry and confused by The Shift as the human inhabitants of The City. In the thousand years since The Shift, something of an equilibrium has been reached. The Shifted and humans go about their affairs, mostly co-existing in a rough semblance of order. Some do not. Some on both sides seek to inflict pain on the rest of the population. Alliances between humankind and The Shifted are made and broken every day. Humans stumble on areas affected by The Shift and descend into abject madness.

The struggles of the first century gave rise to organisations which still exist today. The macrocorps all grew from the ashes, each with their own unique story of war, decimation and survival. Over the coming centuries, The City and its inhabitants would reach a twisted equilibrium with their situation. Society grew and expanded, the population stuttered, fell and then grew again. Sciences and technologies were rediscovered, yet even today, many live in poverty and grindingly primitive conditions. The rediscovered technologies were harnessed by those who had the power and resources to utilise them. The macrocorps evolved into bastions of knowledge, hoarding their precious discoveries, only to find them ripped away by unceasing war and the more subtle calamities of espionage and treachery.

Now, in the present day, The City is a study in contrasts. The majority of the population live in tenements and towers built of brick, stone and concrete. Their dwellings are lit by gas piped in from huge rubbish heaps or by flickering electric lamps, their clothes made from crude fibres and their property that of a society barely reaching the industrial age. In the domains of the macrocorps, things are very different. The corporate citizens have access to the finest food, to unlimited power, to shining vehicles and well made clothes. The soldiers who guard them ward off the unruly, clamouring mobs.

In the slums of Mire End, Dreamingspires and Fogwarren, life is a daily toil, earning enough to buy some food as best you can. The middle classes fear the slums, seeing them encroach upon their own moderately comfortable lives. In the corporate bastions of Luminosity Tower, Konkret and The Forbidden City, the macrocorporates look down upon the teeming millions: their workforce and their potential downfall.

Through the backstreets and alleys, The Shifted Ubel stalk, ripping and tearing those who come too close, leaving only a cooling corpse as an echo of their passing. Simils made of iron and brass, surmounted with a human head, clank their way through the streets or lay down their existences in the hell of the Contested Grounds. Lugner spread rumour, fear and suspicion through their whispers and fleeting dreams.

Some seek to stand up to the despair and hopelessness. Lostfinders investigate the miserable dealings of the common populace for little or no reward while Stringers piece together fragments of information to feed into the hungry newswires and memory cores of the Dataflow. The Provosts of the Three Canals Metropolitan Area Authority (TCMAA) try to enforce some form of law and order in their chaotic collection of burghs, holding on to the belief that theirs is the one place in The City where life is that little bit better. Others believe that the unknown forces which prevent anyone leaving this place are corroding, that soon they will be able to leave this place for a better life above the smog.

Perhaps the clouds will one-day part, and then, the people of The City will once again have that rarest and most precious of commodities: hope.

the shortest distance: transport and travel

Getting around The City is a problem that can tax even the most cunning, intelligent and streetwise of citizens. The massive complexity and interconnectivity of The City makes navigation an extremely difficult proposition. That having been said, there are three main ways which allow you to get about: the canals, the railways and the streets.

lifeblood: the canals

The floating wharves and loitering skiffs rocked violently as the ekranoplan rushed by in a howl of props and a wall of spray. Traders were pitched overboard and stock sank into the impenetrable depths.
"Bastard!" screamed Innes. "Utter, utter, utter bastard!"
"I wouldn't worry, pal. Someone'll get the gadgie." uttered a dripping, brown figure standing unsteadily on a small plastic skiff.
"Fuck that, I've jist lost all me stock."
"Ach, never mind, you'll get more."
"Get more? Fuck you, ya dick. It took me weeks of raking about underground to get that lot. Good scrap it was, too. Don't you blether to me about getting more."
"Steady, man. Didn't mean to cause any offence. Just commenting, like."
"Oh, jist piss off, OK."
The dripping figure scrunched his fists up in his pockets and made to start the engine of his skiff. He turned.
"Hey, pal!"
Innes looked up from what remained of his stock, ready to tell that annoying idiot exactly where to go.
"What the fu..." He found himself looking down the barrel of a massive sparklock.
"Stitch this, ye miserable sod."

The roar of the gun was lost as another ekranoplan roared past, rocking the boats.

If the Dataflow is the nervous system of The City, then the canals are its lifeblood. From the majesty of the Grand Canal to the stinking Capillary Streams, the canals provide transport, food, water and even entertainment. Dominating the canal network are the eight major Lateral Canals. The Laterals are connected by the Concentrics, rings of water spreading out from the centre of the city. At the very heart of the system is Basin, a deep, dark pool of water a thousand yards across. This perfect black circle is home to no drifters, no markets float on its surface. Rumour and superstition abound about Basin. Some say that monsters inhabit the depths, other state with authority that it is a bottomless pit. Whatever the real story, Basin is another one of the mysteries of The City, a mystery no one is in a hurry to investigate.

the grand canal

Largest and most impressive of all the main canals, the Grand (or 'Big Blue' as it is known locally) is walled by sheets of incredibly tough, grey metal which seems impervious to any known force (short of an atom weapon, which no one has tried yet). Completely different in construction to any of the other canals, the Grand is by far the biggest, at a constant 100 metres wide for its entire length. Ancient and ill-understood pump mechanisms ensure that water flows (at a very slow rate) around the canal, preventing stagnation. However, many of the mechanisms have broken down and the Grand has become choked with rubbish at several points along its length. The largest event of the year on the Grand Canal is the GC:2000, the biggest and most impressive ekranoplan race of the season. Teams from all classes and from all over The City line up to make 200 sprints up and down a 10 mile section of the Grand. Hundreds of thousands of spectators line the banks and millions more watch on TV or from the buildings overlooking the canal, all hoping to catch sight of the most impressive crash or spectacular mechanical failure.

the least canal

Narrowest of the main lateral canals, the Least is, at points, totally clogged with waste and rubbish. Indeed, at some points along the canal, settlements have grown up on the solid ground formed by the rubbish blockages. This has created large stagnant ponds fed by sewers and runoff from the streets. Disease is common around these pools, hence the fact that some of the worst slums in The City can found along the banks of the Least.

the black canal

Poisoned by slurry and toxic waste from the mining zones, which straddle the canal, and by toxic waste from rustbelts and landfills to its north, the Black Canal has been closed off at its eastern end to prevent contamination leaking in to the main canal system. All of the concentric and capillary canals leading into Black have also been blocked off.

the red canal

The Red Canal takes its name not from the colour of the water, which is the usual blackish brown, but from the smooth red stone which makes up its banks and bed. Theorists speculate that the Red Canal is the oldest of the main canals (apart from the Serpentine, whose origin may be natural). Nonetheless, the Red is a massively busy waterway, constantly thronged with rowboats, barges, steamers and hovercraft. Many areas of the bank have been cut away over hundreds of years to provide good stone for building and now resemble vast flights of steps.

the nothing

The Nothing is deep. Not just ordinarily deep like the other canals, but really deep. A slab sided trench extending 100 metres into the ground. Why the Nothing was built like this, nobody is sure and any records of its creation were lost long ago.

the green canal

For most of its length, the Green Canal is covered with a thick carpet of hardy waterplants. Traffic along the Green is sorely impeded by the tough, fibrous growths which emit highly toxic compounds when slashed or cut. They also seem almost immune to any form of toxin or parasite, fuelling the theory that they originated from genetically modified stock, created for some forgotten purpose.

the serpentine canal

Winding its way lazily through the western reaches of The City, the Serpentine Canal is an oddity amongst the sharp regularity of the canals. Some topographers speculate that at some point in the distant past, the Serpentine was a river on which the ancient ancestor of The City stood. Now, the Serpentine is enclosed by concrete banks and brick walls, a naturally shaped feature in an unnaturally twisted environment.

the trench

Cutting through what must have once been an upland area, The Trench has steep rock walls, sometimes as much as 200 metres high. The walls are now riddled with dwellings, factories, malls, sewers, traintubes and roadways. The Trench is seldom used as a means of transport and is, for most of its length, ill-supplied with turnoffs and tributaries. However, the canal itself is criss-crossed with a latticework of walkways, traintubes, bridges, conduits and pipelines. On occasion the lattice becomes so thick that it is impossible to view the canal from above.

the concentric canals

Slashing across the main lateral canals are the eight Concentric Canals. Unlike the Laterals, the Concentrics are bereft of romantic names, being referred to as Ring One to Eight. They are uniformly 60 metres wide and are often thronged with watercraft and speeding ekranoplans (in some sections, there are dedicated ekranoplan lanes for safety purposes). Certain parts of the Concentrics are blocked off, especially all of those connecting with the Black Canal. This can sometimes prove a hindrance to traffic, but back canals and capillary waterways usually provide an alternative route.

the minor canals and capillaries

Connecting up the Laterals and the Concentrics are hundreds upon hundreds of minor canals, some no more than a couple of metres wide, water alleys through the heart of The City. In some places they are hemmed in by buildings, only accessible through tight, narrow lanes, sewage outfalls and watergates at their edge. Others have walkways, paths and streets by their sides whilst gangways, bridges, pipes, ropes and cables create a latticework over the canals, often making high-speed travel a distinctly dangerous prospect.

tracks: the railways

An analysis of the rail network prepared for presentation to the 2nd Level Disbursements Committee, Nakamura Yebisu Group.

"While the canals dominate the mercantile life of our city, the extensive railway network operated by the Ancient and Honourable Guild of Fulgurators and the Transit Militia provides a useful adjunct to waterborne transport. Please do not be mistaken that the railway system is anything like our own railtracks used to bring resources in from the Outlands. Our tracks are wonders of engineering. With the city network, one wonders how the engineering holds up.

The tracks spread through the city like a parasitic plant, some

times aping the spread of the canals, sometimes following their own routes. At times they are held aloft on brick arches, iron trestles and concrete skyways. In other sections they dive deep underground, threading through ancient tunnels and passageways, but at no time do the railways run at what we would call 'ground level', i.e.: the level of the canals. They are always either elevated or subterranean.

Power for the railways is provided by the ancient, failing systems of the Guild. We have always denied them aid, as have the other seven, in accordance with our agreements. The Guild maintains rusting, decrepit power production systems at various locations around The City, patching, tending and caring for these decaying mechanisms as best they can. Power outages and flow failures are becoming more and more common in some areas as they fight to maintain a working supply.

The power is routed to the railways through massive overhead power lines, dangerous, deadly systems that have killed more than one wandering unfortunate. Pantographs on the tops of the engines hauling the trains draw power from these lines, sparking and arcing in a most alarming manner. The engines and trains are impressive things to behold. The engine itself is essentially one huge electric motor driving eight or more wheels. They are ornate constructions of black iron and brass, impressive in a primitive sort of way. The coaches are variable in the extreme, no two exactly alike. The trains rumble and crackle along the tracks, the blue sparks from their engines mingling with the orange sparks of the iron brakes. The train drivers are all members of the Guild, clad from head to toe in heavy, insulated suits to protect themselves from the ever-present danger of electrocution.

The engines are jealously guarded, precious things. We hold a strong suspicion, as do other intelligence organisations, that the Guild no longer has the capability or the funds to produce more engines. We feel this is evidenced by the increasing number of engines being stripped for parts in the yards and sidings. It is therefore not unsurprising that the engines are guarded with some vigour by the Transit Militia. Gaining access to one is impossible within the precincts of a station or yard. The Militia are somewhat trigger-happy and will gladly shoot anyone they suspect of interfering with the engines. I personally experienced this while gathering intelligence in CrossBar Terminus, but gladly, I escaped unscathed.

You will note from the map behind me that stations are numerous and widely scattered. Each parish, burgh or area has at least one station, many of the larger areas having several within their boundaries. Stations are very variable in their construction and facilities, but none are kept in particularly good repair. The Militia guards at all stations I visited are, however, highly motivated and devoted to their duty. Any transgression of rail law is punished very swiftly, as I witnessed on several occasions.

The locus of all rail activity in The City is CrossBar Terminus. You will see on the map that all lines converge here. A massive, rambling place, it is the bastion of power for both the Guild and the Militia. I have a firm belief that the Guild maintains its most important power production facilities under the terminus, although I was, sadly, unable to find their location or even to confirm their very existence.

In conclusion, ladies and gentlemen, I would say that our current course of action, i.e.: doing nothing, should be continued. It is my strong belief that the railways are on a downward course and will expire without any excessive outside influence from ourselves.

I do sincerely hope you found this short exposition useful and I thank you for your time."

complexity: the streets

For sheer diversity, complexity and maddening resistance to order, only one network comes close to The Dataflow: the streets, alleys, boulevards, thoroughfares and sidewalks of The City. An ancient tangle, riddled with secrets, with hidden byways and centuries old paths. No one person can claim to have knowledge of the millions of interstices and nodes which make up the street network of The City. However, few need to make such a claim, as only a small percentage of the population ever travels more than a mile or so from the place of their birth.

In most areas of The City, traffic on the streets is primarily on foot. Porters sell their backs for the carriage of heavy burdens, entire families draw small wagons of goods, ground vehicles are rare and treated with a semi-mystical awe. The occasional clanking, stuttering electric wagon owned by a haulage company can be seen making its unsteady way down the wider streets. Only in the more prosperous area, mainly those controlled by the macrocorps, does ground traffic become increasingly vehicular. Vehicles that cost more than the average citizen could hope to earn in their lifetime are used for short trips, for promenading or for terrorising those of a lesser social status. Armed gangs of well-to-do youngsters stream out of their protected areas to cause chaos on the streets. Many never return, ripped apart by real gangs who have lived their entire lives through violence and chaos, their expensive powerbikes destroyed or sold for a fraction of their real value.

Some areas offer alternative methods of transport, such as cablecars, funiculars and trams. In the Three Canals Metropolitan area, the Authority lays on a ramshackle, irregular and somewhat dangerous tram service. These rickety constructions, drawing their power from uninsulated overhead lines, rattle down the streets according to a timetable which is never published. Other parts of The City, such as

Burningfell, are criss-crossed by funicular railways, carrying goods and people up and down the steep sides of the fell. Some areas, in an effort to reduce the chances of their citizens being preyed upon by criminal elements, have even set up cable cars which swing above the streets, carrying passengers between stations perched on top of tenements and clinging to the sides of towerblocks.

However, the most important thing to remember about the streets is that the vast majority of people walk. And that includes the vast majority of people who have designs on the money, property or lives of their fellow citizens. Only a few streets are well lit, wide and easy to stroll down, the vast majority being small and cramped, with dwellings reaching high above on either side. Stalls and ramshackle accommodations make them even more crowded, forcing walkers to press past each other in a constant, flowing mass of bodies. The streets are home to cutpurses, pickpockets, jackers and thieves of all sorts. Wise people keep one hand on their money and another hand on a stout cosh.

The best advice, if you have to travel, is to avoid areas with which you are not familiar. There is a very real chance that wandering through unknown alleys and lanes, you will emerge into places with which you are desperately unfamiliar. Many who, by accident or design, take a stroll into Bankside, Mire End or Fogwarren are never seen again: lost, murdered, eaten or taken into slavery.

Be warned: The streets take no prisoners.

overhead: air

The air above The City is choked with pollution, a permanent brown haze hanging over the buildings. Through this haze comes the occasional thrumming cargo aerostat, screeching mikefighter or wallowing dirigible. Air travel is almost exclusively the preserve of those organisations wealthy enough and powerful enough to be able to afford the massive costs involved in building, buying and maintaining aircraft. Outside of the macrocorps, hardly anyone maintains substantial fleets of aircraft, with most of those outside of macrocorp service being ancient, decrepit, patched up and generally time-worn.

The most common form of aircraft in the skies over The City is the aerostat. Flat, disc or oval shaped craft, they use massive arrays of fans to lift their bulky bodies into the air and further arrays of jets or fans to propel them forward. While not particularly fast, they can carry heavy loads and have the advantage of being able to land almost anywhere. Huge circular cargo aerostats carry heavy loads of resource materials from the outer edges of The City into the factories nearer the centre. Most of the really big aerostats are manufactured by Gorunna Logistics, who have something of a monopoly in the design and building of such craft. Smaller aerostats serve a wide variety of different functions, from gunships to one man personal transports.

Buzzing between tower blocks and flitting across the rooftops are the mikefighters, tiny warplanes optimised for combat in The City. Barely big enough to hold a pilot, an engine and some weapons, they come in a staggering variety of designs, from pure fighters to warcrawl-busters and bombers.

A few centuries ago when the mikefighters first started appearing, they were much larger and heavier than they are now. Then a bright spark working for one of the macrocorps had the idea that by reducing the space needed for the pilot, and the systems which support him or her, the overall size of the craft could be reduced. Fast forward to the present era and the current situation, with that single idea long ago taken to its logical conclusion: mikefighters are piloted by children. Kids as young as five are drafted into macrocorp training academies and instructed to become pilots. Most start their careers aged eight or nine, careers which are over by the time they hit puberty. Very few now question the use of child soldiers in this way, it has become just another part of life in The City. The rate of attrition amongst rookie mikefighter pilots is terrible, with crashes, equipment failures and death in combat all being contributing factors. The majority of mikefighters are either vertical take-off and landing (VTOL) craft or short take-off and landing (STOL) craft. Some users, however, do make use of some rather interesting methods for the rapid launch of their aircraft. Trilhoeven are known to maintain launch and landing areas on top of some of their larger buildings, using magnetic catapults to accelerate mikefighters up to speed before launching them off the side of the building. Others simply drop them from the sides of the tallest buildings, sending them plummeting to the ground before their engines take hold and curve them skyward.

Compared to the mikefighters and aerostats, drigibles (or airships) are slow, ponderous and unwieldy and a relative rarity in The City. They are all homemade, patchwork constructions of dubious reliability, floating under bags of explosive hydrogen. Many areas will not allow dirigibles to pass overhead, due to the risk of fire and explosion, and so they are mostly confined to the outer areas of The City where aerostats are rare. Powered by chugging, inefficient alcohol burning engines, they plough through the skies, sometimes coming to a virtual halt when the headwind becomes too great.

a sense of common indecency (part 1)

The forecast is for rain. Make yours a good one.

Lockkstar was a paederast. Even in a city of millions, with all the evil that surrounds us, there are still some who manage to sink lower than The Shifted. Still, he always had the word on the street.

"Yah, man. Holed up in Vent 54, she is."

"Very good, fuckhead. How so?"

"Guy told me."

"What guy?" Shit, this was hard going.

"Ghostfighter, thin boy, Brigade tattoos on his arms. Thousand yard stare."

"Everyone in this place got the thousand yard stare. Vent 54, eh? So what's your price"

"Those photos? You said you get them."

"Yeh, I got them." Even through the gloves, the ziploc in my pocket felt dirty. I drew it out of the oilskin and threw it in the puddle at Lockkstars feet. "There you go, enjoy." The fucker grabbed at the packet, removing the slim cards inside. Even as the rain dribbled off the squares, I could see his face light up with a sickly glow.

"Nice."

This was too much. As a mikefighter stuttered overhead, I loped across the grass to the park gates. One of the ragged clumps along the path raised his bleeding head. Scrape addict. Bum. "Hirplakker." he whispered.

"How can you know, hotshot was gone too fast."

"Heard 'im. Know the sounds. Heard the sounds."

"Very good" I was out of there before he even started his pitch. I'll testify I heard whispered swearing following me all the way down the path to the gates. The gates were always a thing of fascination to me, even as a kid. Massive, patinaed, rust red edifices they were. Magnificently wrought and solidly constructed. Totally at odds with the decrepit, soiled environment of Mire End. My home. My life, in a way.

Me, I'm Kripitsch. Lostfinder. Seeker after that which has been mislaid, a service sorely required in this troubled parish. See, Mire End doesn't get any help from the Three Canals. The Metros don't want to know about the anthill on the other side of the Green. They got their own problems looking after Dreamingspires and Bankside. Provosts are run off their precious little feet up there. Still, gives the opportunity for greatest freedom of business.

Sideband came down here couple of years ago. At least, one of their market research sub-contractors came down here. Did some sort of survey, questioned folk. Only lost three of their team, not bad considering. Anyhow, they come up with the statistic that Mire End has more pornographers, peddlers and perverts per square yard than any other bit of the city. Well, at least we're famous for something.

Your life is worth nothing. Why bother?

Gneshel was worth a trip with, usually only once. A canal cab driver, she used to race ekranoplans in the Limited class, now she just meanders about the canals in a beaten up old turbiner. The rain coursed down her face, collecting in the tight hem of her slicker jacket and creating the tiniest of waterfalls. Apparently, she didn't notice.

"Ride, Gnesh?"

"'k."

She was a woman of few words, through choice or inability, I didn't care to know. As we skimmed round Circular Three, the architecture failed to change. Miserable plastic and metal shacks clinging to the canalside or to ruined towers and some squatting on barges. Further back from the canal, the buildings were in better shape, even with jagged chunks of rock and masonry missing. This end of the parish had been hit bad during the Hundred Block War. Hirplakker built a fake staging depot at the corner of H-Street and Powell. Arclight knocked the shit out of it. Knocked the living shit out of a big chunk of the parish as well. I saw them that day. Brigade of Light Tentenel troops moving through the cooling rubble. Silent, impassive: armoured angels.

"Where?"

"Eh?"

"Where?"

"Oh, right. Er..Y'know the Contested Grounds?"

"Yes."

"Drop me off the nearest you can get me to there"

"'k."

The boat droned and the barrios streaked by. The water stinks.

The docks at the Contested Grounds were always thronged, twenty five hours a day. Brigade L-Core personnel offloading barges full of weapons. Hirplakker transport troops doing the same. Not to mention the guffers, ghostfighters and militant firm soldiers getting ready to do battle or to pillage the spoils of war. The presence of a Lostfinder from Mire End attracted little comment. My passing went (relatively) unnoticed. Some jezzes' tried to get my attention, thought I was a trooper with cash to burn. A swedge broke out among the Brigade and Hirplakker guys. Usual kind of thing.

The docks was a town of crates, barges, pads and gangways, parts of it were, undoubtedly, off limits to your casual passerby, but mostly you could wander around, undisturbed and unthreatened. My problem was getting out to Vent 54. Right in the middle of the Grounds. Inside The Silo. Bollocks.

Nervous System: computing and communication

The Dataflow has often been likened to the nervous system of The City, twisting through its gargantuan body, sending, receiving and processing information. However, The Dataflow should not be thought of as one consistent, contiguous whole; like The City itself, it is a phenomenally complex agglomeration which has built up over time into a frighteningly convoluted network. Every communications and computer system constitutes a part of The Dataflow. Telegraphs, cablenets, microwave relays and laser comms provide the transfer capacity, while datacores, dingins and electronic computers provide the storage and processing capacity. An important note is that radio systems are unused in The City. Something prevents radio being used, nobody even bothers trying any more, it's just an accepted part of life.

Computing

By far the most common form of computer in The City is the mechanical computer, or dingin as it's more commonly known. They range in size from the massive assemblies of cogs, gears and rods of macroscale engines, down to the tiny nanoscale dingin processor blocks produced by macrocorporate manufacturers. Between these two ends of the spectrum, there are the microscale engines, where the mechanisms are too small to be seen with the naked eye (sometimes only just) but can be easily viewed with a microscope. Some of these are produced on vast automated production facilities, while others are painstakingly constructed by hand by the most skilled of artisans. No matter what scale of dingin is used, there must be a means of programming it so that it will carry out its functions. Macroscale engines are most commonly programmed by sequences of punched cards or slotted tapes which the dingin reads and translates into machine code. Microscale engines use a variation on the tape idea, using tiny spools of coded metallic tape run at vast speed to program the engine. Nanoscale engines are the most complex of all, using strings of individual molecules as the 'tape'.

Dingins have become so prevalent in The City because of the high level of background radiation and the constant threat of viruses. The virus threat comes in many forms: so many have been used over the centuries that many of the viruses have evolved and changed, becoming predators in The Dataflow. However, they cannot attack dingin systems without having some means to physically insert their programming. Also, dingins are far more resistant to radiation and extremes of temperature, making them ideal for life in The City. Most weapons systems with integrated computing modules use dingins for this very reason.

Other forms of computer system are found in The City, but none are so widespread as the dingin. Optical computers are utilised by macrocorporate and corporate organisations, but they are most often separated from the main body of The Dataflow by firewalls and banks of dingin safeguards. These optical computers most often use DNA cores for information storage purposes, giving massive amounts of storage capacity. The DNA systems use crystalline vats containing DNA material suspended in a storage medium. Variable frequency lasers read the information stored on the DNA chains while information is added and removed through chemical enzyme activity. Some of the macrocorps are known to use such things as quantum gate computers on a limited basis for ultra-high level encryption purposes. However, only one of the macrocorps (Hirplakker) is known to have created Artificial Intelligences.

Communication

Like The City itself, The Dataflow is almost incomprehensibly complex, multi layered and incredibly variable in its level of technology. The Dataflow encompasses telegraph lines, phone lines, cablenets, microwave relays, laser comms and many other, esoteric, forms of communication. Something as simple as telephoning one of your friends can be a nightmarish operation, depending on the kind of access you have, where you are in The City and quite often, who you are. In many of the poorer areas, communications are non-existent, or extend only to a battered public telephone kiosk standing on a street corner or by a canal. Wealthier areas usually have contracts with telecomms companies or the macrocorps to provide communications services. These can range from simple telephone systems to full visual conferencing and information access systems. As an example of the complexity, someone calling from Bankside to a friend in Burningfell may have to wander down to a public kiosk and dial the number that they think the individual might be on (these can change with alarming frequency). This will then be routed to the nearest exchange (if the exchange is still working). The exchange will then have to see what systems it can access in order to patch a call through to Burningfell. This might involve linking into a macrocorporate comms network, routing the call through a series of microwave relays to a main processing exchange. This bigger exchange would then prioritise the call and route it through the most appropriate and available network. The call could then be shunted onto a local cablenet and fired towards Burningfell. Luckily, Burningfell has stumped up for local cable access. Then, the call gets routed to the local server system and finally, maybe, reaches the intended destination. As can be seen, this is a ridiculously complex system and it can often take an age to actually get a call patched through to the person you want.

The most comprehensive (indeed, the only) citywide integrated comms network is provided by Barrage Balloon Communications, a subsidiary of Sideband Media. BBC maintains a network of massive gas balloons floating at heights between 4,000 and 8,000 feet above The City. Below these balloons are clusters of microwave downlinks and relays. Subscribers to the service can send a message, a phone call or conduct video conferencing at reasonable speed and with relative security. Messages are routed into the network through an extensive series of uplink/downlink stations and sent to the nearest downlink to the target point via the network of balloon relays. This avoids the vast, complex body of The Dataflow as whole. Users still need a means of access to the ground stations and most use the hardwired cablenets provided by BBC. Corporate users are most common, although private individuals can buy into this expensive system. The largest non-corporate users are the TCMAA Provosts who use the network to route most of their inter-unit comms traffic.

Now, the above is just on the level of actually talking to someone. When it comes to exploring The Dataflow or accessing information, this process becomes even trickier. If you have the right system and access, then entering an information database is relatively simple. Searching the entire Dataflow for information is a much more worrying task due to the different technology levels, connections and processing speeds and means of data transfer, it can often take days to track

down the particular bit of information you're looking for. Specialist software companies such as Firefinger have established a reputation for building dingin programs designed explicitly for information search and retrieval. Even with these specialist programs, it's never easy. The bit of info you might be looking for could be stored on a centuries old macroscale dingin with a ridiculously low retrieval and transfer speed. So, while finding the information might not be so complex, actually retrieving and downloading it would be the time consuming part of the process. Data retrieval specialists (or

flowghosts as they are more commonly known) have developed unparalleled skills for getting information from The Dataflow, cracking secure databases and sneaking off with information that they really shouldn't have.

Sedate the masses: entertainment

With such a huge, factionalised, unstable population, The City could easily explode into mass violence at any moment. One of the few things that keeps the population stable is (relatively) easy access to a vast range of entertainment. From the ridiculously expensive night-clubs of Brightlights to the parasite infested brothels surrounding the Contested Grounds, entertainment comes in many forms.

television

Easily the most widespread entertainment medium in The City, low-grade television is supplied to hundreds of thousands of homes by Sideband Media and other, smaller companies. Many years ago, it was Sideband who took the decision to provide free television to any part of The City that requested it. Hence, even the most impoverished homes will have a television, albeit a battered and scarred one, sitting somewhere in the room. Sideband took this decision (a decision which was followed by other corporations) for three main reasons. The first reason was, in agreement with the other macrocorps, to effectively sedate the population and provide them with an outlet for their fears, hatred and passions. The second reason was to make money from a range of other services. Although TV is provided free, only a limited range of channels are offered, with more popular, diverse channels costing an extra fee. In addition, users can also pay to have their cablenet carry phone signals. Sideband makes a healthy profit from this service, charging exorbitant rates for telecommunications provision. The third reason was that TV could penetrate the home more effectively than any other advertising medium. A full 35% of programming consists of adverts and infomercials. New products are glamourised and glorified, encouraging the huddled masses to purchase the latest consumer goods, even if they can barely afford them.

Actual entertainment programming covers a wide spectrum. The free channels mostly concentrate on cheap fiction shows, often featuring sex or violence as their main themes. Romances, war stories, police dramas and series purporting to give an insight into the lives of the rich and famous are all extremely popular whilst factual and news programming is almost non-existent on the free channels. For anything approximating documentary or serious news, a user must pay for one or more of the additional channels. More popular than these are the film channels, which show an endless diet of the low-budget movies churned out by Sideband, its subsidiaries and other smaller studios. They tend to follow the same pattern as the free TV shows, only with bigger budgets and better known actors. Sports channels are also highly popular, with the Association of Ground Effect Racing Leagues Wingship channel being by far the most heavily subscribed.

Workers come home at night, shrug off their working clothes and place themselves in front of the TV to while away their evenings. TV sedates the population and allows the macrocorps to create demand for their products. A more effective method of keeping the population under control has yet to be found.

live entertainment

Musical trends in The City are very varied, not just from culture to culture but from region to region. The most popular musical style at the current moment is a discordant, almost unlistenable, style named rust. There are many young bands that seek to make it on to TV and the rust scene is a very vibrant, constantly changing part of the music business. Popular new bands in this vein are Deadly Lethargy, WaaWaaWaa and SCB, all signed to small, non-macrocorporate, independent labels. Among the more wealthy, club orientated set there is a fad for fast, highly syncopated string music, quite hard on the ears but apparently great for dancing to. The scene is virtually dominated by bands made up of young macrocorporates. There have been a few good bands in this vein that are not tied to the macrocorps in some way, yet they seldom seem to have much success, possibly due to the stranglehold of the macrocorporates on the music industry. For the more cultured listener, opera and more sedate string pieces are still big business. The Grand Opera House

in Brightlights and the Unsooth Hall in Luminosity Tower both play host to many high profile, expensive events.

Theatrical productions hold a strange place in The City, seemingly being confined to the two extremes of society. The massively rich attend live theatre events as a style statement, to show that they would not watch TV like the common herd. At the opposite end of the spectrum, the most poverty stricken members of society, who live in places where even Sideband refuses to provide TV access, rely on live acts for their entertainment. Ironically, it is crudely satirical plays which are most popular with both audiences.

sports

Newsline

Subject : HSD Launch New Ekranoplan Racing Ship
Stringer : Merryn Lysak

"In a glittering ceremony at the Straits Raceway, HSD launched their new ship for the upcoming Class-A season. Based on last year's controversial fusion-powered design, the new ship is claimed to be faster, more agile and more stable. Regular readers may recall the tragic debut race of last year's design when 2 racers were killed at the Rapid Ring."

The most popular spectator sport in The City is, without a doubt, ekranoplan racing. The sight of these massively powerful ground effect planes careering around the canals, a few yards above the surface, is quite something. From the Class A races down to the lowest of the Limited classes, events draw huge crowds, all hoping for an exciting win or spectacular crash. Racing is co-ordinated and controlled by the all-powerful Association of Ground Effect Racing Leagues (AGERL). The Association controls every aspect of racing and lays down the rules for competition and vehicle design, occasionally enforcing them by rather violent methods.

racing classes

Class A: Class A is the fastest and most popular of the three racing classes. Using cutting edge design and having the best pilots, only teams with massive corporate sponsorship can afford to enter.

Class B: Less expensive than Class A, often using technology from Class A races of two or three seasons ago, Class B offers a more affordable route into the higher echelons of racing for less well off teams.

Limited: Within the Limited class there are numerous strata, from local clubman racing, up to semi-professional teams striving to get the sponsorship needed to enter the big time.

Aside from the three main classes, there are numerous underground and illegal races which take place across The City. These are frowned upon by burgh councils and militant organisations, but they all seem unable to stop them. Home built ekranoplans of widely varying design take to the waters for little or no prize money and often only for the kudos of winning.

famous teams

Alekseyev EKR: Started by three times Class A champion Gregor Alekseyev, A-EKR is one of the more successful non-macrocorp funded teams. While they have yet to win a championship, the three-ship team has consistently placed well and is vying with the more powerful teams for top spot.

Darrat-Emvax: House team of the Arclight macrocorp, D-E won last years championship by one point over HSD. With massive funding and some excellent pilots, they are one of the teams to beat.

HSD: The Hirplakker Speed Division is possibly the best-funded team in the class and this season is no exception. With each of their new craft costing in excess of 6.5 million pounds, they are expected to make a stern challenge for the title which they relinquished to Darrat-Emvax last season.

Kraken: New to ekranoplan racing this season, Kraken is primarily sponsored by Trilhoeven macrocorp.

WaveFront: The only private team in the last ten seasons to win a championship, WaveFront have been on something of a downturn for the last few years, but their poaching of hull designer Vincent Giler from Darrat-Emvax may give them the competitive edge that they need to start winning again.

famous pilots

Gill Willis: Winner of last season's championship for Darrat-Emvax, this year Willis has signed a new contract with HSD. The most successful female pilot in the history of ekranoplan racing, she first won the title three years ago.

Ivan Vassar: Lead pilot for Darrat-Emvax for the last five years, Vassar is reputed to be the highest paid sportsman in The City (his paycheque for last season was reported to be in excess of 30 million pounds). A fierce, aggressive racer, he has an alarming tendency to push other racers into danger-ous situations, especially HSD craft. Some suggest that this may be due to the fact that up to the age of fifteen he was a mikefighter pilot for Hirplakker, before he grew too much and he was pushed out on to the street. Vassar stoutly denies such slanderous rumours. Indeed, several legal battles have been fought over this very fact. Vassar was publicly furious last year when injury caused him to lag far behind in the championship standings, allowing his younger team-mate Gill Willis to win the Class A crown.

famous tracks and races

The Grand Canal 2000: Sponsored by Trilhoeven and organised by the TCMAA, the GC:2000 is the biggest, richest and most spectacular sporting event in The City. Every season, teams from all classes converge on the Grand Canal as it runs through the TCMA. 200 times they race up and down a ten mile stretch of the canal, the leading craft reaching speeds in excess of 450 miles per hour. Fatalities are

common, not only amongst pilots, but amongst the throngs of spectators and those foolhardy enough to slip past the Provosts and stray onto the canal in small craft. On average, 5,000,000 pounds in bets changes hands running up to and during the GC:2000.

The Rapid Ring: A lethal, twisting watertrack, the Rapid Ring was downgraded from Class A to Class B last season after a series of horrific accidents on its numerous tight bends. Hirplakker, its owners, are furious about this and have made numerous threatening advances towards the AGREL.

The Straits Raceway: From the pollution of the Black Canal came something to cheer the population. Two subsidiary canals, cut off by the blocking of the Black were linked up to form the Straits Raceway, a highly competitive Limited Class watertrack. Maintained by sponsorship from the Firefinger corporation, the Straits are located in Fogwarren and often provides the only outlet for the entertainment starved population.

Other Sports and Pastimes

Aside from ekranoplan racing, there are few sports in The City which achieve anything other than limited or underground popularity. Combat sports are, by the very nature of life in The City, rather popular and many variations abound. One of the more widespread and popular underground combat games is Cripplecut. A Cripplecut venue can be almost anywhere: a cellar, a tunnel, a back alley or a factory floor. Games range from backstreet brawling involving a couple of local toughs to major underground events, perhaps drawing as many as a thousand spectators. Cripplecut is, at its most basic level, knife fighting. But the object is not to kill your opponent but, as the name suggests, to cripple him or her. Even in the lawless, violent world of cripplecut, actually killing your opponent is considered rather bad form. Each fighter uses the edged weapon of their choice (although there are informal restrictions on what you can and cannot use) and attempt to prevent the use of the arms and legs of their opponent. Surrender is allowed and takes place generally when one fighter has lost the use of two limbs. The permission of surrender and the prohibition against killing blows are the only two rules in cripplecut. Major cripplecut events are often organised by the big criminal groups such as the 3rd Syndicate. Betting is always keen at these events, whether they are large or small and considerable amounts of money change hands. Due to the huge sums wagered on some events, some groups have taken to bringing in 'ringers' fromoutside the normal cripplecut circles. These are often ghostfighters (a class of stealthy knife-fighters) who have been paid very well to take part. However, much to the dis-

appointment of their backers, the ghostfighters are often at a severe disadvantage, as their first instinct in a fight is to strike to kill.

Card games are particularly popular across The City, mainly because they provide a cheap, convenient form of entertainment. All games are based around the standard eighty card deck, containing five suits (Black, Red, Grey, Green and Blue) of 16 cards each. The numeral cards run from one to ten, while the face cards are named (in ascending order) Assassin, Priest, Temptress, Captain, Warlord and Daemon. Widely played games include 'Railwaymans Bluff', 'Dog' and 'Height'. 'Railwaymans Bluff' originated with the drivers, signalmen and engineers who work on the railways and can have up to ten players. The object of the game is to bluff the other players into getting rid of the face cards which you need in order to complete a run of all the face cards and the one card, of a specific suit. Assassin cards can be used to force the other player to discard a specific face card. If, for example, you suspect that one of your opponents holds Black Warlord, and you are attempting to collect Grey suit cards and have a Red Assassin which you don't need, you can throw the Assassin down a declare an assassination' on the other player's card. However, you need to be careful, because if you're wrong, the other player can randomly select a card from your hand and have it discarded. 'Railwaymans Bluff' can take an excruciatingly long time to play. Needless to say, it helped railway workers while away the hours during strikes.

You are what you eat: food and drink

In a city of millions, isolated from the outside world, one major question arises: how do the inhabitants survive? More pointedly, where does the food come from to allow them to survive? The are no farms, no herds of cattle, no rolling fields. People require sustenance and that sustenance has to come from somewhere.

The sustenance problem can essentially be divided into two categories: the macrocorporate problem and the everyone else problem. Dealing first with the macrocorporates, their situation is somewhat easier due to their access to resources and labour. Over the decades, the macrocorporate institutions have built up vast supply networks, providing them with all the food they require, and more. All of the eight maintain vast underground hydroponics facilities producing fruit, vegetables, and pharmaceutical plants. Usually located away from the centre of The City, these enormous, multi-layered facilities consume extraordinary amounts of power and water. Plants exist in these facilities which are grown nowhere else in The City. Salvaged from the chaos of The Shift and The Bombardment, the genetic codes for these plants are almost all that remains of The City's pre-Bombardment flora. Outside of the macrocorporate facilities, many companies, families and individuals grow their own food, through various means. Some small corporations have purchased equipment and seeds from the macrocorps in order to start their own production facilities. These vary in quality from sparkling clean underground growing houses to dank, pestilence ridden warehouses which barely manage to produce anything edible at all. On roofs and in courts throughout The City, individuals and family groups maintain small gardens to feed themselves and, occasionally, to make a little money. Fertilised by treated sewage (or sometimes untreated sewage) these little gardens are fiercely guarded against those who might steal valuable food. Most law enforcement organisations will look the other way when a garden owner beats or kills a miscreant who has attempted to make off with a vegetable.

The most commonly available foodstuff in The City is fish, in all its varying forms. Bred in the turgid waters of the canals, feeding on the plant life (and other fish) they are perhaps the most valuable resource in The City. Commercial fish breeders use vast cages suspended in the canals to contain and grow their stock. Most famous of the fish producing areas is Bankside, which sells produce far and wide. Many people who dwell beside the canals maintain fish cages on a smaller scale, providing for themselves, their family or their local community. Selective breeding and limited genetic engineering have allowed the fish farmers to breed fish which are hardier and better able to survive and grow in the polluted, dark waters of the canals.

In stark contrast to the fishermen of the canals, the macrocorps maintain huge underground facilities (normally in the same complexes which house the hydroponic facilities) devoted to the production of edible fish. Using the water which has been cycled through the hydroponic growth areas, the fish not only provide food but also provide valuable fertiliser for the hydroponic facilities. Bloated, lazy specimens swim lethargically in the warm tanks, gobbling up food pellets as fast as the tenders can throw them into the water. The fish are a valuable source of food, oils and a wide range of other useful stuff: bones are turned into glue, fish skin is turned into clothing and oils are sold as lubricants.

Outside of the large-scale facilities, fish are still available if you have a line, a hook and a lot of patience. Canal dwelling fish are often ill, diseased and foul tasting, but for many they are the only option available if they wish to survive. However, fish stocks in the canals are sinking lower and lower and the

chances of catching anything worth eating are becoming more and more slim as the years wear on.

Another popular food choice in The City, coming second only in popularity to the ubiquitous fish, is dog. Man's best friend has become man's favourite main course. Dogs, in a wide variety of shapes an sizes were and are endemic, found in every area of The City, adapting to different environments and generally thriving. Wild dogs are hunted for their meat and skin, whilst others are bred for the same purposes. Fat, waddling 'meat hounds' are kept in pens and fed on fish products that even the hungriest human would probably pass up. Here they are fattened for the slaughter, their meat sold for food, their skin made into clothing and shoes, their bones reduced to glue and other useful products.

Some people do keep dogs as pets, but a careful eye must be kept on them, as a stray dog is most likely to be snapped up and eaten. Dogskin is also tanned and made into shoes, coats, trousers hats and bags, another valuable source of raw materials for the imprisoned citizens of The City.

All this having been said, The City does not simply survive on a diet of fish, dogs and vegetables. More sinister sources of food are available. Decades and decades ago, some bright spark figured that there was a huge source of raw material that was being burned to a cinder every day. A valuable resource was simply going up in smoke. What was happening? People were being cremated. Now, the thought of actually eating human flesh was repugnant to the vast majority of the population. Folklore recalled the horrific years after The Bombardment, when vast numbers of people were reduced to cannibalism in order to survive. But what if this resource could be used to create a more palatable foodstuff, one that the population would accept. Hence, the practice of selling the dead to food companies began, slowly at first, but now it has grown so much that it is a fully accepted part of City life.

Large numbers of the dead are bought by so-called Deathdealers who reduce the bodies to a nutrient soup from which tasty treats are grown. Using genetic engineering to modify the growth, meat, vegetable type substances and all manner of foods are churned out by the factories. Even the macrocorps have got in on the act. Macrocorporate workers often have to sign contracts which stipulate that they give up all rights to their body when death finally comes to them. The macrocorps can then use their loyal workers one last time to feed the ravening hordes of The City. In return for this service, the families of the dead are paid a small amount, usually in foodstuffs. One chain of fast-food stalls has even adopted the name 'Meat The People' as a blatant signifier of what it is actually selling. As unpalatable as this may seem, it provides another valuable source of nutrients for a city which is cut off, isolated and in desperate need.

but where does it all come from?: resources

An address by Fion Schleichner, Resource Management Executive, Hirplakker Combine, given to new employees of the Combine. Certain segments have been excised for security reasons.

"Colleagues, friends, co-workers. You're all gathered here today as new employees of Hirplakker Combine to find out one thing. How does this sprawling, chaotic, filthy cesspool in which we live survive? You've all suffered hardships to a greater or lesser extent. Now, you're one of us. Hirplakker shall provide everything you could need. However, I'm not a marketing man, so, enough of the advertising shit.

[laughs from audience]

How do our factories keep producing? Where do we get the raw materials for the steel, glass, fibreoptics, wood, plastics and all the other vital items this company produces? Well, I'll tell you. And this is something that 95% of the people in this city don't know. From The Outlands.

[gasps from some members of the audience, muted laughing from others]

Yes, I know, no one can go into The Outlands, Death waits for us at the borders of The City, blah, blah, blah. Well, that part is true. However, we've overcome that. Out there, under the blistered, cracked sand and rock are billions of tons of minerals, petrochemicals, a storehouse of natural resources. Desiccated forests of ancient lumber just waiting to be hacked down. Lights please.

[lights dim.]

[holo projection springs into life show a shaky view of a seared desert]

This is how we do it. Robots. Automatons. Drones. Whatever you call them, they can go where we can't. We've been sending them out for hundreds of years now, setting up mining installations, prospecting. And not one of them has been touched by 'forces from above'. As long as they don't leave the ground, that is.

[camera pans to a view of a construction of pipeworks, tubing, massive cylinders set on end]

My friends, this is Extractor 34. It mines for ferrous metals, iron to you and me. The iron ore that we turn into steel, turn into weapons, armour, boats, mikefighters. We've got another seven like it, all dragging iron from the ground. Similar plants produce precious metals, light ores anything we need. Now don't get me wrong, we're not the only ones doing it. Gorunna, Trilhoeven, Arclight [sound of spitting] they're all at it. There's an unspoken law: don't fuck with the mining facilities, without them, this place would grind to a halt. Lights.

[lights come up]

We bring the stuff in, along the canals and on automated train lines, right into our factories, smelters and furnaces. That's how we keep going. That's how this city survives. We hold the keys. Only us and the other macrocorps can do this. Only we have the power. The will. The resolve. That's what puts us at the top of the food chain.

Never forget: we rule this city. Not the people. Not the Council. Us.

Thank you for your attention."

a sense of common indecency (part 2)

Darkness encroaches. Buy a torch.

Hiring Simils always struck me as a funny business. They never wanted money (what the hell would they do with it, anyway?) or consumables, always something strange, unexpected. This time it was a potted plant, a picture of a pretty girl and a doll. "Seriously?" It doesn't pay to be too sarcastic with a seven foot tall mechanical freak.
"Yes." Their voices really set me on edge, like two sheets of pitted steel being scraped together.
"All right, wait here for an hour, I'll see what I can rustle up"
"Yes."

The pretty girl was easy to get, plenty of pictures like that around the Grounds. I nicked a doll that had been tied to the gun barrel of a Hirplakker assault gun (the crew were comatose with drink at the time) and bought, at an outrageous price, a small potted flower from a Brigade artillery officer relaxing in his tent. He thought I was mad as well.

"Right, here you go. Doll for you, picture for you, plant for you." With remarkable delicacy, the three Simils took their payment and gazed at it, motionless for quite some time. This was beginning to get on my nerves. Secreting their prizes in massive steel backpacks, they hefted their weapons and turned to me.

"Silo."

"Yes, The Silo. Vent 54. You ready?"

"Yes."

Everyone takes the Simils for idiots, mechanical children with precious little intelligence. Well, let me tell you, if it wasn't for them, I'd have died within five minutes. The Grounds are, quite literally, hell. Ruins of factories and chimneys, houses and cellars, railtracks and canals. Twisted metal and pulverised brick. A wasteland of craters, walls and ditches. The infantry of both sides skitter about, all clad in the same uniform grey dust. Armour rumbles about, pulverising the landscape even more, whilst the mikefighters and aerostats wheel overhead, bombing, strafing, adding to the destruction. The Grounds are never silent, the war seems to be unending.

Things went bad when we rounded a corner and ran bang into a bunch of rippers. They were scavenging a knocked out tank, stripping it clean before the rightful owners could get to it. Apparently they took exception to our presence and opened up. These weren't like the local idiots from Mire End, these guys had been about and had amassed a fair arsenal. I cowered behind a burnt up half-track while the Simils waded in. One of them was carrying a massive electric gatling, tore the rippers apart. Didn't prevent one of the others being trashed by an RPG. After the fight, my Simils didn't seem to care about their dead (do Simils die, or do they just break?) comrade.

"Hey, the other one, what about him."

"Gone."

"That it, you're just leaving him here?"

"Yes."

Guess it just goes to show, you can't apply human values to something you really don't understand.

Don't be scared. We won't hurt you.

I sometimes wonder if the Third Church of God types are right. That this place is a testing ground, built by some mad Architect-God to test us poor, stupid mortals. Then I think of how depressed and downtrodden the Thirders are and get on with things. We rounded a corner into what must have been a vast railyard: rusted rails stood up at all angles and the shells of engines and wagons lay about like discarded drinks cans.

"Danger."

"Beg your pardon? Danger? I thought we were already in fucking danger?"

"Silo. Danger."

Above us loomed The Silo. Black against the dull red sky, it stood higher than any building I'd seen before. Jagged round the edges, pounded by artillery and airstrikes, it stood like a massive grave marker, mourning the loss of thousands of soldiers. The Silo represented what this war was all about. Resources, prestige, influence. Hirplakker realised they couldn't protect their precious resources from Arclight, so they tried to destroy them. Turns out they built The Silo a little too well, even better than the Flak Towers. What with the strictures against atom weapons, there's no way they could bring that beast down. Now infantry infested it like rats, scurrying through the maze of corridors and passages, flitting across the dank spaces of the massive silos themselves. In there, you're more likely to be killed by your own side than by the enemy. So it goes. Now we just need to get to Vent 54, right under the guns of hundreds of paranoid psychotics, armed to the teeth, deprived of sleep and high on a cocktail of drugs. It really does make me wonder why, in the name of all that's decent , I'm doing this.

War is hell. But it's better than nothing.

That was the worst experience of my entire life.

Who knew a flechette through the shoulder could be so bloody painful? I'm really hoping it doesn't get infected or go gangrenous before I get out of here. This sure had better be worth it.

The noise in the place is the strangest I've ever heard. A combination of gunfire, screams, scraping and rattling echoes through the passageways like a never-ending wind. The simils were in a worse state than me. They just walked through the fire, projectiles ringing off their rusty carapaces, punching holes in their armour. They didn't seem to care. Vent 54 leads down, deep into the bowels of The Silo, where ancient machinery rusts and rots away to nothingness. Only the bravest of the scavs come here. Rumour has it that platoons of soldiers, driven mad by the fighting, lurk in the depths, sneaking out to steal food from their erstwhile comrades. Only a rumour, though.

Well, onwards and downwards.

the infernal game: politics

"If elected to represent the ward of Folly Hills South, I promise to campaign for better public services, better policing and better conditions for workers"

"Yes Ms Yelland, but aren't these same empty old promises made by every candidate?"

"Not at all, not at all! We in the Onwards With Confidence party are committed to making these promises become reality!"

"Uh huh. But aren't these, I put it to you, the same promises made by every other party or independent candidate?"

"No. Next question."

"Very well. How do you respond to the accusation that activists for your party have been bribing some of the poorest members of Folly Hills society to vote for your party?"

"I absolutely refute such allegations, they are baseless and totally without any reasonable foundation. Furthermore, I would regard them as scurrilous lies, tantamount to a personal attack on myself."

"So these photographs of Onwards With Confidence party members handing mysterious packets to families living in slum tenements, they're false then?"

"Err...ummm...of course. Absolutely. Fake, without a shadow of a doubt."

"And this set of photos, showing your good self accepting a bundle of what appears to be ten pound notes from someone we have identified as an executive of Trilhoeven macrocorp, that's fake as well?"

"This interview is over, do you hear. Finished. I will not be treated like this, d'you hear?"

"So is that a denial, or an admission of the truth?"

"Bah! Parasite! Gutter journalist!"

The infernal game of politics in The City. The scrabble for power and influence. From the lowliest burgh councillor to the most powerful macrocorporate head, all those in the political game strive and struggle for every last scrap of power and prestige.

Like almost all other aspects of life in The City, the political landscape is a fraught, complex thing. Most areas which have some form of nominal control have representatives who decide laws, policy and expenditure (if, indeed, there is any money to spend). Whether they are tyrants who impose their will on a single tenement or lawfully elected representatives, in office by the will of the people, all fulfil the same function. These local politicians go by many different names: burgesses, councillors, peoples representatives, leiters, deputies, their nomenclature being almost as varied as the individuals themselves. In areas where there is some form of central political control, semi-regular elections are a feature of the political landscape, giving the common masses an opportunity to express their view. However, graft and corruption are rife through all aspects of city life and politics is, unsurprisingly, no exception. Ballot rigging, intimidation, bribery and assassination are tools used to affect the outcome of elections, the desire to have power over others being so great amongst some people that they will use any means necessary to gain that power.

The two most notable 'democratic' areas in The City are the Three Canals Metropolitan Area (TCMA) and the Red Canal Collectivist Republic(RCCR). Both differ radically in their political make-up but both are very similar in that they have regular elections with strictly laid down principles and a clear system of voting. The Three Canal Metropolitan Area Authority (TCMAA) holds elections every two years, with each burgh within the TCMA electing two representatives to the Authority. The system, despite its laudable democratic aims, is open to widespread corruption. Many areas within the TCMA are extremely poor and take little interest in the political manoeuvring of the Authority. Power-hungry politicians will often buy a seat on the Authority by paying the poor denizens of the slums for the votes, normally for pitifully small sums. All of the larger parties use this tactic, utilising the dreadful situation of the people in these so-called 'rotten burghs' to gain a grearter majority on the Authority. Electoral fraud is not of great concern to the Provosts, the police force of the TCMA. They have far more pressing things to deal with than a few cases of vote rigging. The RCCR, on the other hand, has an almost fanatical dedication to wiping out electoral fraud in all its forms. Voters must provide many different forms in order to register, their every move in the ballot stations is watched by electoral observers from the Special Department. The fact that there is only one party to vote for is totally beside the point. Peoples Representatives are elected by and from the people, elected in a komradely fashion to best serve the will of the collective. The entire system, however, is essentially a sham. Large numbers of citizens are prevented from voting by reason of criminal record, past mental illness, Special Department reports or any one of a number of spurious reasons.

Some organisations seek to impose political will over the entire city. The Council is one such organisation, a body which takes representatives from all burghs who can muster some sort of political system, from the major religions and from the macrocorps. Self-styled head of The Council is the enigmatic Councillor Rhilfele, a singularly mysterious individual. To most citizens of the city, The Council is nothing more than a glorified talking shop which never achieves anything.

For the most part, this bears a close resemblance to the truth, in that The Council has never actually achieved any form of unity or direction. The only successes it has had have been imposing a series of Pan-urban Strictures, mainly designed at curbing the most violent excesses of the macrocorps. This has forced (to a certain extent) the macrocorps to take responsibility for their violent actions, especially relating to the use of weapons of mass destruction.

The macrocorps themselves have a byzantine network of political allegiances and relationships. Gorunna is on relatively good terms with everyone, as is GRID. Trilhoeven, on the other hand, are universally despised by the other seven. Most of the other macrocorps find something secretly sinister about Trilhoeven, something which they have never been able to put their finger on. Arclight are seen as rude young upstarts, causing Sideband and Nakamura-Yebisu to side with Hirplakker on this issue.

I-LOK are pretty much the wild card, as nobody truly understands where their power base comes from or how they actually manage to wield so much p o w e r. Allegiances and trade agreements come and go, the macrocorps swing

back and forth, siding with each other for economic, political or military gain. No one of them every truly gains an advantage, well aware that an overt display of premier status could lead to them being crushed utterly by their fellows.

the symbol of the city: the gun

From a lecture delivered by Professor Georg Humbolt, Longshore University, TCMAA.

"The City exhibits a persistent and profligate weapons culture, a culture which law enforcement and legislation seem unable to stamp out. Why is this so? What is it in our society that causes such a reliance on the gun? Where does this attitude spring from? I cannot claim to have the answers to these questions but, hopefully, I can in some small way make the situation clearer.

Our isolation, our lack of knowledge and our lack of awareness of self are all contributory factors in our violent culture. When The Shift occurred, a change so vast was wrought that we are still living within its consequences. The Bombardment, now an event of legend and folk story caused even greater disruption and dislocation. These two events were the defining, shaping points of history for The City. In fact, it is with these two events that our history begins as the devastation of The Shift and The Bombardment stole the knowledge that was once ours. You history lecturers will have gone over in detail the immense loss of knowledge that occurred as a result. We have only fragmentary records of that time, mainly transcription of oral testimonies given by survivors. They are incomplete and at times incoherent. The violent birth of our society filters down today, through the centuries. We are the inheritors of a whirlwind of chaos.

This leads me to our current situation, the isolation which we face every day. An aeon ago, we may have been able to leave The City, to roam far and wide, perhaps even to the stars. Yet now we are trapped within this urban maze, victims of events we can barely comprehend, let alone understand. All who attempt to leave this place are destroyed by the fire from above, from the legendary 'Iron Ring' which surrounds us. Trapped, isolated, breeding and expanding on top of one another, our frustrations as a society must be given vent. Violence rears its ugly head on every canal corner, in every building, in every room. Our hatred of The Shift, of what it has caused to happen to us is given form by violence. We have a collective anxiety about our situation. We fear the unknown, we fear the power of the macrocorps, we fear our neighbours and our colleagues.

As a people, we have no heritage, other than that which has been created since The Shift. We have no true sense of self, who are we, where do we come from, who were our ancestors before the shift? Even though we have been trapped here, evolving for a thousand years, we still crave the knowledge which can never be ours. The Shifted walk amongst us, yet they refuse to provide any useful information. Scientists in this very building probe the secrets of The Shift, at risk to their own lives, and yet we still remain ignorant of the basic facts of our existence.

So why is the gun the symbol of our home? For all the reasons given above, we live in fear. Some feel it to a greater extent than others, some only feel it in the depths of sleep, but we all feel it at some time in our lives. Hence, weapons are seen as devices through which we can protect ourselves from the fear. Unarmed, we are defenceless against fear. Armed, we have something to strike back against the fear. This fear takes many forms: The Shifted, criminals, employers, neighbours. All can be objects of fear and all must, by our own standards, be warded against.

Yet, the gun remains symbolic of other factors. The most common weapon you will see on the streets is the sparklock, a weapon easily manufactured, easily maintained and diabolically dangerous, the perfect symbol of our city. The common criminals carry these weapons as tools of their trade. Status is achieved through better weapons. Gang leaders, powerful underworld figures and crime lords will all strive to have the most expensive, high technology gun they can find. Purloined macrocorporate weapons are immensely popular for their level of advancement and sheer technical artistry when compared to the common sparklock. Men and women will openly display these firearms (in the more lawless areas, at least) as badges of honour, wealth and importance. Like the citizens of Lucent Heights use their property to display their wealth and power, like the macrocorps use their domains as displays of influence, so these people use their weapons as their own display.

It is now easy to see why weapons are so endemic in our home. My findings can be summarised thus:
1) Our lack of self-knowledge and our ignorance of the events of the past contributes to a climate of fear.
2) We feel that we must strike out at the sources of that fear, and hence must have a weapon to achieve this.
3) The gun is a symbol of wealth and status. As the vast majority of the population lives on a low technology baseline, a hitech firearm is a symbol of wealth and power.

From these three simple points we can see how the violent, gun-obsessed culture which surrounds us has developed over the decades. Unless the basic causes of this obsession are acted upon, the situation can only continue to get worse. Despite the bolstering factors which give some limited sense of order to our society, we can only slide further into chaos and dissolution if we do not make checks on the spiral of violence which threatens to engulf us.

Think on how you can effect change, even on the smallest scale. I know that many of you carry arms to classes every day, if only to protect yourselves from the predations of the criminal underclass. I would urge you to cease this practice, to walk the streets with a confident air. We, as an intellectual elite must make the first moves. We are the leaders of society, its opinion formers, its motivators. If we attempt to change things for the good, to make life that little bit better, then society as a whole can benefit. I urge you to think on this, to draw conclusions and to act. Thank you."

Counter/culture: gangs and criminals

The City has its fair share (some would say more than fair share) of gangs and the problems associated with them. There have been gangs in The City since The Bombardment (and possibly before that) but the problem has become steadily worse over the centuries. Gangs can be divided into differing classes according to their motivations and patterns of operation. Here follows the classifications as used by the TCMA Provosts Gang Control Unit.

The most commonly encountered type of gang is the turf gang, one which lays claim to an area of the city and defends it with violence or subterfuge. The Provosts alone have seventy six such gangs registered on their files but there are far many more who are too small or too clever to be noticed by the cops. The more exclusive areas are no-go areas for gangs as the militant organisations and corporations fiercely protect their interests, and those of the citizenry at large. Fighting between neighbouring gangs can become extremely violent, especially if one is trying to muscle in on another's territory. A large number of the turf gangs are also involved in small time crime, mostly drugs, protection rackets and muggings. However, some gangs actively protect the people who live in their territory without resorting to extorting money from them. This sense of community pride is unusual but nevertheless exists in some areas of the city. Most notable of these 'protectionist' gangs are the Nightjackers from Shore Ditch Warrens who regularly fight with the extremely violent Drot from Burningfell to stop them from increasing their territory into the 'Warrens. Violent crime in the 'Warrens is rare due to the Nightjackers' habit of beating up or maiming muggers, rapists and robbers who decide (unwisely) to ply their trade in the area. The gang makes its money from drug dealing (soft drugs only, most of the time) and by selling information collected through its network of members and informants.

Supremacist gangs are a phenomenon grown from The Shift and The Bombardment that has refused to go away and the supremacist gangs can be liable to commit violence against anyone for no apparent reason. They stay well away from the big syndicates and live in mortal fear of the 3rds. Most of these gangs are merely a disorganised rabble with no name or proper territory, but there are a few large, well-organised supremacist gangs based in and around Fogwarren and south of Basin.

In the poorer areas, brightly attired troops of youths race downs the canals on skiffs, brandishing clubs and knives and generally causing mayhem. This 'chaseganger' culture has spread across The City with the rise in popularity of home-made films popularising their antics, often portray the chasegangers as glamorous and heroic. For most of the chasegangs in The City, it is organised ekranoplan racing which provides their inspiration and many try to imitate popular racers and customise their boats to resemble vehicles from their favourite team. Most of these gangs dress in bright colours, often with AGERL team logos on the back of their jackets or on their (rare) helmets.

Each gang appropriates a different logo (some gangs inventing their own) for itself, this becoming the mark of the gang, rather than having any official gang colours. Gangs symbols are also displayed from pennants mounted on masts attached to their boats, a distinctive symbol appropriated from the racing leagues.

Chasegangs tend to cause mayhem on the canals but very rarely indulge in deadly acts unless it is between two gangs. They tend to favour hand weapons which can be used to smash vehicles and people while travelling at speed, utilising anything from hammers to home-made swords and morning stars are used.

Some gangs defy classification, usually stemming from some form of subculture or alternative groups. Some have links to a variety of religious or quasi-religious groups, whilst others have connections to business interests. It is a source of much speculation regarding the use of street gangs by the macrocorps. Some say that this is simply another bit of folklore, others claim that the macrocorps make extensive use of streetgangs to subjugate and control populations in certain areas. Indeed, there may be some truth in this, as gangs in areas such as the Gorunna controlled Merryhell do seem to be unusually well-eqipped and well-informed.

In the Three Canals area the Provosts answer to the gang problem is increasing use of CATCH teams in anti-gang operations, particularly against the more violent turf gangs. It seems though, that the gangs and law enforcers are stalemated, with the situation set to continue for a long time to come.

the Shifted

Mysterious? Misunderstood? Monstrous? The Shifted who inhabit The City are all of these, and more. Where they came from, none can truly say. What they want, no one has the answers for. Suffice to say, there is no group in The City more hated, reviled and mistrusted than The Shifted.

Shortly after The Shift and The Bombardment, the shell-shocked, terror-crazed inhabitants of The City began to notice strange new shadows and hear incomprehensible new voices. Ghastly figures stalked the alleys and prowled the streets. No one could pin down exactly what was wrong or what was causing these manifestations. In the chaos which abounded, most of the reports were discounted as the ravings of starving lunatics. Yet, as time wore on and The City began to haul itself into some semblance of normality, people began to take the tales and stories more seriously. Efforts were made to investigate sightings and discover the truth behind these horrific folk stories. Then the truth dawned. Humanity was no longer the sole inhabitant of The City.

Since the dawning of realisation, The Shifted have been identified and classified into numerous groups. While only a small percentage of the population can say with any confidence that they have encountered a Shifted being (apart from the ubiquitous Simils), they are a real fact of life. From reports, sightings, and horrific evidence, mankind has pieced together fragmentary knowledge of these beings and learned something about their behaviour and existence.

dealing with the Shifted

To all intents and purposes, the motivations and goals of The Shifted are totally incomprehensible to humankind. If a Shifted being is heard to speak, it is, to the casual listener, a relentless babble of noise. Some of the creatures have been heard to speak in human tongues, yet even then their speech is beyond the realms of understanding. Jumbled words and fractured sentences pour from between their lips (if, indeed, they have lips). Some have, to a greater or lesser extent, attempted to deal with The Shifted, to make pacts and alliances. In some cases, these appear to have been moderately successful. In other cases, they have resulted in violence and death.

theories on the Shifted

Different groups across The City have widely varying views on The Shifted. Those who believe in the tenets of the Third Church of God The Architect view The Shifted as the minions of the Great Demolisher, out to destroy the work which God in His wisdom has wrought. Various sects of the Church actively attempt to fight the Shifted, tracking them down and destroying them. Admittedly, their schemes have met with little success, yet they continue to pursue their efforts with unabated vigour. The most easily dispatched are, surprisingly, the Simils. Captured Simils are fed into furnaces and melted down; their component parts reduced to iron ingots that the Church buries in crypts and catacombs. Efforts to destroy other Shifted beings have met with less success. Church Lay Reserves Martial units have often been torn apart trying to capture or destroy an Ubel, a fact which seems to little hinder their enthusiasm for the chase.

Perhaps the most sensible views on Shifted beings come from the Shift Studies Faculty (SSF) of Longshore University. Endowed with massive funds and utilising some of the best scientific brains in The City, they probe the very nature of The Shift and the beings which it threw up. The best guess of the SSF is that the Shifted were brought here from somewhere else, although where that somewhere else is (or was), they seem unwilling or unable to say. Of all organisations attempting to enter some sort of meaningful dialogue with The Shifted, they have met with the most success. According to University rumour, members of the SSF have actually entered into conversation with Lugner and Ubel. What these 'conversations' revealed, the Faculty has not yet said. However, it seems that if any one group of people is going to penetrate the true nature of The Shifted, the Shift Studies Faculty will be that group.

A third source of speculation on these beings is the folklore and rumour which permeates The City like a fog. Pervasive rumours state that The Shifted are in fact the spirits of all those who died during The Shift and The Bombardment. The story goes that they have been brought back to life, to haunt The City and take vengeance for lives cut dramatically short. Other folk tales insist that The Shifted are the product of horrific experiments carried out by the macrocorps in years gone by. All of the macrocorps stoutly deny any involvement in either The Shift or the beings which arose after it. Those who shout too loudly about this theory are quietly disposed of, adding even more grist to the rumour mill. The last of the more common folklore theories is one of the oddest and least well regarded. Some say that The Shifted are in fact beings from beyond The City, maybe from even further beyond. This particular theory states that they were not created by The Shift but they themselves created The Shift for their own ends.

Suffice to say, until things are proven one way or the other, the competing theories and beliefs will continually war against each other for dominance.

the Shifted races

Below you will find the extent of common knowledge on the five most frequently encountered Shifted beings.

drache

Insubstantial, seemingly nothing more than a vague, shimmering haze in the air, Drache are the least understood of The Shifted, mainly because they have no physical aspect which humankind can relate to. Gazing upon a Drache causes the eyes to twist, vision to blur and pain to explode inside the head of the viewer. They seem to be a species which was never designed to be gazed upon by human eyes. Careful research has discovered that Drache can control small electrical currents and manipulate electrical fields. Hence, the Drache are viewed as the cause of most of the cases of 'possession' in The City. There have been documented cases of criminals being shot dead in the act of committing a foul crime, only for those who stand witness to see a faint shimmer depart from the body at the time of death. Reliable individuals will swear to have seen some people surrounded by a faint haze which is painful to look at. While undoubtedly some of the incidences are acts of imaginative fancy, it is certain that Drache are responsible for some of these events.

hager

Tall, powerful, appearing from the dark and fog to kidnap and assassinate. Even in the rarefied circles of studying The Shifted, precious little is known about the Hager. Tales circulate of their immunity to bullets, their massive strength and utter ruthlessness. Many disappearances are attributed to the predations of Hager, but few can be proven. Physically, they are tremendously imposing, standing seven feet tall with a sculpted musculature beneath their all enveloping black garments. Their heads are featureless ovoids of pale, almost white, flesh. Their exposed hands are similarly featureless, six fingered, long and slender, without the knuckles and joints which characterise human hands. Hager never seem to travel alone, unlike other Shifted entities. They are always seen in groups of three or four. Reliable witnesses are, however, rare, for a visitation by Hager is seldom a time of joy.

Lugner

Lugner are seldom seen, but often heard. Of all The Shifted, they appear most adept at utilising human language for their own mysterious ends. Rumours and whispers appear from nowhere. Citizens lying in their beds hear strange voices in their ears, whispering terrible things. Those who claim to have seen the physical manifestation of the Lugner describe them as squat beings, almost obese, with pallid skin and puffy pink lips. Scientists working at Longshore University have theorised that the sole purpose of the Lugner is to spread dissent and misinformation. Why they do this, no one can truly say.

Simils

By far and away the most common of Shifted beings, Simils present an aspect to the world which seems radically at odds with the other Shifted races. Walking juggernauts of iron, brass, glass and stone, they tramp about The City, emitting sparks and gouts of steam. The most disturbing aspect of a Simil is its head: a human head. Seemingly impaled upon the

mechanical construction which is the rest of the Simil, the head is that of a dead man or woman. Some have run screaming from certain Simils, fearing that they recognise certain features in the twisted face which looks out upon the world. The face of many Simils are horrific to look upon, ravaged by pain and frustration. Others present an altogether more calm outlook, a calm so unnatural is highly disturbing. However, such is the strength of the Simils, they are commonly found labouring in hazardous environments, working for bizarre payments such as dolls, plants or photographs. Why they choose to do this, it is, again, one of the mysteries of The Shift. Suffice to say, they seem to be the only Shifted beings who will actually work for humankind, selling their services to whoever will pay them. Some gangs have taken to using these metal giants as hired muscle, relying on their strength and the fear that they inspire to defeat their opponents. In some cases, they have been hired as soldiers. In the Hundred Block War, Hirplakker hired many hundreds of Simils as 'suicide' troops in their fight against Arclight. Their lack of regard for their own physical bodies allowed them to wade through fields of fire which would decimate even the toughest and best equipped human troops.

Ubel

Of all The Shifted, it is perhaps the Ubel who are most feared by the common populace. Many of the most horrific killings and brutal murders have been attributed to Ubel and it is because of the frequency of these acts that Ubel are amongst the best documented of The Shifted. Sightings are relatively commonplace, the unlucky viewers always giving the same description: horrible, creaking beings, apparently with skeletons of rotting wood, strung with sinew and muscle, cloaked with tattered black rags. They are always reported as carrying rusted black iron blades, with which they slice and chop at their victims, all the while gibbering in their own language. On very rare occasions, Ubel have been captured and place in the most secure of detention cells. Here, they slam themselves against the walls, raving and screaming. After a period of incarceration, despite constant watches, they always simply disappear into nothingness.

the lost places

A lone man walks down a darkened alley, never to emerge on the other side.

An emaciated dog runs from nowhere into the middle of a crowded street.

Children scrabbling in cellars and basements, playing to blank out the misery of existence, find one of their friends gone. Forever.

Squads of heavily armed troops disappear while on patrol, their screams faintly floating on the breeze.

Half heard voices from nowhere, partial glimpses from the corner of an eye.

These are the Lost Places.

Even those who are wise in the ways of The City fear some places. Most feared are the Lost Places. Only whispered about on the streets or glimpsed in nightmares, the Lost Places are one of the mysteries of The Shift, places that are difficult to find and impossible to leave.

Some alleys, courtyards, cellars and even whole buildings appear on no map and reside in no memory. They are only stumbled upon by the unfortunate, the desperate or the mad. These are the parts of The City worst affected by The Shift, parts that were twisted and torn by the changes which The Shift wrought. No scientist can explain the nature of the Lost Places, they merely shrug their shoulders and turn away, afraid of what they may find if they look deeper.

Finding a Lost Place is a formidable task, you may only stumble upon one. For a moment, things seem familiar, but then you realise you must have taken a wrong turning, be on the wrong street. Then truth closes in. Buildings in these places seem to loom closer in, they appear to be more threatening. Alleys are tighter and more twisted, cellars more dank and dingy. It is here where The Shifted are at their most powerful. Overhead, the sky is pure black without a hint of colour.

Even aerial photography will not reveal the location of a Lost Place, they remain hidden from sight. Once the casual visitor is within, there is only one way out: the exact way you came in. Any other routes will simply bring you right back to where you started. Entering a Lost Place can be as simple as stepping slightly to the side when entering a courtyard, it can be as complex as winding through a maze of dark tunnels.

Some of these places are recollected in myth and legend. Torture Lane, supposedly a place of unimaginable pain and suffering. Corner Alley, a twisting nightmare which can drive even the sanest, most rational man to the brink of madness. These are only two of the legends. Two out of a myriad of folk tales. Those who claim to have visited a Lost Place are usually discounted as insane, not an unreasonable viewpoint given the state in which these alleged victims are found.

Some have gone so far as to question The Shifted about the Lost Places, seeking arcane knowledge which may give them power over others. Allegedly, no answers have ever been forthcoming. Even the more 'talkative', of The Shifted remain tight-lipped (in those occasions where they are seen to have lips).

a sense of common indecency (part 3)

The worst place in the world? It's where you are now.

It's never pleasant to stagger down a stairwell scabbed with blood and gore. The desiccated remnants of past battles, battles fought nose to nose with knives and sharpened spades. It's easy to sense the despair and confusion of these skirmishes in the gloom. I really don't know how some of the lights in here still work! Must be a generator buried somewhere. Every so often gunfire echoes from far away, usually accompanied by running feet and plaintive screaming. This must be the worst place in the world.

Things were getting tight for the Simils. At some of the corners, they could barely squeeze their metallic bulks round, scraping and scratching on the pitted concrete. It's the disturbing sense of calm which they radiate. It's really beginning to put the frights up me. Through the twisting, bronchial maze we trekked, never out of range of the sounds. Sometimes they were closer, at other times they were almost inaudible. But they were always there. These weren't sounds created by men, but by animals masquerading as men. After the first few minutes in this place, my sense of smell had, thankfully, ceased to function, yet it came back like a punch between the eyes when we crawled into the next chamber.

It loomed far overhead, a massive cylindrical space lit by two flickering, faltering lamps nailed into the scabbed walls. The floor gently dropped away, forming a great bowl into which

all sorts of putrid ordure had gathered, channelled by conduits and dripping from the walls. But it was the collection of wretches clustered around the fetid pool that almost caused me to flee right back to the safety of Mire End. They had probably been soldiers at one point; maybe even some of the first troops sent to defend this place. What they were now was a joke. How they remained alive was a mystery. Severed limbs had been replaced with crude simulacra fashioned from wood, string and scrap metal. Their skins were uniformly rotted and decayed, black in some places, grey and pallid in others. Most were eyeless, all were clad in scraps of cloth and sheeting. They drank from the putrid pool in the centre of the room, sometimes vomiting the contents of their stomachs back into the liquid, to mix with the already diseased vileness.

The surface of the pool shimmered with a deeply unhealthy blackness. Like a scar in the reality, liquid flesh over an otherworld of awfulness. High, high above me was a tiny point of light, barely visible. God, this must go all the way to the roof of The Silo. How deep are we? A croaking wail emitted from the nearest of the figures. He (she?) pushed upright on arms knotted with pustules and boils, questing with pits long bereft of eyes. "Ghoo zag agonn?" Bloody hell, the damn thing could still speak. "Ummm. I'm, aaaa, looking for..." Words quite honestly failed me. What could I say that could make any sense to something that must be destroyed by madness? "Hooarch kor ummmin?" I guessed this was some kind of interrogative remark, or possibly just deranged ramblings. The figure crawled towards me. The Simils crowded the entranceway behind me, leaving me nowhere to go. Blast! Its hands grasped at my boots, feeling for my breeches, clawing towards my waist. For the first time in years I was rooted to the ground with a horrid sense of loathing and fear. Pity did not even enter the equation. It found what it was looking for. My gun. Cooing like a baby, a strange, almost calming sound, it caressed the barrel, lightly tracing the metallic outlines, as if committing the shape to memory. Looking down into the pits that once held eyes, into the grotesquely changed face of what had once been a fellow man (or woman?), I realised what it wanted. Like all of us in the place, it wanted release. My life as a Lostfinder has been spent looking for things which have gone. This wretch wanted the peace which it had been denied. To do any less would have been failing in the oath I swore to myself all those years past.

The detonation echoed round and round the chamber, spiralling upwards like sonic smoke. Other figures stirred, crawled, wailed and scrabbled.
"Kill them. Now. All of them."
Maybe the Simils understood the pain and suffering, maybe

they were just following the orders of their employer. Who knows? They did their job, quickly and efficiently. When it was over, I'm sure none of us felt any better.

The sword of truth is blunted by time. Lies are a razor.

We found her at last, following the instructions Lockkstar had given me. Huddled in the corner of a pump room, behind shattered pipework, lying in a puddle of urine and filth. In all honesty, I should have felt some satisfaction. Suffice to say, I didn't. Seldom have I taken on jobs to pay off a debt and I'll be damned if I do it again. A dull concussive thump came down through the concrete, dust trickled down from the ceiling.
"Artillery." Intoned one of the Simils.
"Really? Must have been a fucking big shell to be felt down here."
"Mortar."
"Brilliant. That's what I need right now, a discussion on siege artillery." For the first time, I realised exactly how menacing the Simils looked in the dim, wan light. How they fitted in here. As if they were a part of the place.
"Anyway, lets get her bundled up and get out of here, shall we?"

Entropy is now declared obsolete. We no longer need rules.

Sitting in Wittens Emporium ("Serving Folly Hills For Over Fifty Years. And No Deaths Yet!"), sipping some java and browsing the Mire End Tribune ("Local News For Local People") , the events of recent days seem strangely distant, like a tale related by someone you don't really like and would rather not be with. The wound is healing nicely and Shroden the radical herbalist stopped the alarming spread of some rather nasty infections. It would be all to easy to slip back into the semi-comfortable way of life, unchanged by experience. Somehow, I do not feel that will be easy. Or desirable. What we witness changes us. If it changes us for the better, making us stronger, more human or more thoughtful, then that can only be a good thing. On reflection, though, was it worth it?

All that to rescue a stolen pet dog.

"Nah, don't care me. Got me boat, got me gun, got me shivs. Fine, I am. Nothing scares me, not a thing. I see one of those Ubel, I spit in his eye. Shifted? It's all just madness. Me, I got me own thinking on that. S'all just a big things those macros got goin'. All this Shift stuff, just a big gag, keep the locals frighted. Blokes in suits wi' knives is all. None of it's real. All a con, if you ask me. Which you did. Now, about that shilling°."

'Mudjack', Nomad/Boatperson, Least Canal South.

the place

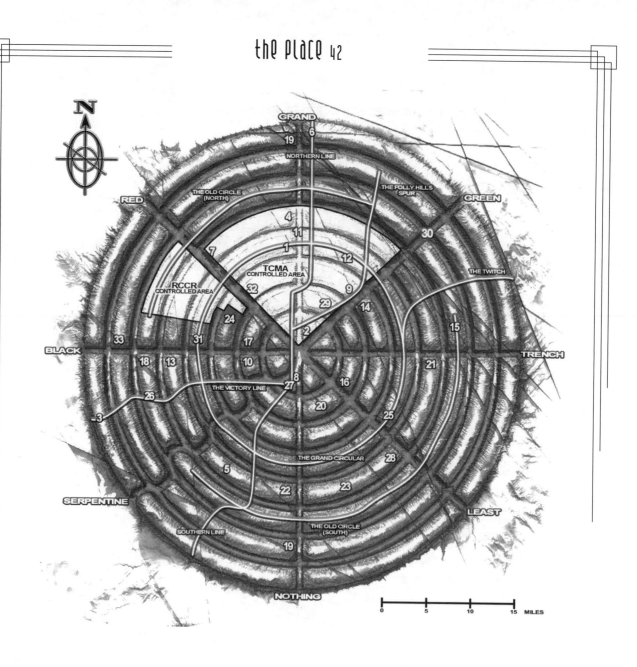

Burghs

1. Bankside
2. Brightlights
3. Calculus Tor
4. Clearwater Break
5. Colsetter Parish
6. Dog Junction
7. Dreamingspires
8. Fogwarren
9. Folly Hills
10. Hangside
11. Long Pond
12. Lucent Heights
13. Merryhell
14. Mire End
15. Project 97
16. Shore Ditch Warrens

Industrial Areas

17. Burningfell
18. Deepdown
19. The Train

Macrocorporate Domains

20. The Cathedral
21. The Forbidden City
22. The Iron Bastion
23. Konkret

24. Luminosity Tower
25. The Powerhouse
26. Trenevier

Notable Buildings

27. CrossBar Terminus
28. Inferno
29. Longshore University

Other Areas

30. The Brackens
31. The Contested Grounds
32. The Forest
33. Smokey Mountain

Within this chapter, you will find details on thirty-three different areas of The City. Each description provides an overview of what the place is like, any security or military presence that the area may have, a highlighted location within the area and a highlighted personality for the area.

The chapter is sub-divided into the following parts:

The Passing Of Time: How the minutes, days, months and years pass in The City.

The Bliss Of Ignorance: Give details on some of the more common drugs that the citizens of The City use.

Sound & Fury: A short essay on language in The City, covering the three main forms as well as a selection of dialects.

Flora & Fauna: Not only does The City teem with human life, it also teems with plant and animal life. Yet, only the hardiest can survive in this harsh landscape, giving rise to strange, sometimes incomprehensible plants and animals.

Burghs: These are areas which are primarily used for dwelling, shopping, working and all the other activities associated with everyday life. They can vary in size from a few blocks to many square miles.

Industrial Areas: These are areas dominated by manufacturing, mining, engineering and other industrial processes. While many people do live within industrial areas (in Burningfell, for example), they are mainly given over to industry.

Macrocorporate Domains: Headquarters of the macrocorps, these areas are imposing, even threatening places. They reflect the ethos and personality of the company that dwells within. You will notice that while there are eight macrocorps, there are only seven domains. This is due to the fact that I-LOK does not have anything which could reasonably recognised as a domain.

Notable Buildings: Particularly large, impressive, ancient or interesting buildings that deserve highlighting and description.

Other Areas: This section covers any areas which do not easily fall into any of the above categories.

the passing of time

A year in The City is composed of ten months, each month consisting of thirty three days and each day consists of 25 hours of sixty minutes each. Months, days and hours are simply referred to by their numbers, nobody has gone to the trou-

ble of devising specific names for them. However, the year is also divided into five two month seasons named Cold (1st and 2nd months of the year), Mist(3rd and 4th months of the year), Burn (5th and 6th months of the year), Damp (7th and 8th and months of the year) and Freeze (9th and 10th months of the year). The most common system of counting the years is to take the alleged time of The Shift as a baseline and numbering from then on. Consequently, the current year is 997, with the time of The Shift being Year Zero.

For the vast majority of the inhabitants of The City, time is not a massively important feature in their lives. They live according to when they have to go to work, when they have a day off, when it's time to eat. Actually taking note of what day it is seems rather pointless, especially when most days drag by in a dull repetition of those which have gone before. Those who feel the need keep track of the day of the month and what year it is through various means. Holographic displays (if you are that wealthy), water clocks, steam timepieces and mechanical watches all have their part to play in keeping those who need to know in the know. For example, if you had to meet someone in front of Luminosity Tower at a given time, you would arrange to meet them at, for example, 18.35/15/5/997. 18.35 represents the time of day (in this case thirty five minutes past the eighteenth hour of the day), 15 represents the fifteenth day of the month, 5 represents the month itself and 997 tells you what year it is.

the bliss of ignorance: drugs in the city

Writer's Note: This section is about drugs in the context of a fictional game world. These are not real drugs, this is only a game. Drug use within the context of the game is up to individual GMs and players. It is a common part of life in The City, an avenue of escape for those living with untold horror. We do not condone or condemn the use of drugs in the real world and do not attempt to make any judgements on those who choose to take any form of drug.

Escape from the horror of life in The City is foremost in the minds of many citizens. Some choose the solace of religion, some turn in upon themselves and vast armies choose the blissful comforts of drugs. The scale of drug taking in The City is completely unknown, suffice to say that is extremely widespread, common in all levels of society. From the casual nebelweed smoker to the pitiful scrape addict dying from his infections, drug users can be seen on almost every street corner. This dependence on chemical dreams has led to the conspicuous wealth of certain criminal organisations, who tap into a rich vein of profit by manufacturing, buying and selling drugs.

Most of the more commonly available drugs are manufactured from the indigenous plant or animal life of The City, grown in greenhouses or harvested from the streets, a whole spectrum of narcotic satisfaction is available. Other, normally more powerful or obscure, drugs require greater ingenuity to synthesize, ingenuity which is beyond the reach of the average peddler. In the shadowy recesses of commercial labs, chemists and pharmacologists turn a blind eye to the production of addictive substances, preferring to live a quiet life and avoid rocking the boat.

Edge

Popular with those who seek greater clarity, Edge has the effect of temporarily improving perception and, some say, increasing creative ability. This may help to explain its wide use amongst artists, writers, poets and the like as well as with macrocorporate managers seeking to focus on given tasks.

Method of Consumption: Pill
Effects: Heightens sensory awareness, improves clarity of surroundings, possibly increases creative ability.
Addictive Potential: Mild potential for physical addiction, moderate potential for psychological addiction.

escape

A powerful hallucinogenic, escape is the drug of choice for those who really want to forget about the awfulness of their lives. Moments after consumption, the user begins to descend into an alternative world, a world under the control of their subconscious. If the user is relaxed, then the journey into their own personal fantasy land is most likely to be pleasurable, if somewhat strange. If they are tense, nervous or worried, then the journey can become a nightmare of horrific proportions.

Method of Consumption: Pill
Effects: As described above, an intense hallucinatory experience.
Addictive Potential: Moderate potential for physical addiction and a mild potential for psychological addiction.

nebelweed

The single most commonly consumed drug (if you discount alcohol) in The City, nebelweed grows in pavement cracks, up walls and along canals. Anywhere moist and dull (which means almost everywhere in The City) will support the growth of this hardy, tenacious plant. It grows at an alarming rate and it seems that only the speedy harvesting of the plant for smoking purposes prevents The City being swamped in greenery. Nebelweed is cheap, as you can go out and collect it yourself. Only specially grown, more powerful variants command any kind of price in the retail market.

Method of Consumption: Normally dried then smoked in a pipe or rolled in paper.
Effects: An overall sensation of calm, with a slight unsteadiness on the feet if too much is smoked.
Addictive Potential: Very, very mild potential for physical addiction with a mild potential for psychological addiction.

scrape

Horrifying in its ultimate effects, scrape is nevertheless a popular, powerful narcotic which always seems to have a market for new users. Nobody is very sure who first developed scrape, yet it is easily manufactured with the right equipment. The major side effect of the drug is a progressive thinning of the skin which causes the user to scratch almost uncontrollably. As the addict uses more and more of the drug, the skin becomes thinner and thinner and the scratching more intense.

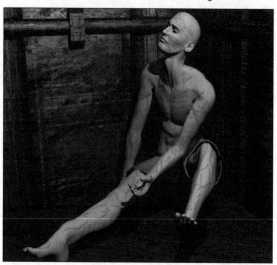

This leads to open sores, infections, blood poisoning and, ultimately, a painful death. Scrape addicts often bind themselves tightly with strips of cloth to stop the scratching. However, makes no difference. As the compulsion soon becomes too strong, culminating in a slow, agonising death.

Method of Consumption: Can be consumed in a variety of forms, injected in solution, taken orally in tablet form or, in some forms, smoked.
Effects: Intense feelings of euphoria coupled with a perception of physical invulnerability. This lasts about ten minutes before a crashing comedown which reduces the user to a quivering, twitching, scratching wreck.
Addictive Potential: Extremely high potential for physical addiction. Most users become addicted after their second or third hit.

Sound & Fury: language

Language in The City is a many splendoured thing. From three broad language groups have sprouted numerous dialects, patois and tongues. From the stuttering, staccato sentences of Broken, to the whispered nuances of Menace, there are as many vernacular language forms in The City as there are burghs.

All language comes from three basic groups, called Common, Culture and Commerce. Most citizens can speak at least two of these forms fluently, or they at least can speak one fluently and have a passing knowledge of another. Common is a straight forward, language, ideally suited to everyday interaction, the expression of technical ideas and the process of teaching. Culture, on the other hand, is a very tonal language, with many subtle variations but a somewhat limited vocabulary. It finds use in the arts, the writing of poetry, songs and plays. Lastly, there comes Commerce, a gutteral language, harsh and didactic, mainly used by traders, salesmen and those engaged in any form of commercial activity. Between the three main language groups, there are some points of similarity and over the decades, some words have been transposed between the languages. The vast, vast majority of people can speak Common with a fair level of fluency, followed by Commerce, with Culture bringing up the rear, as it is most frequently used by the upper and middle classes.

Each of the language groups can be further broken down into the various dialects and tongues which have sprung up around The City. Many burghs will have expressions and forms which are unique to them, whilst some professions have their own dialects, which, while spread across The City, are almost exclusively used by members of a profession, organisation or society. Some of the more common dialects are as follows:

Broken: Seemingly designed to get the maximum amount of meaning into the shortest possible sentences, Broken is a difficult tongue to speak, as it requires many of the tonal skills associated with Culture, even though it is descended from Common. Broken is not encountered very frequently and is most often used by Nomads and boatpeople living on the canals. Common speakers will find it very difficult to understand what is being said.

Cant: An offshoot of Culture, Cant is the high language of the Third Church of God The Architect. While most sermons to the laity are delivered in Common, discussions amongst ordained members are carried out in Cant. It is a flowing, smooth dialect and one which fluent Culture speakers can follow to a certain extent, although they may miss out on many of its subtleties and specific meanings.

Electrospeak: The internal language of the Ancient and Honourable Guild of Fulgurators, Electrospeak is full of technical details, scientific expressions and particular slang which has developed over a period of centuries. Only ever encountered within the Guild, it requires not only the learning of another language but also the learning of a complex lexicon of technical expressions linked to the business of the Guild.

Fighting Talk: Favoured by ghostfighters, soldiers, scops and other combat professionals, Fighting Talk is a clipped, sharp dialect based on Commerce. It is spoken in very fast, short sentences, with the minimum of wasted breath. Those not familiar with Fighting Talk will hear it as a series of sharp bursts.

Menace: Full of low, hissing sibilants, Menace appears to have grown up amongst the criminal elements in and around Long Pond. It has now spread out and is generally accepted as the language of criminals in the TCMAA. A variation on Common, most speakers of the root language will take on board about half of what is being said, the other half being incomprehensible gibberish. Menace has taken some of the tonal elements of Culture and a few of the more utilitarian phrases and words from Commerce.

Flora & Fauna in The City

Even in the harsh, polluted environment of The City, life still manages to exist in all the varying ecological nooks and crannies. From the mineshafts of Deepdown to the towers of Dreamingspires, life thrives and survives in all its variety and splendour.

Fauna

Bleeders: Appearing in a stunning variety of forms, bleeders appear to be descended from one root creature. All bleeders are six legged, with a chitinous exoskeleton and most are capable of flight. Ranging in size from tiny creatures less than half an inch long, right up to beasts measuring up to seven inches in length, they are a plague on the inhabitants of The City. They have adapted to life in The City by utilising the most plentiful food available: human blood. All bleeders, large and small, have splendidly developed mouth parts, designed to efficiently and quickly extract as much blood as possible from their host. While the amounts of blood consumed by bleeders are small, it is the fact that they carry disease which most terrifies the populace. Bag rot, sewer fever, twitching ague and all manner of unpleasant infections are carried by these parasitic creatures. Perhaps even more terrifying is the habit which bleeders have of injecting the target area with fluids to prevent coagulation of the blood. These fluids often play host to all manner of sickening, destructive parasites, none of which are easy to remove without hitech medical support. All in all, bleeders are deeply unpopular, feared and endemic throughout The City.

Dogs: Popular foodstuff, sometime pets and occasional terrifying menace, dogs are to be found in every area of The City, from the scrawny, diseased, feral specimens of the Contested Grounds to the pampered pets of Lucent Heights, dogs are the largest of the common city animals (obviously discounting humans and furies). Over the generations, selective breeding and natural evolution has turned some species into fat, waddling creatures barely able to support their own weight. They loll in pens and warehouses, chomping on fish guts and other unsavoury foodstuffs. When their time comes, they are slaughtered, their meat turned into food, their bones into glue and their hair and hides into clothing. Some dogs have been bred to fight or as guard dogs; squat, bull-headed horrors, all massive jaws and razor claws.

Fish: In cages floating the canals, in massive tanks held in warehouses and cellars, in vats on roofs, fish are everywhere, in every size, consumed by everyone. In the polluted, turgid waters of the canals, fat, bulbous, lethargic fish have been bred over the centuries to feed on the pollutants, sewage and rubbish which floats through the waters. They will eat almost anything which is thrown to them, blinking blindly in the opaque waters, swallowing anything which might serve as sustenance. Famous canal breeds include the Bankside Bulb, Thorsens Leaper (something of a misnomer, as it can barely move, let alone leap) and Quag Eels. All of these are pretty foul tasting but provide a lot of nutrition for many people in The City.

In the more refined environments of macrocorporate tanks and rooftop vats, fish of a slightly better flavour are bred. Immense specimens with tiny heads and massively swollen bodies loll in grubby tanks, ready to be hauled out, gutted, filleted and sold to the hungry masses. Wild fish tend to be bottom dwellers, all the better to avoid the millions of nets and lines of city dwellers desperate for a nutritious meal. Flat,

skulking, dun coloured fish root amongst the silt and garbage at the bottom of the canals, feeding of the detritus which drifts down from above.

Furies: Deep in old foundations, through sewers and train tunnels, splashing through forgotten reservoirs, the furies shamble, run and creep the bowels of The City. The results of torture, experimentation, toxins, pollution, radiation and biological contamination, furies are the mutant offspring of every strand of DNA in The City. No two furies are alike and it is generally reckoned that they are incapable of breeding. Still, they appear, ravaging slums, slaying workmen in the tunnels, screaming their deformed lungs out. With some furies, it's easy to identify what they started life out as. With others, it's doubtful that even the most detailed scientific analysis could determine what they once were. Some furies become famous across wide areas of The City. People in Shore Ditch Warrens still talk of the fury which rampaged through their burgh twenty five years ago. Most observers reckoned it had once been a dog, warped by the experimentation's of some demented madman, bent on creating a biological terror weapon.

Scurts: A plague on the inhabitants of The City, scurts are endemic vermin, infesting every nook, cranny and recess. They are six legged creatures with a hard exoskeleton covered in a rough, bristling 'fur'. Two large and two small multi-faceted eyes glare out balefully above a protruding, segmented jaw lined with tiny rasping teeth. Ranging in size from four to twelve inches in length, scurts destroy stocks of food, carry plague and pestilence and even attempt to eat the extremities of sleeping individuals. Much to the annoyance of most people, scurts aren't even good to eat. Even when pulped and turned into meal, fish refuse to eat their foul smelling, bitter bodies.

Tyrants: Wandering troubadours cluster round gas flames and tell tales of the tyrants. Rumours and legends twist through the minds of the people, feeding the darkest desires of men. The tyrants are ghosts in The City, mere wisps of superstition and fear. Many theories exist about the tyrants, some say they were once men, driven underground by The Shift, never to emerge into the light. Others say they are horrific creatures of darkness, the most tortured and insane of the furies. Some say they are noting but legend. But, sometimes, in the darkest recesses of The City, down in the ancient depths where few dare to tread, gigantic black shapes are seen to flit through the air and skip across the vaulted roofs.

flora in the city

Worming into every crevice, climbing walls or being cultivated in courtyard plots, plant life is everywhere. That having been said, most of the plants which are not cultivated for food are totally inedible. Indeed many of the food plants taste as if they should be inedible, the result of being fertilized with raw sewage and sucking in the pollution laden air of The City.

Nebelweed: Of unknown origin, nebelweed is a tough, fibrous creeper that seems to thrive in the wet cracks of wall and pavements. It's not known who discovered the narcotic properties of this plant, but wild nebelweed provides a modicum of escape from reality for many citizen of The City (see 'The Bliss of Ignorance, also in this chapter, for more details of the effects of nebelweed).

Trees: Only really common in protected areas such as The Forest or Central Park, majestic trees are something that the average citizen can go their entire life without seeing. Ranging in size from the Spreading Hurtlenut (only three of which are actually known to exist, all of which are in The Forest) to the miniature Retiring Oak (a popular accessory for the houses of the wealthy nomenklatura), trees are always valued as a connection with the natural world. Some religious groups, such as the Greenkeepers, have taken this veneration to its logical extreme and made trees the central part of their belief system.

Troot: Tasty, nutritious and full of goodness. The troot is none of these. It is, however, easy to grow and quite filling. Grown in miniature gardens everywhere or in massive cultivation factories, troot is a pale yellow, rough ovoid about the size of a clenched fist. It can be fried, baked, mashed or (in particularly desperate circumstances) eaten raw. Fried troot and fish is a popular meal, served in the traditional wrapping of greasy huyzel vine paper.

Apffel Plants: Prized sources of fresh fruit, apffel plants range from tiny varieties providing shrunken, bitter fruit, to twenty foot high monsters grown in jealously guarded courtyards which provide shiny, heavy, sweet fruits. Owners of apffel plants guard their property with vigour and enthusiasm, as prime fruit can sell for enormously inflated prices.

Fungus: Everywhere there is a damp surface to grow on, you'll find fungus, in a huge variety of forms, colours and shapes. From the deepest sewer to the tallest building, all will be decorated with varicoloured fungal splashes. It is these very funguses which provide the herbalists and apothecaries of The City with much of their raw material, as they refine various parts of the wide number of funguses to make serums, potions, curatives and medicines. Some growths, such as Boatmans Finger, can give rather unpleasant infections to those who touch them, while others, such as Bricktunnel Shroom, are highly sought after delicacies. Particularly despised is Chisel Fungus. The bane of many a homeowner and businessman, chisel fungus has the unhappy knack of being able to eat through concrete (especially the poor quality concrete found in The City). Luckily, it doesn't attack the concrete with anything approaching rapidity. It can, however, spread rather rapidly. This has lead to a thriving service industry of sprayer-toting fungicide merchants, only too happy to take large sums of cash in exchange for ridding poor unfortunates of the pest.

Huyzel Vine: Crawling over, through and around the buildings of The City, huyzel vine endemic in some areas and totally absent in others. Some buildings can be cloaked in the thick, rough vines, while their next door neighbours are clear of any kind of plant life. One endearing attribute of the vine is the tough fibres at its core. These can be stripped out and used for a variety of purposes, including making a rough cloth and sturdy rope. Thanks to the quick growing nature of the vine, it can be harvested on a fairly regular basis.

burghs

From the teeming, stinking horror of Dreamingspires to the antiseptic cleanliness of Clearwater Break, the burghs of The City are as varied as the people who live in them. Some are controlled by lumberingly bureaucratic local governments, others by religions, some by cartels of wealthy businessmen and still more by their own small burgh councils. Each burgh has its own flavour (sometimes literally) and character, with unique sights, sounds, smells and experiences.

bankside

Region: Lat 8, Ring 4
Status: Residential, light industrial
Law: Self-policed
Wealth: Low

overview

An almost palpable odour of fish, sweat and sewage rose over Bankside. As the sun came up, the residents were already going about their business, legal or otherwise. Stories circulated that One Eye Frank had jacked another Provost patrol on the edge of the burgh. Down by the canal, massive cages full of bulbous, lethargic fish were scrutinised by expert eyes. The fish were the lifeblood of Bankside and anyone that fucked with them would have a whole heap of trouble on his hands. Hardly any buildings here were over three stories tall and all were interconnected by walkways, gangplanks, ropes and pipes. This was a place of scum and treachery, but also a place of invention and commerce. The genetically engineered fish were sold all across The City, making Bankside one of the most prosperous slums anywhere. Boats, barges and skiffs began to congregate around the wharves, off loading buyers, keen to get the best fish for the best price. They were met with the steely glares of the fish farmers, who knew a good deal when they saw one. Back from the wharves, more secretive dealers laid out their wares and filthy mod clinics opened their doors for business. Commerce. That was the key. Something which hellholes like Mire End could never hope to achieve. Bankside began to throng and the day wore on.

Running for three miles alongside the hundred metre wide Grand Canal, Bankside is really numerous smaller districts that have become tangled together. The smells of sewage and rotting fish are predominant in this area. Many residents run microcorps specialising in breeding bio-modified fish that can live and reproduce in the stinking, polluted waters of the canals. While not especially tasty, these fish are a valuable source of food. Bankside is also home to numerous back street biosci clinics which, rather strangely, have grown out of the genetic engineering programs used to breed the fish. So twisted and tangled are the streets and so numerous and aggressive the denizens, the Provosts seldom venture into Bankside and as such, it is considered to exist separately from the TCMA.

However, despite the lack of interference from the forces of law and order, there is one conspicuous absence from Bankside: organised crime. For some unexplained reason, even the 3rd Syndicate and the Hohler Gang refuse to have anything to do with Bankside. Perhaps it is the clannishness of the denizens, or that the complexity of the area is too much even for the hardened criminals and then maybe it was because the 3rds and Hohlers found out that the people of Bankside were even more violent and nasty than themselves.

Few buildings in the area rise over two stories and only one could be described as high-rise: Block 54. This is the only remnant of Bankside as it was hundreds of years ago, some say that Block 54 even predates The Shift. Whatever its origins, it is an imposing, looming concrete tower, stretching two hundred metres into the sky. Scabbed with fungus and blackened with centuries of smoke and soot, '54 is uninhabited and feared. Many rumours surround the block: some say it is home to families of cannibals who snatch babies from their beds, others will tell you with authority that it is the lair of a cadre of Ubel who stalk the streets, creaking and rasping in their search for victims. The more hard-headed will tell you that this is all a load of old nonsense and that the block should be used for living space. Regardless of opinions, nobody ventures into Block 54.

Street level in Bankside resembles a cross between and open sewer and full-scale riot. If you want to get anywhere fast, use the walkways, gangplanks and bridges that arc across the streets and between the buildings. Such is the complexity of this overground highway system, that you can often find yourself walking through someone's dwelling without realising it. Most take this as a part of everyday life.

security/military presence?

Despite the fact that Bankside forms part of the TCMAA, the Provosts still refuse to go in. "Too dangerous" they say, "Cannibals" say some. Whatever the reason, you'll only ever find Provosts on the very edges of Bankside, never daring to venture more than a few tens of yards inside its boundaries. The only law in Bankside is that dished out by the citizens themselves. The most heinous crime in the area is interfering with the fish cages. Anyone found damaging cages, poisoning fish or stealing farming equipment is drowned in the Grand Canal without so much as a trial. Nobody asks questions.

highlighted location

the underground market

Description: Black market trade site, below Black Row, Bankside, TCMA

Located under Black Row in Bankside, the Underground Market (known simply as 'The Market') is an extensive series of underground tunnels, rooms and disused cellars. Within this cramped maze, hundreds of people come to deal in various illegal or stolen goods. The Provosts are well aware of its existence but as it lies deep within Bankside, they prefer to leave it alone. Current thinking goes that a campaign to clear it out would prove extremely costly due to the defensive, not say psychotically violent, nature of the inhabitants. Almost anything, from a sewing machine to a machine-gun can be purchased here, from individuals or small groups of dealers. The large criminal organisations such as the Hohler Gang and the 3rd Syndicate have no presence here, only occasionally sending someone in to purchase a particular item.

highlighted personality

wilbur renton

Age: Unknown, looks in his mid 30's
Height/Build: Short/Plump
Eye/Hair Colour: Hazel/Mousy brown
Occupation: Drug Dealer
Affiliations: None

If the price is right, Wilbur Renton can obtain almost any pharmaceutical substance you care to mention. Rumour has it that he has major league connections in one of the big chemical corps, other rumours say that he makes most of the drugs in a secret lab of his own. Whatever the case, it seems he has a never-ending supply of most drugs on the market. Circumspect and cautious, he never seems to be troubled by the police and maintains two tough bodyguards for that little bit of personal protection. If you met him in the street, you'd probably pass him by, being ordinary and unremarkable is his stock in trade, standing out would only be a hazard.

brightlights

Region: Lat 1, Ring 1
Status: Commercial
Law: Strict
Wealth: Very high

overview

The club thumped and the band played harder. Sweating in their suits, they plucked strings, blew horns and rattled drums as the dancers twirled and spun faster. The violinists arm was a blur and the double bass players fingers bled with the effort. A thick haze of nebelweed smoke obscured most of the room. In the curtained booths which lined the walls, couples copulated, argued, whispered or lapsed into drug-induced unconsciousness. Exquisite dishes of canapes lay half eaten on tables on trampled into the floor. Through it all swerved waiters and waitresses, balancing trays containing impossibly huge orders. Perspiring, inebriated patrons barked at the staff, fists were raised and sackings threatened.

In the midst of it all, a solitary figure stood, clad in a shimmering purple suit. The stark white collar embraced his neck, providing a plinth for his sculpted, streamlined head. The band wound up the number and announced a short break. The band members were all drenched, dizzy and dehydrated. The purple suited man strolled towards the band leader, now placing his baton back in a carved wooden case. The man whispered to the band leader, who shook his head and pointed at his watch. The man struck the band leader across the face, leaving a scarlet trail down one cheek. Blood flowed freely from the wound, a neat line from a razor sharp blade. The band leader staggered to his feet clutching his face, blood cascading onto the floor. The other band members gathered, unsure of what to do.

The man in the purple suit grabbed a waitress, forcing her to drop her tray piled with glasses. Dragging her into the middle of the dance-floor, he gestured at the band and their now semi-conscious leader. They took up their instruments and began to play: faster, faster, faster. The man whirled the girl about the floor, clearing a space. He spun and flipped the girl, her red hair spilling out from its tight bun and flailing about her face. Above the sound of the band, there was a sharp crack as the girl landed heavily on her ankle. Her scream was drowned as the man urged the band to play faster. The girl was now a limp rag in his arms, being dragged around the dance-floor in a daze.

No onlookers intervened. Security remained impassive. The waiters and waitresses averted their eyes. The rich operated *by different rules, with standards that were all their own. To step in would be folly. Other people were simply objects, posessions to be used and discarded. The girl knew that and the man in the purple suit knew that. Being forced to dance on a broken ankle was a minor indignity compared to what many in The City suffered. Here in Brightlights, despite the wealth, the opulence and the grandeur, people were just as cruel and vicious as anywhere else.*

Bounded on all sides by affluent districts, Brightlights is the most famous shopping area in The City: Three square miles of high-class boutiques, restaurants, theatres, nightclubs and department stores. Only the well-to-do can gain access to this exclusive area unless you happen to occupy one of the many low-paid service industry jobs which Brightlights has generated.

Initially started two centuries ago by the macrocorps as a place of pleasure and relaxation for wealthy corporates, Brightlights has grown beyond the wildest imaginings of its creators. Citizens from Coldbath Fell and Lucent Heights travel here to spend their hard-earned cash. Due to its location within the bounds of the TCMA, it has become something of a money spinner for the Authority, which continually hikes taxes and business rates in order to have an ever increasing flow of money from the business which choose to locate here. In truth, most of the shops and other facilities are still owned by the macrocorporate of their subsidiaries. Such is the cost of buying land and setting up a business in Brightlights, very few independent retailers can afford to start trading.

Due to its status and reputation, the streets and canals of Brightlights are immaculately clean, with huge squads of sanitation workers tasked with keeping the area looking its best. Micro-trams and cablecars are provided free of charge, funded by the massive amounts of cash which flow through the shops and leisure facilities. This comes as a shock to many nouveau riche, who are used to paying through the nose for public transport. Rather than use automated systems to run

the transport network, uniformed staff are at the beck and call of shoppers, sometimes having to put up with arrogant and unreasonable demands. The cost of products in Brightlights is truly stunning: clothes can be bought here which cost in excess of five hundred times the average weekly wage. Entrance to an average club amounts to one hundred pounds, and that's before any drink or additional services have been paid for. Many clubs offer the services of 'escorts' (they wouldn't lower themselves to using such a common terms as prostitutes) who will (for a price) attend to the every need of a wealthy patron.

security/military presence?

Security in and around the area is very tight. In order to get in, you must demonstrate a credit balance of at least £5000. Wealthy shoppers will travel many miles to shop in the arcades and boutiques of Brightlights. As Brightlights is very close to the residence of large numbers of The Citys elite, security in the surrounding areas is also very good. The main security force is provided directly from Trilhoeven's armed forces. This has led to some unfortunate incidents, as the guards are line troopers rather than trained security operatives, which can lead to a somewhat gung-ho attitude. On a more positive note, it is Trilhoeven's proud boast that they have never killed or injured any person who had actual reason to be in or near Brightlights.

highlighted location

the sparkly blue top

Description: Nightclub, 24 - 36 Trinity Boulevard

The 'Top is one of the most popular night-clubs in Brightlights and combines dining and drinking facilities as well as dancing and floor shows. It is decorated in an extremely extravagant, 'old world' style, with many unique and expensive items of art and furniture. Heavy fines are dealt out for damaging fixtures and fittings. Prices in the club are very high due to its popularity and desire for a better class of client, a night leaving very little change out of £250. Average prices are £10 for an alcoholic beverage, £60 per person for a meal and £25 per person for a floor show. The entrance fee is a rather steep £40.

highlighted personality

rembrandt sanger

Age: 36
Height/Build: 5' 8"/Slim
Eye/Hair Colour: Variable
Occupation: Cabaret Artist
Affiliations: None

Famed throughout the TCMA for his musical comedy routines, Rembrandt Sanger is very much in demand amongst the clubs and bars of Brightlights. A man of seemingly unlimited charm and wit, he can hold an audience spellbound for hours at a time. However, he is also a manipulator and confidence artist of the highest order. He is never seen with the same woman twice and is reputed to have seduced many hundreds into his bed. His sparkling eyes, amusing quips and obvious wealth take in many an admirer, admirers who find themselves used, abused and cast aside without a second thought. Yet these very same people who have been cast aside still clamour for Rembrandt's attention, desperately trying to regain their place in his inner circle of friends and confidantes. Many believe that Sanger wields considerable power within the TCMAA due to his contacts and access to an unending stream of gossip, rumour and innuendo.

calculus tor

Region: Lat 6, Ring 8
Status: Residential/industrial area
Law: Variable
Wealth: Variable

overview

Lollygaggers and gawpers crowded around the scene of the accident. A drunken warehouseman had driven his wagon into the parapet of Basal Bridge and now the heavy vehicle was balancing precariously on the edge of the span. Below, skiffers and gondoliers on the Lyre Canal halted their craft and stared in amusement at the impotent bulk of the lorry.

Vendors and costers, ever with an eye for a quick sale, crowded around the scene of the disaster, crying their wares:
"Smoked fish! Nice and hot! Smoked fish! Thrupence a quarter!"
"Lithos! Get your lithographs here! Preserve this day for the ages! Come along now."
"Stolen dingin parts! All kinds, stolen dingin parts, get them while they're hot!"
The cries intermingled into an unrecognisable cacophony as the sellers bawled their offers.

The warehouseman slumped against the partially destroyed parapet, a broken bottle of booze clutched in his hands. Black dust from the demolished stones coated his overalls with a fine powder. Rhythmically moving his head from side to side, he moaned softly, taking desultory swigs from the bottle.

As the crowd grew, rumours began flying.
"I heard he's just been sacked from Coleridge's."
"Really, that gadgie just told me he was trying to top himself, got debts with one of the tongs."
"Nah, just spoke to his foreman, got the real deal. Just lost his boy. Went up wiv' some uvvers lads to the Tor. Naught's been seen of him since twenty days. Least, that's what I was told."
"Bollocks! He's pissed, is all. Stupid old soak."

Another wagon arrived, its steel driving wheels striking sparks from the stone way. Whines and crackles emitted from its innards, causing the fishwives and gossips to draw back. A stout chain was hitched to the rear of the balancing wagon and it was gradually pulled back from the brink. The warehouseman was hoisted roughly on to the shoulders of rough passers by, spew dribbling from the corner of his mouth.

Neigle put down the telescope and removed the headphones from his ears. Turning to his wife, he smiled.
"Voyeur." she snapped.
"But my dear, how else would I spend my time?"

One of the most arresting physical manifestations of The Shift, Calculus Tor has come to mean both the sinister massif itself and the area of The City surrounding it. Calculus Tor itself is a huge bastion of black rock, thrust from the very earth during the upheavals of The Shift. Towering above the surrounding urban landscape, it casts a huge, brooding shadow over the buildings which cluster like tiny boats around its base. However, the Tor is not the only feature risen from the ground during The Shift. Another upthrust, lower but far longer (and imaginatively named The Ridge) rises to the north of the main tor. To the south are five narrow, jagged spires, equal in height to Calculus Tor, but far more slender. While none live on the Tor or The Ridge, the spires have become riddled with passages, tunnels and shafts, turning them into remarkable natural skyscrapers. Named The Steeple, The Tower, The Edge, The Crag and The Summit, The five spires are home to thousands of individuals and each has a character all its own. Rock quarried from inside these trees of stone has been used in the surrounding area to build houses, factories and all manner of building, lending a very natural feeling to the clogged, misty streets. Unlike the canals and streets of the inner city, the smog is not so thick here and on a good day, the sun can be glimpsed, shining through the haze. As previously mentioned, each of the spires has a different character, characters which have developed over hundreds of years of habitation. The Steeple is a dense warren of passageways and cells, home to the workers who toil in the manufactories located nearer the surface of the edifice. The Tower is home to the wealthier citizens of Calculus Tor. They have nothing but the best, with power purchased direct from GRID and fresh water provided by a well guarded purification plant located deep within the bowels of the spire. The Edge is little more than a ghetto, a haven for criminals of all classes and types. They are drawn there by the lack of any reasonable security presence and the labyrinthine complexity of the place. The Crag is dominated by members of the Shining Sky religion. While not controlled by them in any official way, members of the sect are encouraged to make their homes here, even if means turfing out existing residents who are not cult members. For members, basic power and sanitary facilities are laid on, non-members have to make their own arrangements.

The Summit has become home to a thriving class of middle-class businessmen and women. Galleries, malls and atria are crowded with shops, workshops and service industries, making The Summit is the most popular spire with visitors from the surrounding areas.

The two brooding mountains of Calculus Tor and The Ridge are mysterious, unexplored regions. Adventurers and glory seekers, alone or in groups, have ventured up the sides and into the many fissures and cracks which split the surface of these two giants. None have returned, giving the mountains a fearsome, black reputation. Many organisations have telescopes, sensors and scanners permanently trained on the mountains, hoping to probe (from a safe distance) the inner mysteries of the rocks. Some of the wealthier observers have gone so far as to send automaton probes into the crevasses. Without exception, they have ceased all forms of transmission within minutes of entering the gaps. Reputable scientists agree that all of the above must be the result of some Shift effect, an extraordinarily powerful effect.

Surrounding the Tor, The Ridge and the Spires are thousands of houses and factories. By common consent, the entire area around the seven main rock features, lying between the seventh and eighth concentric canals and bounded to the north by the Black Canal, is referred to as Calculus Tor. The region is made up of numerous small burghs and parishes, each attending to its own activities. Lotech industry is widespread here, buying in power from the Fulgurators Guild and (occasionally) GRID. Most of the housing either receives power diverted from the industries, from gas siphoned off from nearby dumps and middens or through the numerous windmills which sprout from rooftops.

Security/military presence?

Each of the spires, burghs and parishes of Calculus Tor must make their own arrangements as regards security and policing. Some burghs, such as Barren Street, have organised their own police forces. Barren Street operates a system of Special Constables, drawn from the general populace. Other areas hire the services of militant organisations, both large and small. The spires all operate their own systems for security: from the hired guards (provided by Kinetic Energy Incorporated) of The Tower to the thuggish factory security guards of The Steeple. Any infraction which may result in a slap on the wrist in one area, may lead to a brutal beating or imprisonment in another. It is best to have your wits about you when venturing through the burghs of Calculus Tor and avoid doing anything which may offend the locals.

highlighted location

Shadow Street

Description: Main thoroughfare

Running between The Steeple and The Crag, Shadow Street is a crowded, bustling thoroughfare, alive with the sounds of commerce and industry. Numerous bridges cross the small canals which intersect the street, yards open onto the road, emitting sounds of hammering and swearing. The stone buildings are home to all manner of purveyor, from costers selling exotic, macrocorporate produced fruits, to ironmongers stocking metal goods at exorbitant prices. Just above the gutters, vendors pitch their stalls, offering fast foods and trinkets to the passing crowds. Pickpockets are legion here, plying their dishonest trade amongst the shoppers and stallholders. Shuddering electric wagons make their unsteady, arcing way down the street, carrying raw materials and finished goods. If you stand on Shadow Street long enough, all life will pass you by.

highlighted personality

Luther Coleridge

Age: 48
Height/Build: 5' 11"/Muscular
Eye/Hair Colour: Blue/Steel grey
Occupation: Haulier
Affiliations: Calculus Tor Chambers of Commerce, Brotherhood of Cargo Carriers

One of the pre-eminent private businessmen in the Calculus Tor area, Luther Coleridge is a powerful and well-respected individual. Owner and operator of Coleridge Transport & Storage (a firm started by his Grandfather), his wagons and boats travel far from Calculus Tor, taking out and bringing in a staggering array of goods. Despite being a tough-talking, hard-nosed businessman, Coleridge is, at heart, a family man. The extended Coleridge family, covering four generations, live in the rambling upper floors of the haulage yards on Shadow Street. His power, however, is far from secure. Factions within the Chambers of Commerce and the Brotherhood of Cargo Carriers resent his wealth and influence. Moves are afoot (moves which Coleridge is only too aware of) to ruin him, destroy his business and blacken his name. It is doubtful, though, whether they realise what a fight they will have on their hands.

clearwater break

Region: Lat 8, Ring 5
Status: TCMAA Burgh
Law: Strict
Wealth: Very high

overview

"Easy, easy. Wind it back gentle now. Not that hard you arse! Gently. That's it."

Bearnice Micwhat crossed her arms and prayed that the rope would hold. Her colleagues strained and sweated as the pressed back on the levers attached to the winding mechanism of the bastard assemblage which stood in the centre of the roof. Creaks emanated from the spars and lines, iron bars groaned as the pressure increased. Micwhat watched the ropes.

"Easy now lads, just a couple more turns."

"Bearnice, why are we doing this?" The questioner was a small, scrawny figure clad from head to foot in a bulky, matt black suit which looked as if it had been made from lengths of electrical insulation.

"Because, young Hegger, we are striking a blow against the bloody posh nobs what live in that stuck up, dandified, overblown rats nest over there. See?"

"Yeah, I get that, but why?"

"You bloody just stop asking questions and get on with winding that damn thing, right!"

"Right Bearnice, sorry."

Standing out at right angles to the rest of the contraption, two laminated beams of iron were gradually being bent back, the tension increased.

"Whoa, whoa! That's it! Put the lock in place and get back." Bearnice ambled around the contraption, fiddling with lines, checking nuts, applying oil here and there.

"Here's the plan. First off, we fire that bag of iron there at the nets. Then, we crank her up as quick as we can and start slinging those bags of shit through the hole. That should give them a little surprise. Now, Hegger, you sure you got the range right?"

"No worries, checked it again this morning, we should be dead on."

"Right. Load! Stand back! Ready? FIRE!"

There was a thump and an immensely loud TWANG as the catapult arm was slammed forward by the massive crossbow construction. Half way through its trajectory, the bag of iron split open and a rain of scrap fell on the filternets of Clearwater Break, tear gaping holes in the opaque sheets.

"YES!" Bearnice danced about the roof. *"Yes, yes, yes!"* She danced over to a shocked and confused Hegger and kissed him full on the lips. *"Get the crap loaded and wind that thing*

back." She grinned broadly and made a rude gesture towards Clearwater Break.

"Great plan Bearnice. So where did you get the idea for an excrement catapult?"

Clearwater Break claims to be "The Cleanest Place You'll Ever See" and, on the surface, that would seem to be a pretty viable claim. Walled off from the rest of the TCMA, shrouded in fliternets, its canals cleansed and purified, Clearwater Break sparkles with perfection. From a distance, the burgh looks like a low fortress which has been draped with gossamer fine tents. In reality, this is not far from the truth. The gossamer fine nets are filters which purify and strain the rain which falls almost every day, removing pollutants and particulates, turning it into a clear drizzle free from harmful contaminants. The nets themselves are products of Trilhoeven biosci, living creatures which trap pollution and send it to centralised collection sacs, from which it is taken and dumped elsewhere. The canals which riddle the burgh are also clear and sparkling. Complex filtration systems, using some of the technology developed for the filternets, strain the water flowing in from the Grand Canal and elsewhere. However, this has given rise to the bit of a security problem for the burgh. So clean is the water which flows out from Clearwater Break that hordes of the poorer citizens of the TCMA gather round the outflowing canals, filling buckets with water before it can mingle with the polluted filth of the Grand Canal.

It is unsurprising that Clearwater Break is not the cheapest place in the TCMA to live. Many wealthy citizens choose to make their homes here, amongst the clean canals and elegant glazed brick buildings. Some of the macrocorps have also purchased property in this area, gifting it to favoured executives or using the area for rest and relaxation purposes. For those not wealthy enough to live in Clearwater Break but who still have to work in the various service industries which keep the burgh running, cleanliness and hygiene measures are extremely strict. Workers coming into the burgh are thoroughly showered and periodically cleansed of parasites and other noxious evidence of life in The City. Their working clothes are not permitted to leave Clearwater Break and must be scrupulously cleaned at the end of each working day. Actual amenities with the burgh are lavish but not extensive. There are many bars and restaurants, but few nightclubs, limited shopping and no theatres or music halls.

Security/Military Presence?

The very nature of the area and the wealth of those who live in it makes Clearwater Break a target for the spite and vitriol of the lower orders. This leads to a rather substantial and intimidating Provost presence. All entrances are guarded with extreme vigilance by Assault Division Tacticals, clad in their best dress uniforms. On the streets, subtle but effective plain clothed officers patrol night and day, keeping watch for any disturbances or breaches of security. The all-important filternets and canal filters are constantly monitored and any attempts at sabotage are dealt with in the harshest possible manner. At any one time, there will be upwards of two hundred Provosts in and and around Clearwater Break.

highlighted location

the peak

Description: Restaurant, 1-5 Trium Crescent

The only building extending above the all encompassing filternets, The Peak juts into the sky on a slim blue concrete needle, allowing dinners to look down on the shimmering sea of the 'nets. The cost of a meal in its glass walled and glass floored dining room can be far in excess of what the average city dweller earns in a whole year, yet The Peak is always fully booked. Discriminating guests come from as far afield as Lucent Heights and Coldbath Fell to sample the creations of the renowned chef, Filip Horten. Horten is known to scour The City for the best fish to serve his well-heeled diners.

highlighted personality

claudine loftus

Age: 26
Height/Build: 5' 4"/Slender
Eye/Hair Colour: Blue/Black
Occupation: Barmaid
Affiliations: None

Claudine Loftus is a young woman with a long standing grudge. Ordered by her rich parents to do, of all things, work for a living, she spends her days seething about her situation and longing for her thirtieth birthday when she can finally get her hands on some of her parent's money. She feels that working as a barmaid in the 'Yellow Strand Brasserie' is way, way beneath her and that she really deserves something better. In truth, Claudine is not that bright and not that highly motivated, with a self-opinion that far exceeds her intelligence. What got her in to trouble with her parents in the first place was her unwholesome habit of wandering out into The City and picking up boys. Many a time her parents had to call upon a private security firm to pick her up from some sordid drinking den in Folly Hills or elsewhere. Now she either works full time or suffers the consequences.

colsetter parish

Region: Lat 5/Ring 5
Status: Religiously controlled burgh
Law: Harsh, religious
Wealth: Low

overview

Dear Brother Kieron,

May the Blessings of our Mighty Lord, Creator of All, Architect of The City be with you upon this day.

After a journey of days, I have finally arrived in Colsetter Parish, most Sacred of Parishes devoted to Our Lord. I hope that you are keeping the Divine candles lit and are preaching His Word with all possible vigour. This evening, I shall be inducted into the Chosen Path, a most signal honour for this humble Servant of Our Lord. I shall meet His Holiness the High Cardinal Himself. Oh, to be in the presence of that most Pious and Holy man!

I have been given apartments which are way beyond the needs of a humble Priest such as myself. Although, I would not argue with the decisions of my Superiors. I have two whole rooms to myself. One of them measures a whole ten feet wide by eleven feet long! I am also very close to the private Chapel of the Chosen Path, a Testament to the Power and Glory of Our Most Divine Lord and Creator.

I have also been introduced to Cardinal Ducreux, a most substantial and important personage, for he is the Commander of the True Path. He presented me with my sidearm, an item of great value and importance. Inscribed upon its flank was the inscription 'Trilhoeven'. I asked, was this not one of the great non-believing organisations devoted to the work of the Great Demolisher. The Cardinal reassured me that it was Right in The Lords Eyes to use items from such groups against the Great Demolisher, thereby using His Own Instruments against Him. The Cardinal is indeed a most Wise and Perspicacious man!

Anyway Brother, I must now conclude this letter, as I must set about the Lord's Work. May He continue to Bless you in all ways. May our Church continue to stand firm against the unbelievers.
Yours,
Brother Andrew

PS There is a box of shotgun ammunition stored in the Knave. You may need it.

One of the parishes controlled by the Third Church of God the Architect (TCGA), Colsetter contains the headquarters of the TCGA, as well as numerous monasteries, convents and retreats. Surrounded by a high, forbidding metal wall and defended by the Lay Reserves Martial, Colsetter is an austere, indeed dull, place to live. Outsiders are allowed in only under extreme sufferance and are expected to pay a substantial sum to the Church coffers for the privilege of walking on hallowed ground.

To the outsider, the parish represents all that is worst about the TCGA: unending prayer and self-sacrifice, dull austerity and boring routine. For the true believers, it is the spiritual centre of their world, home to the High Cardinal and his priests, the ordained ministers of God Himself. Outsiders admitted into the parish are marked by coloured badges, the colour denoting their moral status as reckoned by members of the Church. Blue badges denote those who are morally safe and it is permissible for ordinary members of the laity to speak with and conduct business with them. Grey badges indicate those who are morally ambiguous and only ordained members of the Church or appointed Deacons may speak with them. Red badges denote those of suspect morals, who have only been given permission to enter the Parish under extreme sufferance and for a particular reason.

security/military presence?

Within the grim byways of Colsetter Parish, all matters of security are handled by the Lay Reserves Martial (refer to 'The Power' for further details). All entrances to the parish are guarded and armed patrols are a regular sight on the streets. Not only are they there to preserve the peace and ensure good behaviour, they also take action against any religious infractions. Visitors to the parish must be aware that they too can be punished for any transgression of the religious law. The Lay Reserves Martial can be very strict in their application of the law to outsiders, but quite a lot of it depends on who you are and what allegiances you hold. Those employed by the macrocorps are unlikely to be hassled, as the church has no desire to provoke a major diplomatic incident. On the other hand, an average person from the Three Canals Metropolitan Area doesn't really carry much weight and will find themselves, and their actions, closely scrutinised.

highlighted location

the southern port

Description: Gate leading to and from Colsetter Parish.

One of the four main gateways leading into Colsettter Parish, the Southern Port is an ominous, dark tunnel, constantly manned by hundreds of Lay Reserves Martial. Non-believers wishing to enter the Parish are subjected to lengthy questionings in order to ascertain the nature of their business, as well as their moral status. On the city side of the gate, the entrance is hemmed in by stalls, carts and assorted merchants, all eager to sell their wares to any members of the faithful who should happen to emerge from the port.

highlighted personality

deacon joseph vespasian

Age: 51
Height/Build: 5' 5"/Average
Eye/Hair Colour: Light brown/Grey
Occupation: Lay Reserves Martial officer
Affiliations: Third Church of God The Architect

Military commander of the security forces guarding the Southern Port leading into Colsetter, Deacon Vespasian takes his orders from Archbishop Mohaim, commander of the Lay Reserves Martial. Secretly, he is composing reports to the Cardinals about the lax attitude of his superior in the hope of removing him from office. At a mere five foot three, Vespasian is a diminutive figure but he has a mind like a cold razor.

dog junction

Region: Lat 1, Ring 8
Status: Independent burgh
Law: Very little
Wealth: Low

overview

The soldier stepped off the train as dust devils whipped across the platform. The air was filled with the sussurus of dust whispering against wood, the staccato yapping of dogs being fattened for the kill. Few people had heard of this place, right here on the edge of The City, a last outpost before the wastelands beyond. A few listless old men watched from benches, blinking slowly at the figure in grey. They scratched and smoked their pipes. The soldier hoisted his pack onto his shoulder and marched out of the station.

"Never heard of the place."
"Honestly? The Contested Grounds? Never?"
"Nope."
"Oh, right. Anyway, I've heard about some bloke, lives hereabouts, watches people as they go into The Outlands. You know him?"
"Oh, yes. Everyone in the Junction knows about The Observer. Stays out by, down near the edge. Old bunker, can't miss it."
"A bunker? How ironic."
"Eh?"
"Never mind."

The soldier wandered through Dog Junction. It was all so different from the interior of The City. Here people had never heard of the Contested Grounds, of Luminosity Tower, Inferno and the rest. Amazing. Here they bred dogs and stared out into the emptiness. Curious pre-occupations. He transferred the weight of his rifle onto the other shoulder. It was the last thing he owned from the 'Grounds, his last connection to another life.

"Are you the observer?
"Yes. I am that."
"Why? Why do you do it? What makes you?"
"Curiosity. The undying human quest for knowledge. Or perhaps it's just sick voyeurism? Who knows?"
"I see. So, when I go out. Out there. You'll be watching?"
"Yes. I watch everyone. You'll live on. As a mark on the line. I'll remember."
"Perhaps you'd better have this, maybe you can trade it for something useful."
"No, you take it with you. Better that way. Keeps things neat."

The soldier stood looking down at the wavering white line on the ground a few tens of yards away. He could feel the observer watching him, could sense him grasping his long paintbrush pole and pot of gluey paint. Why did it come to this, in this place? Death could have come so easily in the 'Grounds. Yet, he chose to come here. Out to the very edge of existence. In order to do what? To find out about himself? To see if it was true? He marched forward, clutching his rifle. A couple of yards from the line, there was a golden glow and a thunderous crack. The ground blackened and the soldier was gone.

Holding on to a precarious existence at the very end of the Northern Line, Dog Junction is a lonely, haunted place, peopled by some of the most marginalised (literally) citizens of The City. Dog Junction sits on the very edge of the city limits, wander too many yards to the north and you disappear in a cloud of dust. The inhabitants live with this constant fear, and as such, sleepwalkers are rare in Dog Junction. In drier weather, dust from The Outlands cakes the buildings and chokes the streets. When rains come, the dust turns to mud, caking clothes, boots, faces and dwellings. Most buildings here are low and ancient, fading remnants of the past. Moving through the area towards the edge, the buildings cease to be inhabited, becoming hollow shells, devoid of life and laughter for centuries.

Dog Junction survives from the foodstuff which gives the place its name. Rank warehouses and yards are home to hundred of fat, waddling dogs reared for food. The trains bring in tons of fish by-products to feed the dogs and take out butchered carcasses to feed the hungry masses in The City. Day and night the air boils with the barking, howling and yapping of the dogs. Men and women stagger home from a days work in the stockyards and butcheries, caked in blood and dung, accompanied by the eternal howling of the dogs. The occasional visitor from the inner recesses of The City sometimes appears in Dog Junction. Most come simply to stand on the tallest buildings and stare out at the limitless emptiness of The Outlands. Some come as the final act in their lives, passing through on their way to walk into The Outlands, to disappear forever.

The buildings of Dog Junction are a ramshackle collection of the ancient, the recent, the sturdy and the flimsy. With the relatively sparse population, people can choose to have fairly spacious accommodations. However, most choose to live packed together like most other city dwellers, preferring the close company of the fellow men. The limitless expanse of The Outlands seems to exert a strange influence over the people. Large numbers spend long hours just staring out into the wastes, gazing at nothing in particular. The barren lands

seem to have a strange attraction for the citizens of Dog Junction, a curiously mesmerising quality. Some liken it to the horrid fascination that people have for mutilated corpses, a sick fascination with something utterly repellent and yet absurdly attractive.

security/military presence?

Dog Junction has nothing in the way of policing and precious little in terms of security. Some of the dog farms retain a few lackadaisical, shiftless thugs to serves as security guards, but even these are merely local bravoes armed with crude billy clubs.

highlighted location

the longest line
Description: Deathslide

For those who require one last adrenaline rush before they consign themselves to oblivion, there is The Longest Line. A tall, rickety tower built on the very edge of Dog Junction, it sways gently in the wind, creaking and groaning as it's ancient timbers and iron spars flex and strain. The tower is capped by a small, time worn shed which holds a massive harpoon gun. When a visitor intent on suicide arrives at the tower, the attendants will climb the tower, load the harpoon gun with a heavy steel bolt, attach a length of rope or cable to the bolt and launch it into The Outlands. When the bolt drives itself into the ground, the line is hauled tight and the 'customer' invited to ascend the tower. Here, they make a nominal payment in kind, grip a strap of thick dogskin and launch themselves at speed down the line. Generally, about halfway down, just as they reach exhilarating speeds, the person, strap, and line disappear in a cloud of vapour. For many, The Longest Line has been the ultimate thrill, the final death ride to oblivion.

highlighted personality

the observer
Age: Unknown, looks old
Height/Build: 5' 7"/Wizened
Eye/Hair Colour: Dull blue/Bald
Occupation: Observer
Affiliations: None

The observer's true name is not known. Where he came from is a mystery. How long he will stay is unknown. The Observer has taken it upon himself to watch all those who make the trek out from the interior of The City for that final walk out into The Outlands. As they go, The Observer watches them, carrying his paintbrush strapped to a long wooden pole. When they disappear, he marks the spot with a blob of white paint. Over the years, he has watched hundreds of suicides and marked the spots where all of them disappeared. The blobs of paint delineate a ragged line, a marked limit that children dare each other to creep up to. As for The Observer, he mostly keeps himself to himself. Occupying the dusty, decrepit confines of an old blockhouse, cooking food brought to him by the people of Dog Junction. For the people, he is something of a holy relic, lucky charm and bogeyman all rolled into one.

dreamingspires

Region: Lat 8, Ring 5
Status: Slum
Law: Vigilantism only
Wealth: Extremely poor

overview

The aerial gun platform wheeled over the rotting towers, turning a lazy circle in the hazy brown sky. Below, the inhabitants of Dreamingspires barely glanced up at the airborne interloper. In the cockpit of the gun platform, dingin processors clicked and whirred softly, calculating vectors and ballistic trajectories. The upper turret swivelled, the two gaping gauss cannons tracking across the scene like hungry mouths.

Rubbish was blown into the sky and mud rippled in the hurricane as the gun platform landed by the Gross Burn. This was something new. Macrocorps never came to Dreamingspires. Why would they? Lift fans whirred down to idling speed as both gun turrets tracked the crowds converging on the aerostat. Within the armoured cockpit, the pilot and gunner glanced nervously at each other, fearful of this place and its reputation.

A throng had gathered around the aircraft now, a pitiful, seething mass of people. Emaciated, scarred and diseased, they jostled for position, wanting to get a good look at this wonder from the skies. A small hatch opened under the craft and two legs briefly dangled, then a man dropped to the ground. He spun nervously, clutching a stubby, menacing weapon in his right hand and a cylindrical object in his left.

The crowd pressed forward. The gunners' clean green uniform contrasted vividly with the filth that surrounded him.
"Stay back! Back!" he barked.
"What you want, fucker?" came a hoarse voice from the crowd.
"Looking for a man. Small man. Name of Murayama. Flowghost. Told he came this way."
Members of the crowd looked at each other in puzzlement, exchanged shrugs, shook heads.
"You seen him? Come on, you must have heard something. Speak up, or there'll be trouble!"

In the cockpit, the pilot could see the crowd become agitated. He made a swift decision and loaded canister rounds into the gauss cannons. Then he shrank back in his seat as the gunner grabbed a small child from the front row of the crowd and pressed his carbine to her head, still clutching the grenade in his left hand. Shouting increased and members of the throng began to pick up lumps of concrete, handfuls of mud, rusting masses of iron.

The girl squirmed out of the gunner's grasp and made a break for freedom. Then the rain of concrete began. Jagged lumps tore into the gunner, sending his weapon arcing away, to land with a fat splash in the Gross Burn. He crawled to the hatch, pummelled by the rain of stones. Then his grenade went off. Within the aerostat, the flash was compensated, outside, people were blinded, torn by incendiary fragments and hammered by the blast wave. The pilot tripped a switch and the gauss cannons opened up.

Fifteen seconds later the gun platform lifted off, turbines and lift fans howling like madmen, leaving behind the decimated crowd and the incinerated, broken body of its gunner. They had failed.

Christened a failure at its very birth, Dreamingspires was never destined to fulfil the dreams of its creators. Built three hundred years ago on reclaimed lands, the burgh was envisaged a place of safety and security for the employees of the Fulgurators Guild. The cost overruns, corruption scandals and stuttering construction process broke the original guild and in doing so, doomed Dreamingspires to life as a slum.

Only half of the fifty concrete towers were completed, the rest were left partially finished or standing as steel skeletons against the cityscape. Now, the towers rot and crumble, patched and shorn with wood, brick and iron, they are home to the dispossessed, the criminal and the insane. For those deemed too poor or too mad even to live in Mire End or Fogwarren, Dreamingspires is the place of last resort.

Thirty-seven towers are inhabited to a greater or lesser extent. The most complete towers are seething fifty storey concrete warrens. Sewage cascades down cracked pipes and rubbish decomposes in vast heaps at their bases. Many inhabitants live by gathering what they can from the piles of refuse, fights and deaths over a broken child's toy or a scrap of bread are commonplace. Ragged, crippled children play by the stinking burns and dart through the middens.

The constant flow of filth and ordure has created the Gross Burn, which flows sullenly and thickly through the centre of Dreamingspires. It eventually filters into the Red Canal where it makes a polluted waterway even more toxic. Slimy, treacherous bridges of scrap criss-cross the burn. Those who fall in are unlikely to clamber back out and even more unlikely to be rescued.

Atop the towers live the Risers, sheltering under their tarpaulins and sheets, venturing down from the rooftops at night to prey upon the inhabitants of the towers. The Risers represent the worst of Dreamingspires, the most criminally insane and brutally psychotic.

security/military presence?

The only security in Dreamingspires is that which the inhabitants provide for themselves. Each must look after their own. Caring for your neighbour can be a dangerous occupation.

highlighted location

the scurt's nest
Description: Gang headquarters

Headquarters of the Tunnel Scurts gang, The Scurt's Nest is located deep in the basement of Tower 23. The tower itself is no more than a shell but within its crumbling walls the 'Scurts have built gantries, rooms and storage spaces. The overall effect is one of maddening complexity, deliberately designed to confuse the visitor. Some corridors lead to deep holes covered with a thin layer of plastic, traps for the unwary.

Although the entire set-up has a very ad-hoc, mismatched appearance it is, in fact, well built and quite secure. The gangs' weapons are stored in an old underground rubbish bin that has concrete walls one meter thick and several booby traps to deter the casual browser. At all times there is at least one gang member on the roof of the tower with a telescope and a rifle (older gang members will get to use one of the big sparklocks, younger ones use small, old, rusted versions).

The 'Scurts are a singularly unpleasant gang who make life for the residents of Dreamingspires even worse than it already is. Emerging at night from their home, they prey on the weak and defenceless, stealing what meagre possessions they have, extorting pitiful sums of money and brutalising those who have nothing. Currently, the gang numbers approximately forty individuals (attrition being what it is, exact numbers vary), both male and female.

highlighted personality

mocking dave
Age: Approximately mid twenties
Height/Build: 5' 8"/Gangling, in need of a good feed
Eye/Hair Colour: Mid blue/Black, long and greasy
Occupation: Gang leader of The Tunnel Scurts
Affiliations: The Tunnel Scurts, minor connections with the Hohler Gang

Brutal, sarcastic leader of The Tunnel Scurts, Mocking Dave is a feared figure within Dreamingspires. His propensity for random acts of violence have earned him the enmity of most residents and the devotion of his gang. Habitually dressing in a long, greasy coat and dirty ruffled shirt filched from another part of The City, he likes to think he cuts something of a dashing figure. In actuality, he resembles nothing more than the cheap, nasty thug that he really is. He dispenses 'justice' to the gang through the two enormous sparklocks which he carries in shoulder holsters under his coat. He is also never without a compliment of knives, from small throwing weapons to huge machetes.

Most residents of Dreamingspires would like to see Mocking Dave drowned in the Gross Burn, choking on the filth that he and his gang do nothing to alleviate.

fogwarren

Region: Lat 5, Ring 1
Status: Independently governed burgh
Law: Moderate-high
Wealth: Moderate low

overview

'Oh, shit!' she thought.

The cracked and filthy flooring was damp under her shoulder blades and thighs. Straight above was the pitted and flaking plaster ceiling.

'Hee, it's just like my brother's infection'.

A lone, long legged insect danced across its inverted world. Blackness returned.

'Aaaaaaa.' Consciousness again.

'Why does it have to be so sore?'.

She raised an arm and brought it into her field of view. Blood, dried and flaking, like the plaster on the ceiling, was streaked down the thin arm. Clenched in the fragile fist was a grey mass, a Brigade survival knife, grey steel merging with grey polycarb.

'Why did I ever listen to Rafter? He got me involved in this, got this damn thing in my head now.' She turned her head and the pain kicked her back in to the dark.

A side on view of the world, dotted with scarlet.

'That must be Jim. Shit, he really did have a lot of guts. He, he, he.'

The floor was littered with drug capsules, rounds of ammunition and foam containers; the dead body was merely an incidental feature in the chaos.

'Someone, please get this thing out of my head, please, please, please.'

Crying in the night, as the rain continued to pour.

A massive tangle of streets, alleys, high rise and low rise buildings, Fogwarren is one of the most densely populated regions of The City. Home to the imposing CrossBar Terminus, the area gets its name from the persistent dense smog that writhes through the streets and underground lanes. The smog issues from the many workshops and generating facilities of the Ancient and Honourable Guild of Fulgurators who have their headquarters here. This veil gives Fogwarren a sinister, otherworldly aspect, an aspect only enhanced the deeper you go into the underground layers.

Despite the twisted nature of the place, it is governed very effectively by the elected local council. The local council is elected from residents of Fogwarren and deals with all aspects of civil government. Transport, sewerage, power and water are all handled by the council, mainly through special deals struck with various other interest groups active in Fogwarren. The Fulgurators provide power for the region, making it one of the few non-macrocorporate controlled areas to have widespread, efficient electric lighting.

Fogwarren is not, however, without its problems. The lower reaches of the underground dwellings have become a nightmare for the local law enforcement forces, a virtual no go zone for anyone with a badge. Shifted beings make their home here, moving into the upper reaches to prey upon the inhabitants or to live out their strange, incomprehensible lifestyles. Certain sectors of the region are controlled by militant turf gangs, violently defending what they see as their ground. Around CrossBar Terminus, the Transit Militia act with supreme arrogance, ignoring council edicts and handing out their own brand of justice. While their jurisdiction does not extend outwith the bounds of the terminus and the rail network, they seem to regard criminals operating in the street immediately surrounding the big station as fair game.

They have even been known to chase alleged criminals right across Fogwarren, coming into tense and sometimes violent contact with the local law enforcement officials.

Architecturally, above-ground Fogwarren consists mainly of three and four storey brick-built tenements, nearly all of which have additional stories piled onto their roofs. Below ground, brick and concrete lanes dominate, stairwells and passages jut off at odd angles, forgotten tunnels lead to nowhere in particular. Near to canals, the underground reaches drip with water and moisture, some corridors having veritable streams running down their centres. Canal wall collapses occasionally flood entire blocks, killing hundreds.

By the strange nature of the place, property values in Fogwarren are determined not by the quality of the housing or by its location, but by how much light the dwelling receives. Apartments in the upper stories of tenements, above the enveloping mist command a premium, while the lower you go, the less valuable your property becomes.

In the underground regions, properties nearest stairwells, tunnel entrances and grids in the road are most valuable. Conversely, you can live in the lowest areas for practically nothing. Not that you'd want to.

Security/military Presence?

Set up by the local council to provide policing services for Fogwarren, the Burgh Constabulary consists of a little over a thousand uniformed and two hundred plain-clothes officers. For a population as large as Fogwarren, the police force is extraordinarily under-manned and over-stretched. Unlike larger police organisations such as the TCMA Provosts, the funds available to the Burgh Constabulary are very limited, hence the equipment they use and level of training they receive are not of the best quality. However, the officers are all dedicated and hard working, often putting in horrendously long shifts to make up for the lack of manpower. Armed with hand-me-down pistols and carbines purchased decades ago as a job lot from the Iron Hand militant organisation, they patrol the mean streets in units of three, always on the lookout for potential trouble.

There is a long running vendetta between the Burgh Constabulary and the Transit Militia operating out of CrossBar Terminus. The Burgh Police believe (quite rightly) that the militia overstep the boundaries of their jurisdiction in their fanatical pursuit of offenders against railway law. This has more than once led to firefights and fistfights between the two groups.

highlighted location

the broken arms
Description: Pub/gambling den, 278 Unter Strasse.

A first glance the 'Arms is your typical, lower class pub. The beer is warm and the welcome less than friendly if you are not a local. But like many things in The City, there is something beneath the surface. Accessed by a secret entrance under the bar, there is a level below the cellar which houses a very large illegal gambling complex. Backed by a local 3rd Syndicate assembly, the sub-basement is spartan but offers Railwayman's Bluff, Up And Out and a variety of other gambling activities. Membership is on a recommendation basis, a member must vouch for you and you must be approved by the 'committee' which runs the illegal casino.

highlighted personality

mikey babbage
Age: 20
Height/Build: 5'10"
Eye/Hair Colour: Yellow/Dyed red
Occupation: Gang leader
Affiliations: Red Death turfgang

Current leader of the Red Death gang, Mikey is a self confident, assured young man, well aware of the power he can exert over others. Coming from a middle-class upbringing in Fogwarren, Babbage quickly grew tired of the so-so surroundings of his life and started to hang out with the rougher elements in the local area. He was shortly accepted into the Red Death and became leader one year ago. Like most gangers he is cocky and arrogant, but has the skill and backing to go through with any action he commits himself to.

folly hills

Region: Lat 1, Ring 3
Status: TCMA Burgh
Law: Moderate
Wealth: Low-moderate

overview

The view from the soldiers' head was incredible. Below, all of Folly Hills, Coldbath Fell, Mire End and father afield were spread out. It was as if the soldier would reach down and scoop The City up in the palm of his mighty hand. Ahead stood the great arch and beyond, the splendid angel, shrouded in a thin mist, reflecting the flares, gas lamps and sodium slights below.

Cordwainer drew breath. Even two hundred feet up, the air was still stale. He looked down. Far, far below the denizens of Folly Hills went about their business, scurrying like vermin, serving their masters, serving themselves. A fight broke out at the base of the giant statue. Some drunk appeared to be having an argument with a Simil. An argument he was going to lose, if Cordwainer was any judge of things.

This was the place to be. Far above the streets, far above the crime, the filth, the despair. One day, he thought, all people would feel like this. The City can't go on forever. Staring up through the brown clouds, there was a sudden break and for moment, a gap. A black space filled with twinkling lights. Then it was gone.

Time to go. Cordwainer balanced on the eyelid of the soldier and gazed around for one last time. Closing his eyes, he smiled and launched himself into space, falling away from the soldier and his mighty hand.

A study in contrasts, Folly Hills combines areas which only just raise themselves above the level of a slum in its eastern end, with expanding areas of middle-class housing in the West End. The eastern half is deemed too near to Mire End for any renovation or area assistance, while the East End abuts Coldbath Fell, one of the more salubrious residential areas in the TCMA. Hence the extensive monetary assistance that the west end has received. The good people of Coldbath Fell do not want to see a slum on their front doorsteps.

The area gets its name from the three hills on which it is built. Sloping up from the Green Canal, the hills rise to a little over five hundred feet. These are the hills. The follies surmount these minor rises, increasing their height to over seven hundred feet. Each hill is topped with a different folly. The southernmost is capped with a concrete angel, wings outstretched, right hand clasping a sword of justice. The middle hill displays a fine stone arch, badly corroded by centuries of acid rain and vandalism. The northernmost of the three hills is surmounted by the most massive of the three follies, a statue of a soldier, clutching a rifle and pointing to the south. Nobody knows why they were built but all are sure that they predate The Shift. Folly Hills has grown up around these gigantic monuments, crowding into their bases. Rumour has it that Folly Hills was once open parkland, where families could stroll and admire the fantastic architecture. Sadly, if this was ever true, it is not now the case.

security/military presence?

Being one of the lower priority areas within the TCMA, Folly Hills has only one Provost bunker, and a small one at that. If additional forces are needed, the Provosts are happy to fly in manpower from Bankside Air Station a few short minutes away. The Folly Hills Bunker can accommodate up to 90 Provosts, which is deemed more than enough. A couple of aerostats are always at the ready on the rooftop pad, but these are always older, less reliable models, with the newer aircraft being used over the wealthier areas. Most of the Provosts consider Folly Hills only one step up from Mire End just across the Green Canal, despite the expanding middle-class population in the renovated buildings of the east end.

highlighted location

boundary street

Description: Street of food stalls, Boundary Street, Folly Hills, TCMA

Lying parallel with Folly Hills High Street, Boundary Street is one of many thoroughfares in The City devoted to fast food. The street is lined with tiny cafes and open-air stalls serving all manner of food and drink. All kinds of cuisine are available here at reasonably cheap prices. Most stalls and cafes are family or individually run, there are no chain outlets in these locations. The street is thronged 25 hours a day, and making your way down the street carrying a full plate of food can be a tricky proposition.

The air is humid from the heat being given off by hundreds of cookers and grease hangs like a fog. Your senses are assaulted by a myriad of scents, some pleasant, some downright disgusting. The clientele of the area are as varied as the foods on offer, from Mire End types trying to bum a hot meal, to well-to-do businessmen from Coldbath Fell (trying to avoid getting mugged).

The most common fare by far is fish, freshly brought in from the tanks and cages of Bankside. Poached, fried, grilled, baked, barbecued, you name it, it's available on Boundary Street. As Bankside fish are not the most pleasant tasting items in the world, the Boundary Street chefs have become adept at whisking up pungent and spicy sauces to coat their wares. It's really better that you don't ask what's in the sauces. Honestly.

highlighted personality

robert baker

Age: 34
Height/Build: 6' 2"/Toned and well-muscled
Eye/Hair Colour: Brown/Black, short
Occupation: Flowghost and Security Consultant
Affiliations: None

Robert Baker is something of an outsider in the Dataflow community. Not only is he a capable and intelligent flowghost, but his training in combat techniques and security make him a formidable physical opponent also. It is this physical aspect that other ghosts dislike, they feel that using violence to solve problems is for the ignorant and unworthy. However, his skill earns him a nice living and his third floor flat in a Folly Hills block is one of the most secure places in the area. Physically imposing, he is not the average pale, underfed flowghost of popular folklore. He works out every day and practices mar-

tial arts. In addition to this, he has a natural way with technology and wears his clothes in a manner which impresses clients. Baker also makes money from repairing and selling firearms as well as computers and security equipment, a large cache of which he has at his flat.

hangside

Region: Lat 6/7, Ring 2
Status: Residential
Law: Gang policed
Wealth: Low

overview

"Internal monologue? Pah! It's the only thing that keeps you sane in this place. Personally, I'm sick, tired and fed up of Hangside. It's a carbuncle, should be burnt away. Lazy, shiftless bunch of good-for-nothings. What? Oh, right. Heron's the name, Sergeant Heron. Iron Hand militant group. We do protection for the good people of Sleeping Vale. And the first thing we should do is get rid of Hangside! Right, I had to go through there the other day, meeting up with a professional colleague in Burningfell. The entrance to that place is like a black pit, wreathed in smoke from cooking and hell knows what else. There's barely enough room to walk two abreast, pushing, crowding, greasy, noisy, nasty. Slum dwelling scum. Any road up, I gets half way through when these cheeky young bastards from the Hangsiders stop me. "What you doin' here?" they say. "Fuck off", I says. It's amazing how a crowd can melt away so quickly, all through these little doors and into the backs of shops, behind food stalls. Cowards. So I do what I'm trained for, I draw my gun. Then this kid points the biggest bloody sparklock I've ever seen in my life straight at my stomach. So I take him out, square in the face. His cannon goes off and plants a round into my thigh, cheeky bastard. The rest of them mugs start pulling knives and guns and shit, so I just sprays away. Few screams from through the walls, sounds like most of the folks were just hiding behind the doors, getting a sneaky view. Serves them right. Managed to take out about five of those Hangsiders, though. Scrawny kids, Hobbled out of that place quicksmart and got back to the patrol house. Yeah, that's the way it happened. So, you from Iron Hand? Nice to meet you. What? What department? 'Repairs'? Oh shit! I'm a dead man."

Looming over the polluted waters of the Black Canal, Hangside is the largest and most notorious of the 'bridge communities' in The City. At Hangsides' core lies the old, forgotten Birdhouse Bridge, once the main thoroughfare over the Black Canal between Sleeping Vale and Burningfell. As the population grew and grew, quality housing became ever rarer and shopkeepers on the bridge, ever with an eye for fast profit, threw up new stories on their properties, renting them out for exorbitant rates. As time wore on, platforms were built out from the bridge and connected to the canal banks by ropes, walkways and pipes. Soon, the bridge was completely enclosed by buildings, turning what had once been a wide thoroughfare into a narrow, gloomy tunnel. Hangside itself became a mind-boggling accretion of levels, platforms, walkways and rooms, all interconnected. East of the bridge, the buildings stretch for 500 metres down the canal, while west of the bridge, they run for a slightly lesser 400 metres.

Underneath the layers of construction, the Black Canal truly lives up to its name, stinking with pollution from the industrial zones further west, reeking with rotting garbage and human waste falling from above. It takes a very brave or foolhardy individual to pilot a craft through the canal under Hangside.

In the current era, Birdhouse Bridge still remains the accepted centre of the district, thronged with tiny shops, food vendors and beggars. Doors and passageways lead off at all angles from the main walk. Private dwellings in Hangside are in the main, tiny. The largest dwellings are on the very edges of constructions, but these are always pushed in as new building work goes on to increase the size of Hangside.

One good thing is that the area is relatively free of violent crime. This is mainly due to the local streetgang, the imaginatively named Hangsiders. They are fiercely protective of the area and of its citizens. Indeed, they seem almost halfway to becoming something of an organised militia. Most families in Hangside have at least one member who is part of the Hangsiders. Local businesses pay a not unreasonable amount of protection to the gang, in return for which they are defended against the predations of outsiders. Anyone, whether they be from the area or an outsider, found committing a violent crime, dealing drugs or stealing from fellow citizens is subject to summary and brutal justice (this usually involves some bricks, a length of rope and the Black Canal).

security/military presence?

As previously discussed, the Hangsiders provide all the security that the area needs. They are fiercely loyal to Hangside and will not hesitate to mete out justice to outsiders. They are relatively well equipped and well led, having a large stock of firearms and melee weapons. Their leader is one Lawrence Gavidge, who has been with the gang for most of his adult life.

highlighted location

superpsykikwar

Description: Games arcade and nightclub

Virtual reality games arcade and sometime disco, SPW is a popular hangout for local gangs and other elements of disaffected youth. This concentration of delinquency and petty criminal tendencies makes it a worthwhile place to visit in order to obtain local information, word on the street etc. Most of the games units are of the 'trode set VR type, with no direct Dataflow linkages. There are a few ancient flat screen video games and slightly less aged holographic screen games. Currently popular games include EkranoStrike War-IV and Tunnel Threat.

highlighted personality

florentina venkatseramany

Age: Unknown, possibly late fifties
Height/Build: 5' 3"/Very slight
Eye/Hair Colour: Sparkling blue/Grey
Occupation: Street healer
Affiliations: None

A tiny, spare woman who makes her home in Hangside, shuffling from place to place with her head bowed and arms clasped in front of her. She has all the hallmarks of one bowed by sad, bitter experience and weighed down by the pressures of life. Only when you look in Florentina Venkatseramany's eyes down you see the real spark of life which dwells deep within. For Florentina is a streethealer of unparalleled skill and ability. When a child is sick in Hangside, it is she who the citizens call for. When a Hangsider has been wounded defending the area, it is she who the citizens call for. Her quick hands make short work of cleaning, suturing and bandaging. It is the proud claim of Hangside that only those who are beyond help have not lived thanks to the attentions of this woman. Some in Burningfell and Sleeping Vale call her a witch, or one of The Shifted. She seems to care little for such slurs, continuing to make her slow, shuffling way about Hangside.

long pond

Region: Lat 8/1, Ring 4
Status: TCMAA controlled area
Law: Minimal
Wealth: Moderate

overview

A constant dull banging echoed throughout the lowest levels of The Barque as dozens of small craft rode the slight swell. Shifting in his narrow bunk, Evlin craned to see out of the porthole. Fogged with condensation and layered with a patina of grime and age, the porthole allowed only the weakest form of light through, grudgingly admitting it into the cramped squalor of the cabin. Wedged between the workshop of a cobbler who sang hymns to God whilst hammering hobnails and the laboratory of a quietly insane chemist, the cabin was barely three feet wide and seven feet long.

Casually picking some wandering lice from his armpit, Evlin gave up trying to discern any activity outside and shrugged on his voluminous grey rubber leggings and rotting dogskin coat. Rummaging through the accumulated detritus on the floor, he finally pulled out a pair of heavy black boots and a set of scratched, blackened goggles. Placing them on the appropriate bodily parts, he shuffled sideways to the door and emerged into the early morning fug of the corridor.

The cobbler was singing again, warbling on in a cracked tenor, extolling the seventeen virtues and chastising the impure. There were precious few punters about at this time of day as Evlin tramped towards the bows, hoping to avoid scurrying scurts. The generators beckoned once more, needful of his loving care and delicate touch.

Strine wandered over as he emerged into the generator bilge's, pulling a set of heavy insulated gloves from her hands and fishing in her pockets for a nebelweed smoke. She smiled, displaying a half set of brown, cracked teeth.
"Late again, Ev. Might decide to clock off on time one of these days. Leave you right in it."
"Cut it, Strine. Had a bad night, Deckster was having another one of his mad fits.
"That old freak? Should punch his lights and stop him once and..."
"Ach, he's harmless. Just loud, is all."
"Yeah, but keeps you from the good work."
Strine finished the sentence by stamping up the companionway and slamming the hatch shut behind her.
"Minger." thought Evlin.
Generator Three was throwing its usual tantrum, barking and spitting coolant all over the floor. Evlin grasped the corroded iron lever, heaved on a couple of switches and declutched the drive. The generator started revving maniacally until he

kicked the all stop, cracking the metal with the force of the blow. The core was just about shot, fried wires black with soot. The big stationary magnets were caked with fine metallic dust, blown through The Barque from the workshops above.
"Crap."
Evlin would earn his keep today. This and every other day, as far as he could see.

Largest of turning circles along the Grand Canal, Long Pond is fiercely contested territory, disputed by the 3rd Syndicate, the TCMAA Provosts and the Hohler Gang. The floating markets are the scene of almost daily gunfights, robberies, assassinations and random acts of terrorism. Despite this, Long Pond supports a thriving business community, selling any kind of ware imaginable from shops floating on the surface of the pond or clinging to its edge. Business located on and around the 'Pond must pay various kinds of protection to the 3rds, the Hohlers or even to corrupt Provosts. Most stall owners and shopkeepers accept this as an inevitable part of life, just like the rain. Paying protection does not necessarily guarantee any level of protection from other factions. Indeed, the gangs and the Provosts seldom seem to bother about attacks on businesses nominally under their protection.

To the curious shopper, Long Pond seems to operate on laws of physics as yet undiscovered by scientists. Carefully drawn maps are out of date in an hour due to the randomly shifting clumps of boats, barges and hulks. Fires, violence and the sluggish movement of the canal itself serves to constantly twist and change the waterborne topography of the Long Pond markets. Cargo captains, teamsters and taxi drivers have become adept at an intuitive form of navigation, equipping their vessels with tall masts mounted with telescopes, mirrors or small children to spy out landmarks around the edge of the 'Pond. Orienteering in this manner is the only realistic way of navigating about the swirling, watery lanes. In a remarkable display of level headedness and common sense, waterborne Provost patrols make strenuous efforts to keep a central waterway open to allow craft heading up and down the canal to move freely. They also attempt (with slightly less success) to keep a number of channels leading to the banks open.

Visitors to Long Pond will be instantly captivated (according to a local poet) by the gaily-coloured flags which the stallholders use to identify their position. They will be enthralled by the sights, sounds and smells of this vibrant, energetic location. The truth is somewhat more prosaic. While Long Pond does indeed look colourful, a sea of waving banners, its energy is more directed towards fleecing as much money from buyers as is humanly possible. Encounters with 3rd Syndicate Assemblies and Hohler Crews are always possible, normally with violent (or possibly deadly) results.

security/military presence?

As has been previously mentioned, the TCMAA Provosts are nominally in charge of Long Pond, providing the same level of law enforcement that any area of the TCMA can expect. In truth, the Provosts stationed at Long Pond are, if anything, more corrupt and violent than most of their colleagues elsewhere. Robbery, embezzlement and savage beatings are their stock in trade. In attempting to beat down the gangs through use of force, they have become like the gangs themselves, feared by the populace and despised as much as any criminal. In turn, they have made many citizens look towards the gangs for protection from the police. The 3rd Syndicate is especially fond of tracking down and eliminating Provost patrols. In fact, it has become something of an initiation rite for young gang members.

highlighted location

the barque

Description: Barge containing numerous small businesses.

One of the few unmoving parts of Long Pond, The Barque is a huge, derelict barge, taken over by scores of traders, tinkers and artificers. The pitted, rotting hull is encrusted with ramshackle buildings and disused boats capsized on the deck to form workshops and stores. There is one industry which The Barque has an enviable reputation for: the production of dingins. There are always at least thirty tiny factories, labouriously handcrafting miniature mechanical computers. Bathed in harsh light, complex arrangements of lenses strapped to their heads, the artificers cut, shape and place thousands of minuscule components. Encased in flat steel, burnished copper or soft dogskin, the little boxes give the power of computing to those who can afford such craftsmanship. Whole subsidiary industries have grown up to support the artificers: miniature metalworks run smelters and presses, opticians grind lenses and shape frames and toolmakers craft the tiny implements needed by the dingin artificers.

However, The Barque is not only home to skilled artisans. Here you can find clothes shops, fishmongers, shoemakers and herbalists. All of these services thrive and survive in the midst of the chaos that is Long Pond. Within the moisture ridden bilges of the vessel, ancient, wheezing generators provide power for the lights and machines required to sustain the community. Here, within the dark confines of the lowest holds live disgraced Fulgurators and excommunicated macrocorporate technicians, surviving by selling their hard-earned skills to the community of The Barque.

highlighted personality

Eulin Pireque

Age: 34
Height/Build: 5' 4"/Emaciated
Eye/Hair Colour: Black/Greasy, black, greying at temples
Occupation: Generator technician
Affiliations: None

A disgraced former Fulgurator, banished from the order for a series of unspecified but presumably dire crimes, Pireque has carved himself a life as one of the technicians who service the generators of The Barque. Never the most forthcoming of individuals, he jealously guards the details of his past misdemeanours, something which goes pretty much unremarked in technician circles, as all of those who toil in the bilges have their own secrets which they wish to hide. Small and thin, his face and arms are covered with numerous burn marks, the legacy of working with dangerous, unpredictable machinery. His face is especially scared, being pocked with the leftover marks of childhood disease and malnutrition.

Lucent Heights

Region: Lat 1, Ring 4
Status: TCMA secure residential burgh
Law: Very high, militant organisation policed
Wealth: Very high, upper class

overview

Morgan Kusei hated his life. Living in luxury, with no worries about money was all very well, but he felt that his life lacked certain experiences. The world outside of Lucent Heights was unknown. The massive city was an unexplored wilderness. From the great windows of his parents' mansion, he could see places he could only dream about visiting. Mire End, Folly Hills and Dreamingspires. Places of excitement and adventure. His parents even refused to let him join the Brigade of Light as an officer. Instead, he sits in this ivory tower, unable to touch the world. Tonight that would change.

*The stupid, hidebound guards at the Boulevard Gate were under strict orders not to let him pass. Judicious application of makeup and an ID purchased at ruinous cost from a more bohemian acquaintance allowed him egress. Free at last.
The ferry to Mire End was a revelation. Here were people unsullied by wealth and prosperity. The smells, sounds and sights danced on his nerve endings, he was alive with joy. Rotting tenements and crumbling walls appeared as works of*

art. Until some locals decided that here was someone who could do with guidance.

Morgan Kusei hated his life. He knew there was something wrong, some past that he was failing to remember. Still, he gripped another rough pallet with his bleeding hands and put his back into it. The overseers lash fell on his back despite his efforts. He hated his life.

Built upon a hill directly overlooking the Brightlights shopping zone on the north side of the Central Park area of the TCMA, Lucent Heights is one of the most prestigious residential areas in the entire city. The most sought after are the houses located on top of the hill, sprawling mansions of unbelievable plushness and luxury. Many high ranking macrocorp execs maintain houses and apartments in here, hence the excellent security services provided. Kinetic Energy Incorporated provide a round the clock armed presence and have constructed a mikefighter base at the foot of the hill with pilots on thirty second standby, should anything occur.

The architecture in Lucent Heights varies from street to street and from dwelling to dwelling. Some live in ornate mansions and garish villas, while others choose to live in more minimalistic apartments and houses. What amazes the visitor most is the quietness and cleanliness of the place. There is not a single piece of litter to be seen, no collapsed figures lie in the road and above all, there is a lack of constant background sound. All dwellings, large or small, are exceptionally well soundproofed, the residents valuing their seclusion from the rest of The City. Every dwelling is also protected by a state of the art security system, connected into the main datacore of Kinetic Energy Inc.

When one enters the area on foot, the visitor is first confronted by three rows of walls and fences, set up by KEI as the first line of defence. Once past these, you come upon the 'cheapest' houses and apartments, modest one and two bedroom abodes. Proceeding up the hill, the buildings gradually become even more expensive and large. At the summit are the most expensive pieces of property in The City. Owned by the elite, they are huge, fabulously constructed affairs, guaranteed to strike awe into any city dweller.

security/military presence?

As has been previously mentioned, security for the entire Lucent Heights area is provided by the militant organisation of Kinetic Energy Incorporated. Their troopers patrol the area with a fervour that borders on fanaticism. Nobody gets in without the appropriate identification. Lucent Heights is probably the best protected area in The City, after the macrocorporate domains. The TCMA Provosts have no jurisdiction within the area, a point which irks the Provosts no end. Mikefighters stand ready to intercept any airborne intruders which attempt to pass through the airspace above the enclave.

highlighted location

the lucent heights sportspersons club

Description: Private sporting club and dining establishment

Opulent, richly decorated and heavy with the smells of fine wines and rare foods, The Lucent heights Sportspersons Club is the club to be a member of in this status-obsessed society. Founded many, many years ago, the 'Club is stringent in the application of both it's membership criteria and house rules. To join, one must be recommended by at least four other club members in good standing, be a resident of Lucent Heights and pass an un-nervingly lengthy series of interviews and examinations. Most members use the club simply to socialise, yet a few do actively participate in a variety of 'sporting' activities. From illegal ekranoplan racing to hunting convicted criminals, they obtain their kicks mostly at the expense of the rest of the population. The Provosts tend to turn a blind eye to their activities, realising the power and influence that some of these wealthy adrenaline junkies wield.

highlighted personality

keiko harland-weiss

Age: 31
Height/Build: 5' 5"/Very slight
Eye/Hair Colour: Violet/Blue
Occupation: None
Affiliations: None

A ghost amongst the outrageously wealthy citizens of Lucent Heights, Keiko lives in her vast mansion, attended only by her automaton servants, interacting with other people only through telephone, never leaving the confines of her home. For, in a city of millions, she has the most unfortunate of afflictions: agoraphobia. She lives in fear of crowds, the press of bodies, the smells of sweat and rain. Isolated for ten years, she lives off of the money which her father, a successful and astute businessman, built up. Keiko is considered something of a joke among the people of Lucent Heights, her name is mentioned with derision in the trendy bars, her house is pointed at in passing, the pointer laughing and joking with their fellows. Yet, she remains sealed within, fearful of the urban chaos which surrounds her, dreading the day when it all comes crashing down and the unwashed hordes batter down her door and take her out into the streets, into the crowds.

Merryhell

Region: Lat 6, Ring 5
Status: Macrocorporate housing area
Law: Moderate
Wealth: Low

Overview

"Good morning, faithful employees of Gorunna Logistics, your caring, considerate employer.

This morning's top story is a great one for all workers in the steel mills. Production rose last week by fifteen percent, a testament to the forward planning of Gorunna and to your hard work. Operations Controller Stephane Almovar stated 'I am overjoyed at this latest production increase. However, I believe we can strive for more. I would encourage all employees to contribute to our great efforts and ensure continued increases in the future.'

In other news, Hirplakker continued to show poor performance figures, continuing the trend of the last three years. Heavily damaged by the insurrectionist Arclight Corporation, Hirplakker no longer represents any kind of competition to the might of Gorunna.

Here is a public service announcement: In sectors four, seven and eleven of Merryhell, there will be a power shortage during the hours of darkness. This is due to a new smelting furnace being brought on-line in the Deepdown mining zone. We are sure our employees will understand the vital neccessity of this operation.

On the tube tonight, there will be a special report on the tireless labours of your colleagues in the railheads. These vital workers assist in the important flow of resources for Gorunna. All employees are urged to view this thrilling presentation, as questions may be asked by your shift supervisors.

Now, step out and enjoy your working day. Gorunna: we're there for you, you will be there for us."

Home to workers for Gorunna Logistics Ltd, Merryhell is a giant, sprawling zone of low class housing. 60% of the population actively work for Gorunna, the rest exist as workers families and illegal transients. Almost all of these workers toil in the neighbouring Radstrip or Deepdown (see 'Industrial Areas' in this chapter for details on Deepdown) industrial zones. Security on the edge of the industrial zones is moderate to good but the further into Merryhell you go, the worse it becomes. The majority of housing is crumbling old high-rise and underground deep-rise tenements, infested with rats and even less pleasant creatures.

The above having been said, the residents of Merryhell are considerably better off than the people of slum areas such as Mire End and Dreamingspires. They, at least, have the luxuries of electricity, running water (sometimes) and relative security. Gorunna knows full well that spending too little on the needs of its employees would result in a workforce that would be, frankly, unable to work. Hence, the corporation spends the absolute minimum it can get away with and not incur a workers revolution. Gorunna corporate security patrols most of the area, only leaving out the worst, central areas occupied by the lowest paid workers. The peripheral regions of Merryhell, despite their proximity to the industrial zones, offer the best quality housing (relatively speaking) and the most reliable facilities. Here you can find shops (some operated privately, with permission from Gorunna), public baths, cinemas and other civic attractions. Every change of shift, the streets are thronged with people going to and from work, doing their shopping or bringing their children home from the corporate schools.

Residents of Merryhell like to moan that their lot in life is hard, that it's tough working under the heel of one of the mighty macrocorporations. In actuality, they have a far better standard of living and of health (excepting the high level of industrial illness and injury which is prevalent amongst workers) than many other denizens of The City. Crime is kept to an acceptable minimum by the corporate forces and justice handed out in a swift, uncompromising manner. The people are lucky; the prevailing winds generated by The City's many microclimates flow over Merryhell from the centre of The City. Were it the other way, the entire area would be bathed in fumes, soot, dust and radiation from the industrial zones.

Security/Military Presence?

As previously mentioned, security within Merryhell can be variable. The regions bordering the industrial zones are the best protected, while the interior zones and underground housing are the least frequently patrolled by the corporate forces.

Employees of Gorunna are treated with a fair amount of respect by the security forces; non-residents come in for fairly harsh treatment if caught without a permit or valid reason for being in Merryhell.

highlighted location

the kicked inn

Description: Public house, 19 Needleman Street

The Kicked Inn is a small public house located on Needleman Street, alongside the Black Canal on the extreme northern edge of Merryhell, its main notable function is being a front for Gorunna corporate security surveillance operations. Rather than being based out of an official facility, surveillance and investigating officers for the surrounding area are often based out of the pub's extensive underground network of rooms. This provides a secure, trouble free environment in which to carry out important undercover operations.

The landlord, Mr Felix Laughton, is your average, cheery barkeep. This conceals the fact that he is an experienced undercover officer with fifteen years service behind him.

highlighted personality

hideki murayama

Age: 24
Height/Build: 5' 5"/Slim, fine featured
Eye/Hair Colour: Brown/Dyed blond, spiky
Occupation: Flowghost
Affiliations: None (that he is willing to tell anyone about)

Skilled in his art, Murayama is the bane of many a datacore. Slipping through the dingin and computer defences like a wraith, he spirits away data and sells it to the highest bidder. These activities have not gone unnoticed. Both Gorunna and Hirplakker are seriously interested in this man and would love to have a short, private conversation with him. Hence, he decided to hide right under the very nose of one of his biggest enemies.

His one room apartment in a deep low-rise is lined with gadgetry, from microscale to macroscale dingins, rare electronic computer parts, communications gear and scavenged parts. He is highly intelligent (one of the reasons he has managed to stay one step ahead of the macrcorps) and possesses a keen sense of humour. However, time is running short. The macrocorps have immense resources that are slowly being marshalled against him. The time will come to move again, always jumping that fraction ahead.

mire end

Region: Lat 2, Ring 3
Status: Uncontrolled slum
Law: None
Wealth: Poverty stricken

overview

Slap. Slap. Slap. The sound of boots hitting concrete through an inch or so of water. Water was everywhere here. A pervasive dampness, a state of decay. Across the canal was Folly Hills, even that had been taken in by the TCMAA. But, they wanted nothing to do with Mire End, too deprived, run down and plain hellish for the Burghers and the Provosts to deal with. Three men came round the corner, ducking the jagged ended pipes jutting from the rotting brick wall. Sparklocks in their hands, heavy, ugly weapons. Not guaranteed to kill you straight away, but kill you they will in the infected waters of Mire End. A single gas lamp above the alley caught their pale, waxy faces, almost the same sheen as their slick oilskin coats.

"Cardyouthere?" It was almost like hearing a machinecannon speak. The man's comrades shifted uneasily and hefted their guns. One was a bit too nervous and held the trigger that little bit tight. The sparklock boomed and emitted a huge gout of smoke. There was splintering sound as the heavy ball embedded itself in the brick.

"Youutterprick!" said the leader and stabbed the shooter in the throat with a long stiletto. He fell backwards into the scummy water, gurgling and moaning. But only for a while. I lowered myself from the rusting fire escape and stepped out into the middle of the alley.

"Brady, you should really be more tolerant."
"Hefuckin'! Miss Card, how nice to see you." He spoke slowly, stilted, like a man unused to enunciating individual words.
"Likewise Brady, likewise. So, what you want?"
"Needafighterfor... I need a 'fighter to take out Frontier, he's stepping in on my territory."
"Expensive, what you got?"
"This." He grinned, exposing a row of broken, brown teeth. In his hand he held out a small, matt grey object. An Arclight computer. An exceptionally rare sight in these parts.

"You could sell it for a pretty sum, Miss Card."
"Deal." It's not a nice way to make a living, but in Mire End, your choices are few and far between. I took the comp.

Mire End is a forgotten, forlorn place. Denied help by the powerful TCMA sitting just across the Green Canal and despised by its citizens, it is a place of crime, indolence and apathy.

A few square miles of brick and concrete tenements, Mire End is slowly rotting into the ground. Drainage system s destroyed years ago have given rise to a permanent layer of water to cover the streets. The ground floors of most buildings are left empty, the inhabitants moving to the higher levels in order to escape the dampness and rot. With little indigenous industry or employ-ment, Mire End has had to turn to crime in order to survive.

Most of the citizens are engaged in some form of illegal activity, whether it be shopkeepers selling blatantly stolen goods or young toughs soldiering for the Hohler Gang, crim-inality is endemic. Out of this, Mire End has become some-thing of a trading ground for those dealing in items that the Provosts across the canal may take a dim view of.

If any one group can be said to control Mire End, then it would be the Hohler Gang. They moved in countless years ago and began swallowing up the smaller outfits and local gangs. More than half of the population of Mire End is now connected in some way to the Gang. The gang ruthlessly runs all the prostitution along the bank of the Green Canal facing Folly Hills, with any freelancers being dealt with in the most ruthless of fashions. The pitted, worn concrete bank with its jagged stumps of rebar ready to slice the unwary is a 25 hour a day flesh market, with girls in their flouncing skirts and young men in their frock coats selling themselves to punters from across the water. Scattered amongst the flesh peddlers are sellers of trinkets and assorted wares. The Hohler Gang

tolerates these individual enterprises, as long as they don't get too big for their boots. Here you can find ammunition being sold from rolled up blankets, drugs from trays and pornography from coat pockets.

Most activity is concentrated around the ferry, the ancient, creaking, highly dangerous means of getting from Folly Hills to Mire End. There are few sizeable bridges connecting the two areas and the ferry provides the main link for those trav-elling between the two areas. A decrepit, flat-bottomed wooden con-struction, the ferry is guid-ed by two huge chains strung across the canal. Sparking, arc-ing, diaboli-cal electrical engines beneath the decking power the gearwheels which grip the chains and drag the ferry across the carpet of green. Sparks shower down from the pantograph which runs along the electrical cables suspended above the canal, pow-ering the ancient vehicle. At both landing stages, there are always crowds of passengers, prostitutes, pickpockets and assorted gawpers. A one way trip on the ferry will cost you a shilling, handed over to the bent and bewhiskered ferry-master, a man of venerable age and spiteful temper.

security/military presence?

The only thing that could be described as a 'security service' in Mire End are the internal strictures of the Hohler Gang. They police themselves brutally and efficiently, weeding out the weak, the traitorous and the incompetent. Unlike many other organised crime groups, the Hohler Gang does not extort protection from the citizens. On one level, this is to make the citizens more amenable to their activities and on another level, and certainly in Mire End, the people are just too poor to pay protection money.

highlighted location

the corner of h street & powell

Description: Ruined, semi-inhabited area

Devastated during the Hundred Block War, this was already one of the worst bits of Mire End. Hirplakker, in their wisdom, decided to build a fake staging area here, on the other side of The City from the main fighting in what are now the Contested Grounds. The residents of Mire End were in no position to argue, while the TCMA turned it's back and pretended nothing was happening. Nobody expected Arclight to strike as massively as they did.

Eleven days after the fake staging area was built and manned, the Brigade of Light attacked. Two armoured Tentenel companies, backed up by aerostat gunships and swarms of mikefighters descended from the skies. On the canals, Brigade gunboats pounded the supposed Hirplakker positions, caring little for the poor, forgotten inhabitants of Mire End. When the dust settled, the only corpses were those of the unlucky residents. The Brigade quietly withdrew. Now, H Street & Powell is home to the most wretched of Mire End's residents, living in hovels constructed from scrap brick and iron sheeting. Disease is rampant here, even more so than in the main body of Mire End. Cripples, orphans and the insane all cluster together through sheer lack of somewhere else to go.

highlighted personalities

Janus Kripitsch

Age: 28
Height/Build: 5' 11"/Thin, slope shouldered
Eye/Hair Colour: Deep green/Black, cropped
Occupation: Lostfinder
Affiliations: The people of Mire End

One of the few Lostfinders in Mire End and the only one not to be completely under the thrall of the Hohler Gang, Kripitsch is a man of moral principle and utter practicality. Born in Folly Hills, he moved to Mire End because of a girl. The girl went a long time ago, but Kripitsch remains. Standing a little above average height, he has a slightly lopsided appearance due to a head injury sustained as a child. His cropped black hair, sallow complexion and deep green eyes combine to give him an appearance which is not immediately trustworthy.

However, his appearance belies his manner, which is kind, caring and compassionate. He believes deeply in helping the people of Mire End and, unbeknown to all, he is conducting a long letter writing campaign to Markus Heilige in the TCMAA, begging that the TCMA give Mire End some assistance. Letters scrawled in his scratchy handwriting arrive on Heilige's desk every few weeks, beseeching that notable man to offer succour of some kind.

Jane Card

Age: 25
Height/Build: 6' 0"/Muscular
Eye/Hair Colour: Blue/Light brown
Occupation: Ghostfighter
Affiliations: None

Card is a hard woman, and one that it is best not to cross. Even the Hohlers leave her alone, pretending to themselves that she is not worth the trouble. Her skills are in great demand and she travels far across the City, wherever a job may take her. She grew up in the Third Church of God the Architect orphanage in the eastern half of Mire End, enduring an upbringing of toil, prayer and abstinence. Aged thirteen, she left the orphanage and set out to make her own way in the world. The hard life of the streets quickly taught her that she had a natural talent for fighting and she soon saw that there was money to be made from this talent. Now twenty-five, she has been fighting on the streets for over a decade, honing her skills and establishing a fearsome reputation. At six feet in height, she is tall and also very broad. She is also exceptionally light on her feet, almost a prerequisite for being a ghostfighter. Always the professional, she has made many enemies in her life. Yet nothing seems to perturb her dour, humourless exterior. She always maintains the same blank expression of total disinterest. It is only when fighting that a faint spark of life comes into her eyes.

project 97

Region: Lat 2, Ring 6
Status: Independent burgh
Law: Very little
Wealth: Minimal

overview

The Outside. A place called The City. Beyond the walls of the Project, streets stretching into infinity. Fallenbeck's Grandfather had told him tales of Outside, clustered around the communal lamp, numbed fingers reaching out for the meagre heat or slumped in the draft cooled corridors during one of the interminable heatwaves. Now the decision had been made. The Outside beckoned. The death of Nemeth

decided that. A death deep in the cores, amongst the fog and fungus, had made that a necessity. Most people in the Project did not care for the Outside, the Project was mother and father to them, the only place they had ever known. Those who left were seldom welcomed back, only the Skinners had real dealings with anywhere else, and they were hated because of their privileged position, a position in the light and air.

Bu the Project was cruel mother and uncaring father. Little did it care for the tiny, fragile creatures who swarmed through it. Travel all you want within the corridors, but going to the Outside carries the stigma, of being a traitor to the motherland. Still, it was a journey which would have to be made. Nemeth had known the sacrifices which were needed, known in those last suffocating moments that Outside held truths which must be uncovered. Tales told by old men had a grain of essential truth to them, Fallenbeck knew that. He had gazed from the vast expanse of roof, squatting amongst the cisterns and windmills, quaking at the immensity of open space around him. Beyond the limits of the roof were other places, whispered in dreams and tales. The Luminous Tower, the Infernal Asylum, the Dreaming Spires of the Three Canals. Places of glory and wonder

"He'll go, you know. Outside. He'll die."
"Of course, it's a certainty."
The first speaker coughed, a hollow rasping noise, a staccato burst in the darkness.
"Yes, he will. But slowly, a seeker after such knowledge does not deserve a quick or easy death."
"Yes. Let him quest for a while, let him dream and ponder. After all, who are we to take dreams away from the people."
"Indeed. Who are we."

Probably the largest single building in The City, a vast, sprawling hive reaching up into the smog and delving down into the ground. No one knows how many people live in Project 97, such is the shifting, ever changing nature of its demographics. Whole sections and levels operate by different rules, different laws and different morals. Parts of the building lie rotting and abandoned, ignored, avoided or feared. In the gloom of the cores and sub-levels, gangs prowl for prey, devouring the weak and helpless. In the lightwells and shafts, stinking masses of rubbish give off toxic fumes, spoiling the already foetid air. Dwellings on the outer skin of Project 97 are held on to with violent force, handed down through generations, protected with a fanatical zeal.

Project 97 is truly a huge building, covering many acres of ground and towering high into the smog of The City. A public works project of unparalleled size, expense and extent, even at its current scale, it remains incomplete and unfinished. Its poor concrete splits off in lumps, occasionally crashing down onto a poor unfortunate below. In these troubled days,

no one cares to remember who built Project 97 or why, it just remains home to tens of thousands of citizens, citizens who rarely leave the confines of the concrete warren. Many individual levels and sections are communities in themselves, with markets, gardens, hydroponics and a rough, riotous semblance of public law and order. Others are lawless corridors and basements, ruled by fear and violence, dark realms where combat is carried out in gloom and silence.

Within this mind boggling concrete tangle, there are some remarkable examples of innovation and invention. Some communities tap the stinking refuse mounds which gather in the lightwells and shafts and use the gases they produce to power lights and generators. Others make use of the winds which blow constantly up and down ventilation shafts and through some of the winding corridors, using them to power dynamos giving light, heat and power for tiny industries. The roof levels of Project 97 are festooned with tanks, cisterns and ducting to collect water, siphoning it down through rusting pipes and jerry-built aqueducts to the levels below. Water theft is rife, with pipes constantly being diverted, reconnected, broken open and generally fiddled with. In the very lowest levels, the inhabitants have to rely on the streams which pour down the lightwells, thick with filth and dirt.

security/military presence?

Within Project 97, there is no official security presence. However, this does not mean that some areas are not guarded with a certain amount of zeal. Many corridors have banded together to protect themselves against the depredations of roving gangs and water thieves, most arm ing themselves with staves, clubs, spears and the occasional sparklock. Some artisans within the Project have become very adept at manufacturing compact, powerful crossbows for use within the tight confines of the snaking corridors. Most enthusiastic in the defence of their homes are those who have dwellings which form part of the outer skin of Project 97. These are highly prized, with their access to 'clean' air and the weak, sickly sunlight. Large numbers of outer skin dwellers have set up primitive communications systems involving flags or primitive speaking tubes in order to warn of an imminent attack. To attack one is to attack many. And the many will fight back with the ferocity of cornered dogs.

highlighted location

the funhouse

Description: Makeshift pit-fighting arena

One of the few outlets for the citizens of Project 97 are the many poorly organised, brutal bloodsports carried out at various locations within the ramshackle, meandering structure.

Makeshift arenas have sprung up over the centuries, catering for a variety of bloodthirsty entertainments, largest of these being the inappropriately named Funhouse. In times past, three floors in one of the many wings of Project 97 collapsed, leaving an immense space floored with rubble and twisted metal. Over time, it was used as a dumping ground, storage space and eventually reached its current status as an arena for fighting games. Piles of rubble have been stacked up around the edges of the space, forming impromptu seating galleries. The most prized positions are in the gantries which have been hung from the vacant ends of old corridors and rooms left over from the original collapse. The remains of ancient lightwells allow two shafts of dim luminance down into the arena, casting a deathly glow over whatever grisly combats are being staged. Games of cripplecut, fights to the death, fights against furies dragged up from the sewers and tunnels, fights between madmen found wandering the corridors, any kind of fight is staged here. Betting is often rapid and furious, with food and water being the most common currencies.

highlighted personality

derwent gavidge

Age: Unknown
Height/Build: 6' 5"/Lean and muscular
Eye/Hair Colour: Grey/Red, shaven
Occupation: Pit-fighter
Affiliations: None (that anyone is aware of)

Current king of the Funhouse, undefeated in 57 fights, Derwent Gavidge is reckoned to be one of the most formidable fighters in Project 97. As to where he came from, nobody tells the same tale. Some say he used to serve with Hirplakker in the Contested Grounds, others maintain that he's a former Provost from the TCMA, whilst yet more will place their hand on their heart and affirm that he's in league with the dark powers of The Shifted. Whatever his background, he appeared in the Funhouse one day and asked for a fight. He's never stopped winning since.

A tall, rangy man, his body seems to be made solely of knotted muscle and scar tissue. Yet, he moves with unmatched grace, elegance and speed. Seasoned observers of the carnage in the Funhouse confidently say that he's one of the best fighters they've ever seen. Such is his skill and mounting fame, rumour has it that various powerful outside interests are seeking to tempt him away to the big money of the professional cripplecut circuit. Whenever he is questioned about this, Gavidge simply shakes his head and blinks his watery grey eyes. For him, there seems to be no place better than the gore caked floor of the Funhouse.

shore ditch warrens

Region: Lat 3, Ring 2
Status: Independent burgh
Law: Moderate, local Police force
Wealth: Low

overview

Deer jurnal,
Wurked many long ours in the faktori this day. However!, this leeves mee not without profit! I kan say now that it may bee onli just mor than a yeer hense I will have thee muny I need to attend thee faybeled Longshor Universiti.

Myster Maybell was exceeding kind this day in that hee gifted to mee a Fish on my brake from wurk. Myster Maybell sed to mee: "U make shure u eat enuff lad. Ur a good wurkr and I will bee mighty sorry to see u go when u have enuff muny to go to Longshore. Maybee one day when ur al edukated and suchlik, u will come bak and help mee run this place in my old age?" I thot this most generus of Myster Maybell. He even yet called mee "Sun", which I thot most decent of him as hee lost his own Sun many yeers ago.

I have just this eve begun reeding a Book of which the name is 'One Hundred Storis For Children'. I find the language difikult, as it wos write many yeers ago that it was made. I buyed it from a Vendor who told mee in confidens that it dated from befor The Shift!

Must finish now, as I hav wurk to attend to in the morning.

A dense tangle of industry and housing, the fortunes of Shore Ditch Warrens have fluctuated wildly over the years, leaving the region dotted with disused factories, crumbling housing projects or deeply incongruous areas of gaudily upper-class accommodation. Like many other parts of The City, the highways and byways of Shore Ditch extend deep underground, housing the masses of a literal and metaphorical 'underclass'. Centuries old concrete tower blocks back on to decaying, dusty red brick factories, with chimneys belching noxious vapours and clinging, carcinogenic dust.

The industry of The Warrens is concentrated primarily on lotech manufacturing, producing tools, consumer goods and processed food products for the hungry masses. The factories are dirty, dangerous places to work; safety being one of the lowest on the list of priorities for profit obsessed owners. The Burgh Council exercises nominal control over the area, but in reality, it is riddled with corruption and has little in the way of real power. The local police force has been whittled away until it barely amounts to fifty ill-equipped officers. Bribes from militant companies increased the speed of downgrading and now most business owners use hired thugs for protection, rather than relying on the local constables. The Burgesses of Shore Ditch Warrens have become fat with graft and corruption, a fact which they do little to disguise from the vast majority of the population.

As far as housing goes, most of the population live in crumbling, ill-lit, badly ventilated, damp one or two room flats. Flats above ground level are considered choice properties, even those in the crumbling, teetering tower blocks. Below ground level, the accommodation becomes even less salubrious and the deeper you go and the farther from the sparse lightwells you move, the more rotten the rooms become. In contrast, because of its varied past, there are many impressive, substantial residences in The Warrens. Most of these are occupied by the Burgesses or factory owners, who live in warmth, comfort and security.

However, one startling feature of Shore Ditch is the level of unemployment. In comparison with other areas similarly afflicted with poor housing, bad services and corrupt government, unemployment runs at a remarkably low level. So labour intensive are the factories and mills that they often run short of employees, especially when injuries are running high. Some owners even go so far as to employ Simils in their factories, using their massive strength and apparent fearlessness in dangerous (and deadly) occupations.

security/military presence?

The security of Shore Ditch Warrens is nominally the responsibility of the Burgh Constabulary, an underpaid, undermanned, under-resourced force which seems to have little enthusiasm for catching criminals. In truth, nobody really blames the Burgh Constabulary for this. With only fifty men and little in the way of the resources, they have absolutely no chance against the ravening mobs of gangers, thieves, muggers and other assorted criminal lowlifes. The best officers from the Burgh Constabulary were tempted away to militant companies by the promise of fat pay packets and hitech weaponry. All that is left now are alcoholics, psychotics, slackers and the occasional hopelessly dedicated constable.

Far outnumbering the beleaguered officers of the Constabulary are the thugs, mercenaries and militant troopers employed by the factory owners and other businessmen to keep their premises and businesses secure. The vast, vast majority of these are swaggering bravoes, intent on impressing people with their weapons and armour. To a man they despise the Burgh Constabulary and will go out of their way to make life difficult for them at every turn.

highlighted location

renniks museum of interesting things
Description: Private museum and art collection, Gall Alley

Turn the corner at the end of Stras Kreps, turn down Gall Alley and knock on the blue door on your right. Step inside and find a treasure trove of art, culture and history. Run, seemingly forever, by Marla Rennick, The Museum of Interesting Things is a place of wonder and amazement. Ancient books line the walls of some rooms, drawings, paintings and print festoon the corridors, shelves hold innumerable curious objects, all carefully labelled and tagged for reference. Marla Rennick squeaks through it all on her rickety wheelchair, gliding up and down the ramps which allow her access to all four levels of her museum. From the outside, it looks just like any other anonymous tenement, from the inside it is a storehouse of wonder. The strange thing is, the museum has never been robbed. Ever. The occasional person attempts to steal something from the shelves and they rather curiously find themselves unconscious and minus the stolen object, dumped on the far side of Shore Ditch Warrens.

highlighted personality

chief constable bridgitte leflur
Age: 30
Height/Build: 5' 9"/Wiry
Eye/Hair Colour: Yellow/White
Occupation: Police officer
Affiliations: Shore Ditch Warrens Burgh Constabulary

Being in charge of the Shore Ditch Warrens Burgh Constabulary is probably not high on anyone's list of best jobs in The City, a fact that Chief Constable Leflur knows this only too well. She tries, oh she tries, but the pressures are just too much to bear. Working twenty hours a day drains the body and Leflur is on a constant diet of illegal stimulants just to keep going. Her office is piled high with ages-old reports, her constables either drunk, mad or dead, she cries for hours on end, wishing that it would all stop.

Once a handsome woman, her features are now ravaged by stress, marked by burst capillaries caused by the stimulants, her eyes sunk into black pits, her fingers twitching and writhing in constant motion. She sometimes thinks about ending it all, taking her gun and blowing her own brains out. Then she remembers her ammunition ran out months ago.

Then she cries.

Industrial areas

Alive with thrashing machinery, pounding sound, oppressive heat and strange odours, industrial areas are the beating heart of The City, providing food, manufactured goods, vehicles, clothes, weapons and all the other necessities of life. Hundreds of thousands of individuals work, live and die in the industrial areas, places often more horrific and dangerous than the worst slum or warzone.

burningfell

Region: Lat 7, Ring 2
Status: Independent industrial burgh
Law: Industrial police
Wealth: Low

overview

Gears crunched and metal rubbed against metal as the funicular hesitantly slid to a halt in the station. A faint slapping sound issued from the rusting water tanks slung beneath the passenger deck of the car. In the wan light illuminating the interior of the vehicle, a single figure could be glimpsed, staring back up the hill, following the black lines of the tracks as they narrowed through the maze of black brick and grey concrete.

a sheaf of notes and pressed several into the breast pocket of the attendants jacket. Replacing the money in an inner pocket, he casually strode down the wrought iron staircase, an ornate black fence separating him from the crowd of pushing, sweating workers. Rain began to patter down on the mans hat. It deposited its cargo of soot, ash and dust in clinging globules, staining the fine fabric with the dirt of Burningfell.

The funicular slowly filled with bodies. Moisture from the now dampened workers' clothing caused the windows to quickly mist up with condensation, attenuating the light spilling from the cabin even further. Slamming the door home, the attendant shuffled back to his bothy. Once within, he grasped the massive brass lever which dropped the indicator in the top station, telling his counterpart up the hill to release the upper car. Gradually, the car creaked and rattled its way up the hill, the remnants of water splashing from the ballast tanks.

Halfway up the hill, the two cars came level, workers hanging from the windows to shout hoarse greetings to friends and colleagues. Just then, there was a massive concussive thump

Everywhere furnaces roared and chimneys belched huge gouts of thick, toxic smoke. The door of the funicular rattled as the filth covered, grimy attendant ostentatiously tried to catch the figures attention. Behind the bowed figure of the attendant, a small crowd of workers jostled and coughed. Bright spots could be seen here and there amongst the uniform grey and brown. The workers had been shopping in Sleeping Vale and were laden down with bags and brightly wrapped packages. The figure turned towards the door and tipped his hat to the attendant. With a flourish, he produced

from under the ascending car. A fraction of a second later, the car exploded in a gout of brilliant light, flinging iron and glass high into the air. Knocked from its rails, its retaining cables sheared by the explosion, the descending car began to plummet down the track, weaving from side to side, the faces of its passengers pressed to the glass, only able to stare at the station with which they were about to collide.

At the canal's edge, a figure momentarily glanced back towards the sound of the explosion. Then, he stepped carefully into the water taxi and continued on his way.

Sitting on an eminence above the Black Canal, Burningfell lights the surrounding burghs with the fires of its furnaces and the glare of its retorts. The area is home to numerous small heavy engineering concerns, churning out barges, engines and all manner of industrial goods. In between the factories, works and yards housing projects have grown, designed to accommodate the workers who toil in the smoke and heat. The largest employer in the area is the smelting works owned by Gorunna Logistics. Located in a prime position on the southern slope of the fell, facing the canal, the smelting works gobble up ore from transit barges coming down the canal and spew out processed metals for the Gorunna manufactories or for sale to the smaller works within Burningfell. The Ancient and Honourable Guild of Fulgurators also maintains a sizeable presence in Burningfell, operating a substantial power station located on the north slope of the fell. The Guild also maintains a stormy ongoing relationship with the many small companies who operate the funiculars and cable cars. Around half of these companies are tied to the Fulgurators and the Transit Militia, the rest staunchly maintaining their independence. The Guild and the Militia have, however, held back from taking any action against what they describe as 'wayward' elements, for fear of angering some of the more powerful business interests in Burningfell and beyond.

While not a slum, Burningfell is not exactly the most pleasant place to live. Rain mixes with the heavy soot and dust from the chimneys, coating the streets and houses in a sticky, heavy mud. Most of the housing is constructed from something very similar to this mud. The slag and waste from the furnaces is mixed with a variety of bonding substances to produce bricks for the construction of buildings. Most of the buildings here are built of these rough, black bricks, which, combined with the ever present smoke and dust, conspires to give the steep streets of Burningfell a singularly dark and oppressive feel. Funicular railways grind up the hill between the houses and factories, carrying ore, finished goods and exhausted workers. Indeed, the funicular railway and the cable car are the most common forms of transport in Burningfell, running from the very edge of the canals to the very summit of the fell. They range in size from tiny, one man cable cars to the massive Grimhole Line funicular, which can carry two hundred people and a hundred tons of cargo up and down the fell. Railway lines branching off from the main network terminate at several locations around the bottom of the fell, connecting with the cable cars and funiculars and allowing easy transport of items to other regions of The City. The canals, as would be expected, skirt Burningfell. Only a few travel any distance up the fell, using complex systems of locks and barge lifts to reach about one third of the way to the summit. Civic amenities in Burningfell are somewhat sparse. The occasional cinema or pub can be found wedged into any available space, but most of the citizens prefer to take their leisure in neighbouring Hangside or Sleeping Vale. However, a proportion of the factory owners maintain small clubs for the exclusive use of their employees. These clubs are usually dank,

dingy and exist mostly to provide cheap alcohol and the occasional lacklustre cabaret act. Basic necessities such as water, power and policing are controlled by the Civic Syndicate, an organisation made up of the wealthiest factory owners, businessmen, macrocorporate and Guild representatives. They act as a ruling council for the burgh, organising a basic structure for living as best they can. However, the Syndicate is made up of the controlling business interests in Burningfell and they therefore have a vested interest in running things as cheaply and efficiently as possible.

security/military presence?

Security personnel are very common in Burningfell, with each factory, mill or works retaining at least a couple of guards. Some of these are just local toughs employed for their build and tendency towards violence. Others are professional operatives hired from militant companies or sometimes from the macrocorps themselves. Regardless of their origin, guards are endemic within Burningfell. However, a local police force is not. The burgesses who nominally run the burgh have many times tried to set up some form of constabulary, with a singular lack of success. They have reached a stage where they no longer even bother trying to pass motions to have committees set up to look into the possibility of establishing a board of review to investigate the economic viability of maintaining a police force (or something like that). Instead, most citizens rely on the security provided by the company that they work for, ensuring even closer ties between company and employee.

highlighted location

the happy dog packaging factory
Description: Packaging works

Half way up the Fell, facing south towards the Black Canal stands the slimy, fungus encrusted edifice of the Happy Dog Packaging Factory. The Massive black gates hold up the symbol of the company, a huge dog's head, fashioned from steel, grinning down at the workers at the start the day's toil. Beneath the grinning head is suspended the company motto: 'Happy Dog = Happy Work'. Most workers would wholeheartedly disagree with this. Happy Dog has one of the worst safety records of any factory in Burningfell. Within its dripping brick walls, labourers sweat for many hours a day in cramped, hot foetid conditions, tending the gigantic steel packaging machines which rend flesh and tear limbs with alarming regularity. Happy dog will package almost anything, food, toys, clothes: if it can be packaged, Happy Dog will do it, for a price. Labour organisations have long petitioned the burgesses to have Happy Dog investigated, but as the owner is one of those self-same burgesses, nothing ever comes of it. The factory is a meat grinder which happily swallows up all who step into its maw.

highlighted personality

mr yau

Age: Unknown, looks very old
Height/Build: 5' 4"/Slender
Eye/Hair Colour: Brown/Grey
Occupation: Food stall owner
Affiliations: None

Mr Yau sells fried delicacies at the corner of Fog Boulevard and Bank Way, his tiny stall wreathed in steam and delicate aromas. Customers are never too sure what exactly goes into the dumplings and parcels which Mr Yau pulls from his pots of bubbling oil. Suffice to say, no one has ever complained of illness and the food is always tasty. Especially favoured are the pungent 'No.5 Dumpling in Hot Sauce' and the 'No.12 Mystery Parcel with Greens'. Nobody in Burningfell is entirely sure how long Mr Yau has been a feature on the corner. Grandparents tell their grandchildren that Mr Yau was there when they were but kids, although, they say, that was probably his father. Whatever the story, this wizened, hunched old man does a brisk trade in fast food and pithy aphorisms, with queues stretching far down the street when the factories change shifts.

deepdown

Region: Lat 6, Ring 6
Status: Macrocorporate industrial zone
Law: High
Wealth: High

overview

Ignoring the screaming, be-winged, rifle wielding babies that assailed him from all sides, Sephori put down his sandwich and turned again to the crumpled sheets of his newspaper. In the dim electric light, the large typeface was scarcely visible against the dun-coloured, rough paper. A giant insect walked by smoking a pipe. Sephori ignored this as well. It was better to ignore them. If he concentrated too hard on the strange beasts, he would start wailing and singing again. Then the big men with clubs would come and knock him down, beat him, stick needles in his buttocks.

He had started seeing things as they really were after the cave in. Six days trapped in the blackness. After four days, he began to see things as they really were. After six, the beasts were with him constantly. A rather stand-offish man in a grey coat had intimated to him that he, Sephori, may well be

insane. He had laughed at that and beat the man with a crutch. After that, they put him down here. Him! In the Mad Shafts! He was as sane as the next man. Well, maybe not. Given that the next man was currently trying to beat his own brains out (with some success) on the rough rock walls of the tunnel.

A train trundled past, spitting sparks as it went. Corpses were liberally scattered on the narrow, flat wagons. Men and women screamed, clutched parts of themselves or simply sat, shaking uncontrollably. Poor fools. All of them quite mad. A man with a dog's head and a sword of fire sat down next to Sephori, nodded and produced a cup of tea, seemingly from nowhere. Hmmm. Strange.

Ah well, time to get back to the shaft. He folded his paper and jammed it back into the slot in the wall that contained his worldly possessions. More of the chittering, be-winged babies had attached themselves to his shoulders, so he brushed them off. Mad? Ha! Not likely.

Surrounded by massive fences and constantly bathed in powerful halogen lights, Deepdown is Gorunna's primary in-City mining site. Extending over 10 square miles, the mines of Deepdown extend thousands of yards below the planet's surface. Deepdown is a hellish region of massive vertical shafts, ponderous slag heaps and roaring machinery. Those who work in Deepdown, whether in the mines or on the surface, are the most desperate and unlucky of Gorunna's workforce, driven to work in the appalling conditions due to a sheer lack of any other opportunities. Safety is of very little concern to the executives who run the mining zone, the death and injury rate is truly awful. Even worse is the incidence of mental illness amongst workers. The constant danger, the sheer pressure of being driven for twelve hours a day and the never-ending sensory overload can drive even the sanest person stark raving mad. Those who finally crack are still put to work in the mines, digging in the so-called 'Mad Shafts', galleries and tunnels so dangerous that even the callous management wouldn't put valuable, sane workers into them. The death rates in the Mad Shafts are ridiculous, even by Deepdown standards. Injury is rare. You either die or you carry on mining.

The most obvious physical features of Deepdown are its mine-head towers and gigantic slag heaps. The mine-head towers carry the lift cages for the workers, while the raw ore is brought to the surface by clacking, rusting, continuous belt bucket lifts. The slag-heaps contain the leftovers from the smelting and crushing of the ores. Even they find their uses, with the slag being taken to brickworks to be made into cheap building blocks for housing around The City.

security/military presence?

Because of its place at the heart of Gorunna resource operations, Deepdown is extremely well guarded. The Internal Order Cadre (IOC) maintains a substantial presence, not so much to repel incursions but to suppress unrest amongst the workers. Over 2000 IOC troops are stationed in and around deepdown, controlled from a network of command bunkers built into disused mine-shafts. High speed transit tunnels dedicated to the IOC allow platoons to quickly travel to almost any area of the site, giving a rapid reaction time second to none.

highlighted location

brickworks y-10
Description: Disused brickworks

Now disused after a disastrous strike a few years ago, Brickworks Y-10 lies as a mute reminder of the futility of resistance in the face of macrocorporate power. When manual workers in Y-10 organised a sit-in to protest against working conditions, they found themselves quickly surrounded by IOC troops, hemmed into the building with little food or water. Attempts at negotiation were met with gunfire from the troops, requests for food were denied. Gorunna decided to make an example of the strikers and bricked up the entrances and windows of the factory and left the strikers to starve.

Y-10 has been left as a silent testament to the utter pointlessness of resisting macrocorp power. It's chimmney crumble and chinks gradually appear in the bricked up entrances. It lies desolate and alone, the wind whistling through its workshops and machine halls.

highlighted personality

hannah drake
Age: 32
Height/Build: 5' 11"/Lanky
Eye/Hair Colour: Green/Dirty blonde
Occupation: Miner/Union activist
Affiliations: Various minor movements advocating workers rights

Hannah Drake is woman under surveillance. This she knows, as does almost everybody else in Deepdown. As one of the most fervent campaigners for workers' rights, the Internal Order Cadre keep a close, and not very subtle, eye on her activities. Her phone is tapped, her conversations monitored and every movement tracked. Very little of what she says or does is not picked up by the ever watchful lenses of the IOC. That having been said, Gorunna have so far done nothing to stop her. She is still free to evangelise to gatherings of workers, to sing protest songs in the taverns of Merryhell and meet with known troublemakers from as far afield as Burningfell and Folly Hills.

A lanky woman with a strident, nasal voice and a curiously penetrating stare, Hannah Drake does have the best interests of the workers at heart. Even while encouraging non-violent protests and mass meetings, she still turns up for her shift in the mines every day on the dot, putting in as hard a day's work as any other faithful servant of Gorunna Logistics.

the train

Region: Trans-urban
Status: Independent mercantile lands
Law: Extremely strict
Wealth: High

overview

Like the plunger in a massive syringe, the train accelerated down the tunnel, pushing a vast column of air, dust and debris ahead of it. In loading bays and stations ahead of the onrushing mass of metal, klaxons screamed a warning. Workers scurried from the platforms and docks as the juggernaut hammered towards them.

In the cabin, all was calm. Driver Third Grade Guy Jaenecke watched the bouncing dials with a calm satisfaction. Behind him, insulated by a full yard of soundproofing, the gigantic electric engines spun furiously, driving the megatonne mass of the train along. Ripples intersected in the steaming mug in front of him, interference patterns in a tiny pool. Another lighted loading bay flashed by, a fleeting oasis of light and humanity in the bowels of the earth.

Up to their waists in water, four figures determinedly worked away, disregarding the increasing violence of the gale around them. Splashing in the filth and ordure which had accumulated between the gigantic tracks, they fastened matte grey boxes to the rails, making them fast with reels of wire.

In the cab, a phone rang. Jaenecke picked up the handset.
"Driver 243 speaking."
"Jaenecke, this is Floris. We may have a problem in the tunnel."
"What sort of problem?"
"We apprehended a Fulgurators Guild lookout at one of the emergency vent shafts. He squealed eventually."
As the engine of the train rounded a shallow bend, Jaenecke saw, outlined far ahead, four figures.

"Shit!"

He yanked the massive red emergency braking lever as hard as he could and was flung towards the glass of the canopy as immense plates of steel forced themselves against the spinning wheels. Fountains of sparks flew from the wheels, illuminating the tunnels with a crazy fireworks display. Through a haze of concussion, Jaenecke pressed a small green button embedded in the centre of the dial board. Relays snapped closed. Firing pins dropped and the foot-wide tubes mounted on the front of the train belched their load of ball bearings, nails and assorted scrap.

The last thing the four saboteurs saw was a sparkling dragon, screaming from its lair to belch fire and fury at them. All the cleanup crews could find were a few particles of flesh and torn clothes. The Train was secure again.

Built during the brief reign of the Water Trade Federation (between one hundred & ninety one and two hundred years ago), The Train was designed to carry cargo and passengers from one side of the City to the other. It was initially conceived that the Train would have eight lines, following a similar pattern to the canals. With the collapse of the Water Trade Federation, only one line was completed, running North to South across the City. The two tunnels each carry the massive trains which comprise the system. At ten metres high and four hundred metres long, the trains are the largest vehicles in the City. The Train was never intended to compete with the existing network of passenger only trains, but to challenge the heavy cargo carrying capability of the canal barges.

The two main termini of The Train system lie at opposite ends of The City. The northern terminus lies just beyond the junction of the Grand Canal and the seventh concentric canal, while the southern terminus lies just before the junction of the Nothing and the sixth concentric canal. The original construction of the tunnel system took advantage of long forgotten sewers and storm drains. The construction engineers struggled to widen and strengthen the passages, coming up against all manner of hazards, from long forgotten reservoirs to hidden narcotics labs. Eventually, after fours years of work, the tunnels were completed and the trains were finally able to run.

Security/Military Presence?

To preserve the impeccable reputation of the train system, security is almost watertight (a fact which the operating company constantly points out to the canal cargo companies). Each train carries fifty heavily armed militant personnel and all stations and hoists are guarded by upwards of one hundred troops. Linewerks, a subsidiary company of the opera-

tors provide security, although it has been noted that a large percentage of their personnel are ex-Hirplakker or Trilhoeven troopers. It should be noted that the two main termini of The Train have a round the clock picket of Transit Militia at their gates, the Militia being somewhat aggrieved that it is not they who provide security for The Train.

highlighted location

Cafeteria 11

Description: Cafeteria and rest area

Thronged at almost every time of the day, Cafeteria 11 serves the vast hordes of maintenance workers operating in central section of the tunnel. Seating up to 500 individuals, it is a vast, low ceilinged open area, cluttered with crude benches and tables. Workers are served by a small army of catering staff who toil over gas fired pots and pans, fryers and ovens. The atmosphere stinks of grease, sweat and refuse. Rubbish is only removed from the cafeteria stores once per week and by the end of that week, the stench filters into the kitchen and dining area. All life can be found here, from tracklayers mulling over a cup of tea to electricians discussing union politics.

highlighted personality

Guy Jaenecke

Age: 37
Height/Build: 5' 6"/Stocky
Eye/Hair Colour: Blue/Blackish grey
Occupation: Train driver
Affiliations: Independent Workers Co-operative for Mutual Defence and Assistance (IWCFMDAA)

Guy Jaenecke loves the tunnels. So great is his love for underground life that he even requested assignment to an apartment as close as possible to the train-lines. Most drivers are glad to get away from the confines of the tunnels at the end of the day, not Jaenecke. He always leaves with a faint sense of sadness and always turns up for work early the next day. A few of his colleagues consider him slightly mad, yet none can dispute his efficiency or punctuality. More insidious are the mutterings surrounding his membership of the Independent Workers Co-operative for Mutual Defence and Assistance (IWCFMDAA). This trade union, backed to some extent by the Red Canal Collectivist Republic, is disliked by the management of the train line and by many of the workers. Yet, this does not seem to bother Guy Jaenecke as he turns up for work, early as ever, keen to get back into the tunnels.

Macrocorporate domains

Bastions of ultimate power within The City, the domains of the macrocorps are at times sinister, threatening, welcoming, fascinating, inspiring or deadly. Some ordinary citizens view them with quasi-religious awe, others with unconcealed hatred. For those who live and work within their walls, they are sanctuaries from the dirty masses of The City. Yet, even for those within the domains, there are dangers to be faced.

the Cathedral

Region: Lat 4, Ring 2
Status: Macrocorporate domain
Law: High
Wealth: Extremely high

overview

07.37: Fired sub-editor Breskine. The man was a weakling anyway, too attached to his subjects. Took a couple of tabs of edge and some nice strong tea Mrs Gurtiev brought in. Good old Mrs Gurtiev.

07.59: Re-hired sub-editor Breskine after finding out we couldn't get anyone else on short notice. News of protests outside Luminosity Tower. Ha, ha, ha. Arclight getting it in the neck again. Run that as second item. In fact, must get Shape to send down a few people to stir some trouble.

08.45: Had to bawl out Breskine over the Matta story. Load of old bollocks. Little twit wouldn't know a story if it came up and jumped on his toes. Had to take some pills for raging headache. Mrs Gurtiev brought me a pastry and some more tea. Lovely woman.

10.27: Gorunna aerostat crashes into tenement in Merryhell, suspected terrorist activity. Slot that to front news item. Many

killed, bodies everywhere, grieving families. Great copy.

12.18: Good old Shape! Riot in progress at Luminosity Tower. Brigade troops firing on unarmed civilians. Fantastic. At least thirty dead, many wounded. More tea. More edge. Headache getting worse.

14.50: Fired Breskine again, this time for good. Had some sort of 'thing' about the Luminosity Tower riot. Fool. Damn headache.

15.26: Ha! Arclight claiming that 'outside elements' instigated the riots at the tower! Morons! Brigade apologising to survivors. Footage being brought in of horribly burned victims of Gorunna aerostat crash. Great copy!

16.08: Breskine found dead in toilets, slashed wrists. Weak, very weak. Took the easy way out. Must try and fight this headache.

The heart of Sideband's media web, The Cathedral is a vast, rambling, buttressed edifice which dominates the surrounding area absolutely and completely. Thought to date from before The Shift, details on the history of The Cathedral are sketchy at best. It is assumed that it was, prior to The Shift, an actual place of worship, possibly the prime religious building in The City. However, all of this is mere conjecture and no historians can say with any certainty that they have confirmed the twisted history of The Cathedral.

Through its echoing halls, the thousands of employees of Sideband Media scurry, each intent on their own business. The four wings and the great central hall make up the main body of The Cathedral. These vast vaulted spaces are among the largest enclosed areas in The City, with striated columns thrusting towards the ceilings high above. However, the main work of Sideband goes on in the upper stories, within the immense walls and in the buried cellars. Here are kept the newsrooms, recording studios, sound stages and transmission systems. Visitors to The Cathedral seldom see this frenetic warren which lurks behind the gloriously buttressed and vaulted façade. Such is the diversity of the Sideband operation, almost every type of media imaginable is handled within the walls of The Cathedral. TV, films, telecommunications, Dataflow, news and every other means of communication available in The City.

The Cathedral also serves another purpose, as one of the major communications nodes in The City. Tight-beam transmitters, balloon uplinks, telegraphs and landlines all converge on The Cathedral from all parts of The City. This serves two purposes for Sideband. Firstly, it allows them to keep a tight rein on data transmission over a wide area and secondly, it also allows them to tap and monitor a vast range of communications activity. Not that Sideband admits this or would it use any information gathered for its own political or fiscal advantage, oh no. However, in deep crypts and high galleries, armies of technicians sift through the streams of data, extracting morsels which can be banked for future use. All this activity makes The Cathedral one of the greatest repositories of knowledge on activity within The City.

All this knowledge is filtered through the complexity of The Feed, Sideband's own internal equivalent of The Dataflow. Nobody outside of Sideband is entirely sure how The feed operates. Even those within the company have only the sketchiest knowledge of its workings. Suffice to say, it seems to have something to do with pipes and liquids, although how this serves to communicate information and operate computers, nobody is entirely sure.

Security/Military presence?

Security, both internal and external, is provided by Media Break, Sideband's paramilitary arm. While fairly benign and moderate when compared to many of the other macrocorporate security forces around The City, Media Break do carry out their work with a certain amount of distasteful relish. Their main task is breaking up the fights and squabbles which are always occurring between the various other Sideband departments, resulting in the cracking of a few heads and the twisting of a few arms in an attempt to impose order. Clad in smart black business suits and garishly coloured ties or bow-ties, Media Break personnel are almost all affable and approachable, a fact which seems to make people even more worried about them. It is only when trouble is brewing that the mask of civility slips and the hard professionalism beneath begins to show.

highlighted location

the archive
Description: Media storage facility

Deep in the bowels of the Cathedral, in vaulted chambers running as far as the eye can see, lies the Archive. Miles of corridors loop and twist, feed lines glow gently as they run across ceilings and floors, stacks of cabinets rear up into the darkness. Within the Archive lies the summation of Sideband's knowledge, hundred of years of films, programmes, reports, analysis and books. Hardcopies of almost everything Sideband has ever produced lie in the silence of these vaults. Some items are stored in formats so old, nobody knows how to access them. Rare books are held in hermetically sealed lockers, their contents guarded from decay by inert gases. Other books are left to rot in vast shelves, creaking under the weight of accumulated knowledge. Whole sections of the Archive have been abandoned for years, as researchers and stringers rely on the feed for their information. Only a few dedicated employees maintain the Archive, attempting vainly to preserve the stored knowledge for future generations. As always, rumours twist about the corridors of the Archive, whispers about ancient films and books, sources of horrible, terrible knowledge.

highlighted personality

veridiana van eyck, media personality
Age: 27
Height/Build: 5' 10"/Voluptuous
Eye/Hair Colour: Blue/Blond
Occupation: Media personality
Affiliations: Sideband

Bubbly, lively, irritating host of 'The Sideband Family Fun Hour', van Eyck is darling to thousands, a shiny, clean, sparkling icon in a world of dirt and degradation. Families cluster round their hazy black and white TV sets as she prances in front of the camera, introducing cheap, titillating acts and promoting the latest Sideband entertainment products. Viridiana is recognised by almost everyone in The City with a TV and consequently finds it rather difficult to lead a normal life. Gossip shows and papers are full of innuendo and rumour about her private life, linking her with all manner of people, from ekranoplan pilot Ivan Vassar, to Matt Kenzie, one of the leading figures of Arclight. On the whole, she is a somewhat abrasive, antagonistic character, mostly as a result of being closeted in the Cathedral from much of the time.

the forbidden city

Region: Lat 3, Ring 5
Status: Macrocorporate domain
Law: Very high
Wealth: Very high

overview

Snow collected gently on the bridges and pipes which criss-crossed The Trench. Dirty flakes spiralled down from a grey sky, softening and blurring the outlines of walls, turrets and cupolas. The walkways along the walls of The Forbidden City were free of snow, melted off by concealed heating ducts. Armoured figures tramped through the gloom, keeping their lonely vigils on the walls.

From a tiny door set into the wall emerged a fragile, lithe figure clad in deep red furs. The figure strolled along the wall top to meet with another figure coming in the opposite direction. They met at a lumpen projection which emerged from the surface of the wall, a corroded mass of iron, perhaps once part of some weapon system.

"My Lady."
"Ah, Ruse. Fairing well?"
"Very well, my Lady. Yourself?"
"Ah, moderately well. Thank you. So, how goes it with your plans?" The man shifted his stance and let his eyes flick out over The Trench, something of a worried expression passing briefly over his face.
"Mmm, they are progressing slowly. Achieving, ah, penetration is proving harder than we anticipated. Our assets are being compromised at an alarming rate." He looked down at his feet, at the pools of gently steaming water which covered the walkway.
"They are more wily than we imagined, then?"
"Very much so. This is not some silly little manufacturing concern that we can compromise, this is far more, um, substantial."
"I see."
"Yes. Your uncle, how is his health these days?"
"He survives, in a fashion. However, perhaps not for much longer."

The snow continued to drift down as the two figures stood in silence, both gazing down into the depths of The Trench. A light flickered below, flashing on and off in rapid sequence.

"One of your men?"
"I think not, my Lady."
"I see. So, how do you propose to expedite our problem?"

"Covert tactics have met with singular failure, my Lady. I would propose a more direct approach, using proxy forces of course."
"Of course. And then?"
"Then? Well, something of a probe against their defence would be in order, perhaps leaving sleepers behind. We still need to get the others onside though."
"Yes. Leave that to me Ruse. I believe I can handle that."
"Very well, my Lady. Is there anything else?"
"Yes. Would you care to join me for tea?"

A secretive and sinister place, the Forbidden City is the heartland of Nakamura-Yebisu Group, a grim construction of brick and concrete. Outsiders are seldom permitted to enter the complex, a sprawling collections of buildings occupying a couple of square miles near the southern edge of The Trench. High defensive walls surround the entire area, topped with watchtowers, searchlights and gun emplacements. Troopers in sculpted armour patrol the walls and droning aerostats hover overhead.

Within the Forbidden City, the elite of Nakamura-Yebisu live out their lives, seldom leaving the protection of its high walls. Despite the fact the Forbidden City is surrounded on all sides by lands owned by the macrocorp and occupied by its employees, the company still retains a paranoid fascination with defending its headquarters against any possible form of attack.

Unlike many other macrocorp domains, the Forbidden City contain no manufacturing facilities, storage depots or factories of any kind. It exists purely to service the needs of the top personnel within the company. Luxurious apartments, restaurants, sporting facilities, health suites and conference rooms are all contained within its heavy defensive walls. Very few people within the company ever actually get to set foot inside the fortress, even those who guard it are chosen from the best of the Weapons Division.

security/military presence?

As previously mentioned, elite units of the Weapons Division guard the Forbidden City from any form of attack. Numerous armoured guards patrol the crenellated walls and many the searchlights and sensory facilities. As you would expect from NYG, many mikefighters are on stand-by, ready to intercept any perceived threat. Those living in the areas around the domain have become used to the mikefighters zooming and wheeling overhead at odd hours
of the day or night. Upwards of one thousand troops guard the Forbidden City at any one time, with many more ready to be mobilised from widespread company facilities.

highlighted location

barracks 205
Description: Living area for NYG military personnel

When not on duty, the soldiers of the Weapons Division who are assigned to protect the Forbidden City are almost exclusively confined to one of the barracks within the walls. Largest of these is Barracks 205, which serves as the dormitories and recreation areas for the troops which guard the eastern walls. Low-ceilinged and smoky, Barracks 205 is a series of large, open rooms on several levels within the eastern wall itself. Most of these are given over to bunks and hammocks where the off-duty troopers while away their hours. Alongside these hot, crowded sleeping spaces, there are also canteens, fitness facilities and a number of tightly controlled armouries. Troopers are prevented from entering the main body of the Forbidden City except when they are on duty. Seldom do they have the chance to glimpse the luxury and opulence in which their masters and mistresses live.

highlighted personality

ernst ruse
Age: 36
Height/Build: 6' 2"/Sturdy
Eye/Hair Colour: Green/Sandy
Occupation: Intelligence operative
Affiliations: Nakamura-Yebisu

For a highly placed member of the NYG structure, Ernst Ruse spends very little time actually within the Forbidden City itself. His manifold missions and interests take him far afield, making him one of the better travelled and more streetwise of the ruling elite. His position as intelligence adviser to Lady Karen Nakamura has gained him no small amount of power but has also gained him a fair number of enemies within the company. All this, however, he takes in his stride. Whilst respectful to the controllers of the company, he does not adopt the craven , cowering attitude that many of the lower ranks do, preferring to maintain a certain air of independence. In Lady Karen's service, this has actually served to increase her respect for him and she now relies on his services for all matters relating to external policy. In truth, Ruse could, if he wished, have a very substantial effect on the policy of Nakamura Yebisu, a level of influence which he has so far declined to use.

the iron bastion
Region: Lat 5, Ring 5
Status: Macrocorporate domain
Law: High
Wealth: Extremely high

overview

Ochre slime lay across everything. Even with the windows tightly nailed shut, the slime still managed to find it's way in. Across the street, down towards the junction, she could see the black face of the Bastion, it's surface stained with orange, gouged with pits and crevices. Sighing, she twisted the spokes of her wheelchair and turned away from the window. Below, her father moved about in the tiny kitchen. The clanging of cheap pots and pans announced his attempts at cooking.

The hissing gas lamp lit the room with a faint yellowish glow. It's iron bracket was spotted with rust and festooned with the trails of long deceased insects. The smell of pungent yellow tea drifted up from the floor below, overlaying the odours of rot and decay. It used to be the case that she cared for her father in his advancing years. A lifetime slaving for Hirplakker in the manufactories had aged him prematurely, giving him the shuffling gait of an old, old man. Now, he cared for her, trapped as she was in this upper floor. He went about the daily routine in a daze, carrying her to the toilet on the landing, dressing her, preparing her food.

Ever since the interrogators came for her it had been this way. They carted her off, yelling false accusations of spying, of espionage and sabotage and treachery. They broke her kneecaps, tore the tendons of her legs, smashed her pelvis. She screamed that they had the wrong girl, that she was no spy, that her entire family were loyal to Hirplakker. Only when she had almost breathed her last, did they relent and conclude that she was telling the truth. By then it was too late. Crippled and broken, they pensioned her off, paying a small stipend each week, far from enough to support her father and sister.

Her sister brought in a little money. Sometimes. She didn't want to think about the abuses her beautiful little sister suffered at the hands of faceless strangers. Her father blankly ignored everything, shuffling around with a fixed gaze, brewing tea and cooking watery fish soup. She had never done anything to harm the company. What could one girl do against the might of a macrocorp. Yet, they had chosen to cripple her and condemn her family to a life of squalor.

The door opened and her father struggled in with the tea tray, staring blankly at the wall of iron outside the window.

Like a series of shrapnel splinters thrown from the sky, the Iron Bastion looms above the surrounding dwellings with an ill-concealed air of menace. The iron-clad surface is rusted and pitted from centuries of exposure to the corrosive atmosphere of The City. The metallic gargoyles and waterspouts have become fused orange lumps projecting from the sides of the building at disconcerting angles. Upper surfaces are studded with disused communications dishes, tight-beam transmitters and signalling towers. Lazily creaking wind turbines cluster at various points, groaning and wailing in the stiff breezes. At street level, people walk round the Iron Bastion with a hunched aspect, fearful of falling scabs of iron oxide and gigantic flakes of corroded iron slamming into the pavements. All the buildings near this grim construction are coated in orange-brown layers of rust dust, the substance of the Bastion mingling with the rain and particulates to produce a gluey smear over everything.

The Iron Bastion is the one true home of Hirplakker Combine, a place of faded glory and rusting ambition. Not one inch of the walls are not rusting and decayed, everywhere there is a feeling of a gradual slide into irreversible decrepitude. For a macrocorp as powerful as Hirplakker, the Iron Bastion is a singularly uncared for, gloomy place. Inside, all is stone and iron, giant vaulted rooms, low, winding corridors and steep, slippery staircases. In the core of the building, four giant black iron elevators, massive cages of wrought metal shuddering their way between floors. The lift core is pierced by beams of wan light which filter down from the only large expanse of glass in the building, the shit-streaked, soot encrusted dome which caps the lift core. The dome arches over the gantries and girders which support the mechanisms of the lifts, its own walkways and stairs connecting with those of the lifting mechanisms. In this cyclopean, echoing space, Hirplakker employees come to bask in the light, enjoying a brief glimpse of the outside world while on a break from their working day.

Hirplakker carries out no manufacturing in the Iron Bastion, it is purely administrative and organisational centre. In the depths of the building are located the seven Intellects, the artificial minds who control the affairs of Hirplakker. In these guarded crypts, technicians maintain the Intellects, tending the systems as they would care for a child. Some technicians can even be said to love the Intellects, spending hours in conversation with tiny fragments of their personalities. Such behaviours are overlooked by higher management, as they realise how valuable the cabal of wide-eyed scientists is to the continuing good running of the company. Throughout the rest of the building, secretaries, analysts, clerks and executives sit at dingins wired into the Intellects, organising the work of the massive creature which is Hirplakker.

security/military presence?

Since the debacle of the Hundred Block War and their humiliating climbdown in the face of the rampant Arclight macrocorp, Hirplakker have become increasingly paranoid about security in their headquarters. Every minor incident is viewed as sabotage, with the Intellects formulating increasingly unlikely plans that Hirplakker might use to finally smash Arclight. Workers are randomly carted off for interrogation, fuelling the rumours of torture chambers maintained in the hidden places of the Bastion. Heavily armed guards are stationed at all entrances, with stringent security checks to make sure only authorised personnel manage to gain entrance. Stuttering cameras allow the Intellects to watch the security guards, tabulating and processing their movements, projecting possibilities, occasionally suggesting changes in policy. The Intellects, as with all things within the company, have absolute control. Their word is to be obeyed as the word of God.

highlighted location

the crush

Description: Entrance/exit into the Iron Bastion

The main entrance for shift workers entering and exiting the Iron Bastion, the Crush feeds out onto Defiance Crescent, a boulevard lined with spattered statues of great figures from the company's past. A tight corridor, lined with observation portals and gunslits, The Crush extends a hundred yards into the building and can be blocked at either end by hydraulically operated gates constructed from three foot thick slabs of steel. The impassive eyes of cameras watch workers as they enter and exit. Tight-faced guards peer out from the slits in the walls. Barriers route those coming in and out, allowing the guard to open doors and snatch workers for random searches. The Crush is not a place for the claustrophobic or easily panicked.

highlighted personality

ansell cole

Age: Indeterminate middle-age
Height/Build: 6' 0"/Slender
Eye/Hair Colour: Pale brown/Dusty red
Occupation: Scurt catcher
Affiliations: Hirplakker

Occupying a curious position within Hirplakker, Cole is Scurt Catcher In Chief for the Iron Bastion. The age and extent of the building means that it has a terrible problem with infestations, hence the need for team of individuals whose sole purpose is to root out scurts and other vermin from the interstices of the building. Physically, he is a saturnine man of indeterminate age, with long, thin fingers and a quizzical, faintly amused countenance. He has a cutting sense of humour, sharp wit and displays an intellectual ability which few expect in a man of his station. Deep in the basements of the Iron Bastion, he and his troop of scurt catchers construct intricate traps, brew noxious poisons and hone the various weapons in their arsenal. Cole runs his squad with military precision but with a fair and even hand. With permission to travel almost anywhere within the Bastion, he instills in his underlings a sense of responsibility, duty and not poking their noses in where they are most certainly not welcome.

Konkret

Region: Lat 4, Ring 5
Status: Macrocorporate dominion
Law: Very high
Wealth: Very high

Overview

Internal Memo
MaxEncrypt	6702438589464/fiend45
CodeCrak:	Archer-K
From:	Feuer, Agneta
	(WepSysDevTek 'Lancer')
To:	Fegelein, Brooke
	(Gruppenkommandant, Grauschjager)
Subject:	Project 'Spiker'

Fegelein,
Thanks for your help with Operation 'Ivy', the entire thing proved to be a great success. If there's anything I can do to help you out in the future, just ask.

That aside, we appear to have further developments on Project 'Spiker'. Intelligence has been passed my way by one of our assets within the target which disturbs me greatly and I feel that you should know in order to take any appropriate action. The source was not particularly clear about the exact nature of the information or how it would affect Project 'Spiker', but it does seem to be of a particularly sensitive nature. Apparently, it relates to a fragment of conversation overheard by our source, referring to the 'device workings'. It would seem that the 'device workings' refers to a place rather than a project or item. The fragment was overheard during a conversation between Kenzie and another unknown individual (assumed to be a high-ranking individual within the target).

I would appreciate it if you could do all you can in order to facilitate the retrieval of further information regarding the 'device workings'.

Respectfully yours,
Feuer.

Internal Memo
MaxEncrypt	6702539589565/fiend48
CodeCrak:	Sling-D
From:	Fegelein, Brooke
	(Gruppenkommandant, Grauschjager)
To:	Feuer, Agneta
	(WepSysDevTek 'Lancer')
Subject:	Re: Project 'Spiker'

Feuer,
Information retrieved and acted upon.

Have abstracted several assets from target and utilised information extraction techniques (see attached programme reel for footage). No useful information retrieved. Have dispatched asset 'Eugen' to target for further search. Apparent information security level v.high, no access to those under board level, it would appear. Suggest abstracting higher level target. Have team standing by to conduct abstraction. Suggest Kenzie to be appropriate target.

Please advise.
Fegelein, Gruppenkommandant Grauschjager.

Forbidding. Dominating. Massive. Konkret echoes the very ethos of the macrocorporation which it houses, a three dimensional image of a corporate mentality. No other structure in The City looks quite like Konkret, a gigantic angular arch straddling the fifth ring canal. It utterly dominates the surrounding cityscape, seemingly sucking the tenements and tower-blocks in through sheer architectural gravity. Built out of stained, weathered concrete, the building has a ponderous, immovable solidity and a sinister implied threat. Of all the macrocorporate dominions, none presents such a visible image of violence as Konkret. Gunslits and sensor turrets sprout like fungus all over the surface. Ack-ack defences lie in wait in concealed bunkers on the roof, ready to demolish any and all intruders. Hordes of soldiers and knots of sinister Grauschjager are omnipresent.

Internally, once you have passed through the fifteen foot thick walls), the guts of Konkret twist and writhe, with miles of corridors and ducts connecting the myriad internal spaces. The structure extends deep below ground, whole labs, manufactories, testing grounds and barracks are situated deep below the surface.

security/military presence?

Trilhoeven, being Trilhoeven, have vast numbers of troops both in and around Konkret. For a two block radius around the building, soldiers patrol the streets, operating with no legal authority, yet with the power of life and death over 'suspects'. Less visible, but feared to a far greater degree of magnitude are the small groups of Graushjager (see Trilhoeven's entry in 'The Power' for further details on the Grauschjager), emerging from the squat portals on missions of dire intent.

highlighted location

the viewing gallery

Description: Intelligence gathering centre

Heart of Trilhoeven's intelligence network, the Viewing Gallery nestles in the ground deep under Konkret. Hundreds of information feeds converge on this relatively small space to be poured over by highly trained analysts who extract every last useful scrap of information. The walls of the 'Gallery are lined with viewscreens and projectors, with employees hunched below them, tapping commands into

their computers, examining photographs and ordering surveillance. The air is filled with a wash of noise from tens of tapping fingers, clicking dingins and murmuring speakers. The Grauschjager control the entrances and exits to the Viewing Gallery, assiduously monitoring the employees, watching for treachery or subterfuge of any kind. Analysts are often dragged from their chairs and taken off into the bowels of Konkret, never to be seen again.

highlighted personality

susanna devore

Age: 19
Height/Build: 5' 5"/Athletic
Eye/Hair Colour: Dark brown/Dyed red
Occupation: Message runner
Affiliations: Trilhoeven

Devore is a runner, a message carrier scurrying through the twisting corridors of Konkret. Runners are entrusted to carry messages deemed too important to send via the normal channels. Their bright red uniforms with flashing red strips and blaring klaxons alert other employees to their approach, warning them to move aside as the runners streaks by.

Susanna has been a runner for three years now and is extremely happy in her work. Like all runners, she is extremely fit, a consequence of running everywhere at top speed for hours on end. She prides herself on always being ahead of schedule, getting messages to their destination in the quickest possible time. Within her head she carries a mental map of Konkret so accurate that she can determine the quickest route from any point in the complex to any other point in an instant. She has customised her uniform with a flashing readout which gives a countdown of how long she has to get to her assigned destination. Many view this as unnecessarily flash, but Devore is proud of her abilities and thinks nothing of telling everyone and anyone about them.

In her off duty hours, she spends a lot of time training in the company gyms or indulging in her hobby of building scale models of famous buildings from tiny bricks. When questioned about this rather unusual and somewhat uncharacteristic pastime, she states that it helps her to calm down after a long day speeding around the twists and turns of Konkret.

luminosity tower

Region: Lat 7, Ring 3
Status: Macrocorporate domain
Law: Extremely high
Wealth: Extremely high

overview

"It is a work of the deities. Man cannot have built so wonderful a structure. Man alone has not the strength or the genius to draw such a splendid thing from the earth. I come here every day to gaze in wonder. I petition the guardians at the portal to grant me access, to see the wonders kept sealed within. Yet, they continually deny me. They are harsh men and women, the light of suffering and torture is in their eyes. Although, behind it all is pride, pride to stand guard of the greatest wonder man has ever gazed upon.

I have contacted those who serve the builder-deity. I beseech them to allow me to serve, even in the most humble fashion. Continually, they reject me. What can I do to make them think me worthy. I know that there are those who would seek to destroy the tower, to smash its wonder into dust. Perhaps if I strike against the defilers, then I will be granted access, even if it is in the next life.

So here I stand, gazing at the holiest of holies for perhaps the last time. I stand with this device, this assembly of wires and clockwork parts, ready to strike with all the power of my faith. This corporeal body may be struck down in the process, but my spirit will live on. I will be granted access. Some day."

A gigantic building, dwarfing all those around it, Luminosity Tower is home to Arclight. A slender, glass pyramid, the tower reaches 700 yards into the air, making it easily the tallest building in The City. How Arclight mustered the resources to construct such a magnificent building in only three years is unknown, speculation is rife. That having been said, Luminosity Tower succeeds in putting all other macrocorporate domains in the shade by quite a margin.

In the weak sunlight, the glass plates shine gold, bathing the area surrounding the tower in heavenly light. The main entrance is ablaze with light. When the main doors open, brilliant white light shines out, turning night into day. Arclight knows the value of impressing the public and people will travel over large distances to see the wonder that is Luminosity Tower. The structure itself is divided into 110 floors. The vast majority of levels are taken over by administration and research facilities.

security/military presence?

Security is provided by elite companies from the Brigade of Light. It is considered a great honour to be chosen to guard the tower and competition is fierce to be chosen for this most prestigious of duties. It is often given as a reward to units which have performed particularly successfully in the Contested Grounds. On average, there will be eight companies (each containing 110 men and officers) guarding the tower, including at least two Tentenel companies. The main entrance is always watched over by Tentenel troops, ready to crush anyone who attempts to enter the building.

Dotted in a half mile radius around the tower are numerous mikefighter and aerostat bases, providing round the clock combat air patrols. There is a three quarter mile diameter no fly zone around the tower; any and all aircraft breaching this zone without permission are automatically attacked. Concealed within the tower is an impressive array of anti-missile weapons. A mix of laser and gauss weapons are used to provide defence against anything from an RPG to a cargo aerostat.

Within the tower, the Brigade guards are vigilant but unobtrusive. Tentenel troops guard the most high-security areas, while regular Brigade of Light infantry are posted about the rest of the building.

highlighted location

the atrium

Description: Ground floor of Luminosity Tower

Designed to awe those who enter the tower, the Atrium is a massive space, a giant gap running up through ten stories of Luminosity tower.

Massive glass cases hold items which Arclight is proud of, including a Hirplakker powersuit captured during the initial phases of the Hundred Block War. The sole purpose of the Atrium is to give an impression of power, wealth and strength. This it manages with singular aplomb. Cunningly fashioned into the massive support struts, gauss lifts run to all levels of the tower, although some require higher clearance to enter than others. Lush greenery, tended by an army of low paid workers manages to introduce an organic feel to the place, offsetting the prominence of technological sophistication. No inhabitant can fail to be struck dumb with wonder at this most magnificent of sights.

highlighted personality

Shigunda Bundabbie

Age: 57
Height/Build: 6'/Wiry
Eye/Hair Colour: Watery blue/Grey
Occupation: Head Gardener, the Atrium, Luminosity Tower
Affiliations: Arclight

A man of fierce devotion to his duty, Bundabbie cares for the plants within the Atrium of Luminosity Tower with a fervour that approaches fanaticism. Ten hours a day, his knurled hands prune, water and landscape, driving his minions to greater exertions in the name of the macrocorporate. His loyalty surpasses even that of Brigade troopers, he will brook no dissension and will absolutely not tolerate any form of criticism of Arclight. Orders from above are to be obeyed without question and without delay. Those who tamper with the plants, walk on the grass or pollute the soil will rue the day they ever met Shigunda Bundabbie. A spade to the head is the most likely consequence, and rumours circulate that he has used certain 'fertilisers' to make the blooms in the Atrium grow with even greater vigour.

the powerhouse

Region: Lat 3, Ring 4
Status: Macrocorporate domain
Law: Very strict
Wealth: Very high

overview

"It's the heat exchangers, you see." Yelled the thin man above the clamour of machinery and the hiss of steam.
"Yes, I see. Very impressive." The younger, fairer man almost shouted back.
"Never been down here before, have you? Down to the reactors?"
"No sir, never had the need to. That's why I was surprised when you offered to show me around. Grateful, but still surprised."
"No need to be, young man. No need to be. Just wanted to show you the heart of what makes us great, raises us above the common mass." The thin man leaned out over the edge of the gantry and gazed down at the heat exchangers below. Water dripped from the curving concrete ceiling far above, vapourising as it hit the blisteringly hot metal of the exchangers.
"Excuse me sir, but should the exposed surfaces be like that? That hot? Is that not a bit inefficient?"
"Well spotted, we're running a pressure test with some of the exchanger jackets removed. Normally you wouldn't see that."
"Oh. You can really feel the heat, even from here."
"Yes, you can, can't you?" the thin man put a lanky arm around the other's shoulders, twisted, and flung him over the edge of the gantry. The figure hit the heat exchanger surface with bone breaking force, the sound of impact deadened by the fearsome noise from all around. The figure's mouth was wrenched wide in a spasm of pain as his clothes began to smoulder. Where his bare hands touched the searing metal, flesh came away in blackened gobbets. With tremendous effort he hauled himself upright, his knees seared down to the bone, shoes melting, staggering towards the edge of the heat exchanger. His face red and blistering, he stumbled towards the edge, flinging himself the last few yards towards the edge.

The body tumbled down the curving surface, tumbling head over heels, shedding fragments of scorched clothing, disappearing from view in the darkness. The thin man turned and walked back along the gantry, ambling towards a cluster of men in thick black overalls.
"You can put the shields back on now, get things working properly again."
The men nodded, gulping nervously, and edged past the thin man. As for the thin man, he left.

Standing firm since time immemorial, the central tower of The Powerhouse rears above The City, solid, impassive, menacing. Closer to hand, it quickly becomes apparent that the tower has been patched and repaired numerous times during its long history. Scabs of concrete flake from its surface, buttressing girders hold up sections of wall. Beneath the tower lie the eight great hangers, the vast spaces which house the main reactors which give GRID its power. Sheathed in metal and concrete, the reactors have been running for as long as anyone can remember, kept alive by the tender ministrations of an army of technicians. Festooning the hangers, spreading out over the land like an encroaching cancer are the numerous newer buildings which house GRID personnel. From the air, The Powerhouse resembles a vast, eight pointed star overgrown with brown, red, black and green growths.

At the very summit of the tower, where it spreads out to six times the width of the slender supporting column, is the Control Room. From here, platoons of analysts control and direct power across The City, connecting, disconnecting and re-routing. This is the epicentre of GRID operations, decisions made here affect the lives of citizens many miles away across The City. From the Control Room on down, The Powerhouse is a tangle of interconnecting passageways, yards wide pipes, maintenance runs and tens of levels. The corridors echo with a hollow bass thrum, while the air in the lower levels is hot and damp, as coolant pipes leak steam from worn and cracking joints. Most of the massive cooling pipes connect to one of the eight great cooling towers, conical structures of black brick, clinging to the roofs of the hangars like fungi. Steam billows from their gaping mouths and on still days, the entire area can be wrapped in a thick, cloying blanket of fog.

Through the fog, in between the cooling towers, hangars and encrusting buildings run hundred of cable-cars, ranging from tiny one man affairs to large constructions, capable of carrying two hundred workers. They transport equipment, raw materials and personnel about Powerhouse, swinging along above the crazy topography of the building. Deep below the hangars, GRID maintains a secondary transport system, a double ring of train tunnels designed to assist those technicians who work on the reactors.

The air in the tunnels is almost unbreathable, thick and humid. Leaking coolant from the reactors above drips into the tunnels, creating toxic pools along the tracks. Most of the technicians do not relish travelling through the tunnels, fearful of the folklore which surrounds them. Stories abound of furies coming into the tunnels through ancient passages and sewers, of swarms of diseased scurts bigger than a man's arm as well as of other less identifiable creatures. Executives discount such talk as superstitious tosh, but every now and then a work party disappears, leaving only a few traces of their presence. Occasionally sounds are heard, not the mechanical sounds of the reactors and pipes, but animalistic, feral sounds, welling up from deep underground. The stories proliferate and the fear grows stronger.

Security/military presence?

Like any other macrocorporate domain, The Powerhouse is well guarded by the best troops that GRID can muster. The reactors are a tempting prize for a rival and an almost magical target for terrorists, so GRID keeps a close eye on movements in and around the sprawling structure. The ongoing mistrust between GRID and the Ancient & Honourable Guild of Fulgurators only makes the situation worse. The occasional guild-sponsored terrorists give the guards targets to practice their aim on: few of them get near the hangars. Troops are drawn from GRID's small but effective EyEwiRE Corps and are equipped to the very highest level . Most weapons are bought in from Trilhoeven and Gorunna, as GRID lacks the large scale facilities to produce hitech weapons. The troops also have a dedicated network of fast cable-cars which allow them to move about the facility with all possible speed.

highlighted location

the Shield Works

Description: Manufacturing plant

A small but vital part of the GRID operation, the Shield Works produce and maintain the vital radiation shielding which surrounds the all-important reactors. Cramped into a concrete bay at the rear of Hangar 3, the Works are alive with the roar of machinery, the pounding of great hammers and the hiss of cooling vats. Labourers and technicians toil round the clock, producing new sections of shield, repairing old, worn out segments and generally making sure that there's always enough shielding for any conceivable emergency. Workers have developed their own particular sign language, allowing them to communicate in the deafening clamour. Their gesticulations are unintelligible to outsiders, a blur of waving hands and twisting fingers. The most hazardous job in the Works is disposing of old shielding, breaking it down into manageable chunks before dropping it down the dark, limitlessly deep disposal shafts.

highlighted personality

Letitia Rarity

Age: 27
Height/Build: 5' 3" (due to hunched posture)/Slim, slumped
Eye/Hair Colour: Light blue/White
Occupation: Janitor/Cleaner
Affiliations: GRID

Letitia Rarity used to be a trusted reactor technician, one of the elite corps who tend to the needs of the ancient power sources. Sadly, her fall from grace was both rapid and alarming. She speaks only in monosyllables, hunched over her broom as she sweeps out the cable-cars. Prior to this, she was a vivacious young woman, popular with her peers and superiors. Then there was The Incident In The Train Tunnel (as it is referred to in guarded conversations). She has never spoken about it, and few have pried. All that is known is that, out of a seven person team sent into the tunnels under the reactors to carry out routine maintenance, she was the only one to emerge. Three days after the team disappeared, she emerged, covered in dried blood, almost dead from dehydration.

Of the team, there was no sign. Whatever happened in the tunnels, she is either unable or unwilling to talk about. Yet she pushes her broom, casting the occasional glance at ducts and hatches.

trenevier

Region: Lat 6, Ring 6
Status: Macrocorporate domain
Law: Very high
Wealth: Very high

overview

Always the wind. It's a thermal island effect, they say. Caused by the mass of flat concrete. I say it's just a pain in the arse. Twelve hours on, thirteen hours off. Then thirteen hours on, twelve hours off. Boring. Dull. We maintain our gun, an antique thing, manually loaded, single shot. Still, we oil it and maintain it as best we can. Sometimes, the Captain lets us take some practice shots against the old fence stanchions, scares the life out of anyone who happens to be wandering by. We call her Ursula, after a girl the Captain once knew. Captain doesn't say what happened to the real Ursula, but we look after our one like she was our first love. We get Internal Order Cadre troopers coming by sometimes, mostly off duty and drunk. They push us around, piss on Ursula and slag us off. Captain says not to react, not to get provoked. Just clean Ursula up and make sure she's OK. Once, Jannssen got really wound up and brained an IOC guy with a spanner. She got sent away, never seen since. Captain got very sad over that. IOC guys came back a few days later, lots of them. Kicked the shit out of us.

The company doesn't care for us. A few hundred forgotten souls, not good enough for the IOC they say. We keep a lonely watch out here, with the wind howling through the gunslits. We train, we drink tea, we keep Ursula ready. An IOC trooper came by on her own, showed us pictures. Pictures of what they'd done to Jannssen. We all just stayed very quiet. Sergeant Vath went really white, started twitching. I thought he was going to shoot the trooper there and then. He didn't, just kept quiet. It was the Captain who reacted. Punched that IOC woman in the face until you couldn't recognise her. Got us to drag her out to one of the fence stanchions, tie her there with wire and tape. We loaded Ursula up with an armour piercing round, aimed right for that woman's chest. Fired. Made a hole as big as your head. Had to clean up pretty quickly, dropped the body down an old inspection hatch.

Nobody really speaks about that day, least of all the Captain. He's started talking to Ursula, just now and again, when he thinks we're not listening. We stand watch, because we're the only ones who don't believe that the company is invulnerable. We're the only line of defence. So we polish and oil Ursula and wait for the day when we're proved right.

A flat concrete wasteland stippled with pools of stagnant water, the occasional cooling tower and entrance bunker poking above the dull monotony of the level surface. Centuries of defences ring the area, rusting chainlink fences, abandoned pillboxes and collapsed gun emplacements. An air of decrepitude hangs over this place, like a factory long abandoned of workers, bereft of the clanging of machines and the sounds of toil. Yet, this is Trenevier, home to Gorunna Logistics, if not the most powerful, then certainly the biggest of the macrocorps. The corroded surface conceals the hive beneath, an underground fortress, factory and community.

A few square miles of centuries old concrete, Trenevier is not the greatest advert for the might of Gorunna. Its defences have long since been left to rot, its surface become pitted with age, scarred by rain, fungus and fire. It is below the surface that Gorunna spends valuable resources. From below the surface lies the true enormity of Trenevier, a spiralling, twisting, convoluted labyrinth of passages, rooms, workshops, factories, bunkers, armouries, lifts and ducting. Here, Gorunna maintains its most vital manufacturing and administrative functions, closeted away from the light and air. Tens of thousands of souls work here, maintaining the vital position of the macrocorp. Many citizens see the light but once or twice a year, emerging from the ramps and lifts onto the surface to take in the scenic views which surround them. They return below, satisfied that they are missing nothing.

On the surface, Trenevier is a rough rectangle of grey-black concrete, two miles long on its longest side. The only hints as to the activity beneath are the dozens or so cooling towers and entrance bunkers which cling to the surface. Near to the bunkers are hardened landing pads for the massive aerostats employed by Gorunna and a single spur canal slices across the surface at an angle, connecting to a massive basin hold many large barges. The ruined defences are testament to the position in which Gorunna finds itself. Relied upon by many of the other macrocorps, too massive to be brought down, the company has become fat, lazy and complacent, letting its defences crumble, sure that its very size is protection enough.

The first sight that most visitors will have of the interior of Trenevier are the colossal lifts which descend from the entrance bunkers down into the depths of the structure. Grinding slowly down into the interior, these cyclopean machines disgorge their contents into the receiving chambers: vast spaces filled with running figures, noise, speeding vehicles, crates and the smell of hot oil. These spaces serve as collecting grounds for products heading to the surface or resources heading down into the factories. From here, corridors and passages of various sizes branch out in a bewildering network. Lifts descend to even deeper levels, conveyor belts creak off into darkness and squat cargo vehicles grumble down spiralling ramps. Entire sectors of Trenevier are devoted to single activities: manufacturing, administration, dwelling, education.

security/military presence?

Confident in its position within The City, Gorunna spends very little on external defences. Instead, most of it's security budget is ploughed into the Internal Order Cadre (IOC), a force designed to keep peace and order within the company itself. The External Order Cadre (EOC) is a tiny, pathetic, often ridiculed force made up of a few hundred demoralised and ill-equipped troops. The EOC maintains a few of the crippled defence stations around Trenevier, and attempts to impose some sort of border control. Their weapons are outdated and failing, with most troops resorting to buying weapons from other manufacturers. It surprises many visitors to see Gorunna troops hefting second-hand Trilhoeven rifles and wearing cast-off Hirplakker armour. Some EOC officers and NCOs attempt to maintain some form of reasonable military discipline, parading their troops on the pitted surface of Trenevier, their parade-ground chants echoing across the lonely spaces.

Almost anyone can wander onto the surface of Trenevier and only be challenged once they actually get into the complex. Here, they have to deal with the better equipped, far larger and better trained IOC. The IOC consider themselves an elite, issued with the latest in Gorunna weapons and afforded immense prestige by the company. They take every possible opportunity to go down the EOC, mocking its members and going so far as to sabotage their activities.

highlighted location

the neutral ground

Description: Entrance bunker leading into Trenevier

The only one of the entrance bunkers which is accessible to non-Gorunna personal, Bunker 3A has become known as the Neutral Ground. Here, traders and wholesalers come to purchase Gorunna items for selling on to the larger populace. Centred around the gigantic main lift shaft, the Neutral Ground is divided into a series of bays, each dedicated to a particular commodity. There are bays dedicated to food, clothing, weapons, vehicles and everything else that Gorunna produces.

The area is open for six hours each day, from the 10th hour of the morning to the 16th hour in the afternoon. During this window of opportunity, hundreds of traders scramble to get what they or their masters desire, often fighting to get through the crowds to the bay they require. Fights are commonplace, with armed squads of IOC troopers keeping some form of order in the middle of the melee. Most traders bring their own security to protect their purchases on the way back home, leaving the entire area awash with suspicion, guns, paranoia and envy.

highlighted personality

captain sylas pangborn

Age: 39
Height/Build: 6' 2"/Lean
Eye/Hair Colour: Dark brown/Grey, flecked with black
Occupation: Gorunna EOC Officer
Affiliations: Gorunna

Downtrodden commander of the 3rd EOC Gunnery Platoon, Pangborn's task of monitoring and defending Trenevier is a thankless one. Yet, despite the insults, abuse and sabotage from within, he still manages to instil a certain sense of esprit de corps in his troops, encouraging them to maintain their failing equipment to the highest standards, to place themselves above taunts and petty threats. He is the prototypical firm-but-fair officer, respected by his men but regarded with amused contempt by his superiors in the company.

Tall and lean, with a stiff shock of greyish-black hair, he has the demeanour and bearing of a down-at-heel actor or lounging aesthete. Beneath the peak of his decades old cap, his lined, tired face peers out with seeming disinterest, making him appear far older than his thirty nine years. His shabby, hand-me-down uniform is always in as good a state as he can muster, buttons shined and boots polished to a high shine. Even serving in the despised EOC, his reputation as a leader of men has not gone unnoticed. Several attempts have been made to transfer him into the ranks of the IOC. All have met with abject failure. Pangborn would rather stay with his troops, carrying out his duty, than serve with those who have spent their lives tormenting him.

Notable buildings

Some buildings have stood the test of time and become legends in their own right. Others are mysterious places surrounded by rumour, folklore and legend. Others inspire awe and deep feelings within the observer. These places are highlighted here, from the bizarre warrens of CrossBar Terminus to the academic splendour of Longshore University.

crossbar terminus

Region: Lat 5, Ring 1
Status: Independent mercantile area
Law: High
Wealth: High

overview

Nells' blood pounded in her ears as she sprinted down the platform. Perhaps it hadn't been such a good idea to dodge the fare. Behind her, a whole posse of Transit Militia pursued with single-minded determination, barrels of their sparklocks weaving unsteady arcs in the air as they ran. She faced a stark choice: jump onto the tracks to one side and try and climb down the elevated track which extended over The City, or jump to the other side and attempt an escape down the intestinal tangle of service passages.

She was buffeted by hot air, her hair began to stand on end as a train careered into the station, its brakes showering sparks and its massive electrical engine arcing with power. A corona of blue flickered across the overhead wires, making them shine with unworldly fire. It would have to be the passages then. Above the noise of the train, a shot rang out and everything slowed down. Nell stumbled forward, a hot wetness on her lips, staggering towards the passages and the hope of escape. It was not to be. She collapsed to the wet, oily floor, yards from her goal.

"She'll come round, they always do." A voice from above. A dark place. Tight. Unable to move. She opened her eyes to see a small, low room, lit by a single flickering electric light. Before her stood a plump, avuncular man in a shabby, pinstriped three-piece suit, a silver pocket watch in his hand.
"Aaaaah, the young lady awakes." He spoke gently, turning to smile at the gaunt, narrow figure standing behind him. The figure craned to see and Nell caught sight of a young, pale man, handsome in the dark blue uniform of the Transit Militia.
"Wh..whe whe"
"Where? Where, you ask? Well, young miss, you're in the Guardhouse." The man smiled.

"I'm sor sorr" The pain was returning, the taste of blood in her mouth, the difficulty breathing, the chair felt sticky.

"Sorry? Yes, they're always sorry. Even the pretty ones like you. Still, young girl, you committed a crime and that can't go unpunished, now can it?"

"P pay." she blurted.

"Pay? Oh yes, you'll most certainly pay" The pinstriped man smiled in a fatherly fashion and reached to the small wooden table beside him. In the dim light, the object he held was dull, almost black, she could see the spots of rust on its surface.

"Now. Time to pay the fare."

Central point of the traumatically torturous network of train tunnels and elevated lines that run through the city, CrossBar Terminus is a massive, ponderous topographically twisted set of interconnected buildings squatting in the middle of Fogwarren. Stretching below the ground further than it looms above it, the gigantic station was rumoured to have once been a museum, a storehouse of treasures from far afield. How it came to be used as a train terminus and whether or not the rumour is true are questions that will probably never be answered. Many of the lower levels of the station are now disused, blocked off or abandoned. Vast numbers of the homeless live out their lives in the deep shadows, emerging during the rush hours to beg, peddle and steal.

The higher levels of the structure are home to diverse organisations, from the headquarters of the Transit Militia to the Guildhouse of the Ancient and Honourable Guild of Fulgurators. Businesses jostle for space on the main concourse, selling every possible item that the traveller could wish for. The air is heavy with the odours of cooking, damp, ozone from the arcing electrical engines, oil and of the press of thousands of transient bodies. Most notorious among the warren of rooms in the station is The Guardhouse, the headquarters and prime interrogation centre for the Transit Militia. Here, the Conductors practice their painful art, extracting confessions from ticket dodgers, cutpurses and vandals. The worst fear of someone caught committing a crime on the railways is to be taken back to The Guardhouse.

Security/military presence?

As with all other train stations, large and small, CrossBar is guarded by the Transit Militia. However, those who guard the CrossBar are even more fanatical than their brethren elsewhere in The City. Within the precincts of the station, the Militia live in fear of terrorism and riot, the most dangerous threats to the good running order of the network.

As the income from running the train system is not great, the militia are poorly equipped and badly trained. Many of them are simply brutal thugs, hell bent on causing pain for others. Although the carrying of firearms is mandated by militia statute, officers must purchase their own weapons out of their own pockets. Consequently, there are wide variations in the type and quality of firearms carried. The vast majority of militiamen own sparklocks, with some owning semi-automatics and a few high-ranking officers even having hitech weapons purchased at ruinous cost. Any transgression within the precincts of the Terminus is dealt with in harsh fashion, as the militia answers to no one but the Transit Company. Sentencing is swift and punishment brutal.

highlighted location

the guardhouse
Description: Transit Militia headquarters

A warren within a warren, the Guardhouse occupies an entire wing of CrossBar Terminus and is comprised of a vast number of interconnecting rooms, passages, halls and landings seemingly designed to confuse and disorient the visitor. Transit militia officers scurry about the Guardhouse, dragging prisoners, carrying stacks of files or pounding to an urgent call. The low ceilings and smoky atmosphere only serve to heighten the sense of unease that the Guardhouse provokes in most people. The air is alive with muffled shoutings and clangings from the antiquated speaking tube system, allowing communication between different parts of the wing. Accompanying these sounds are the hollow rattles which issue from overhead as message capsules slide and bump their way through the p-mail system. Deep within this dark maze are the interrogation cells. Within these cells, the Conductors practise their ancient, painful art. Often, a perpetrator will confess without torture, yet the conductors proceed for the sheer satisfaction of hearing their victims beg for mercy. Some organisations claim that the Guardhouse holds even deeper secrets, that within the bowels of CrossBar Terminus there lie secrets lost for centuries, secrets which could hold the key to ending The Shift and freeing humanity from The City.

highlighted personality

ticket collector hyman ferenz
Age: Late 60's
Height/Build: 5' 8"/Thin, stooped
Eye/Hair Colour: Watery grey/Bald
Occupation: Ticket Collector, CrossBar Terminus
Affiliations: Honourary membership of the Ancient & Honourable Guild of Fulgurators

Ancient, bent and almost as worn as the station which he serves so well, Ferenz is venerated by the staff of CrossBar Terminus. Able to spot a fake ticket in a split second, adept at spoting fare dodgers, rigid in his adherence to regulations, he would like to think that he alone keeps the Terminus running smoothly. His connections with the Transit Militia and his membership of the Ancient & Honourable Guild of Fulgurators make him effectively immune from any form of criticism. He is a man who can do no wrong. Time, however, is wearing on, and Ferenz is not getting any younger. His eyesight is failing, his joints are stiffening and spending eight hours a day on his feet is not getting any easier. There will come a day when CrossBar Terminus will have to do without Hyman Ferenz, but for now he remains a stalwart figure, a buffer against change, guardian of what is right and good.

inferno

Region: Lat 4, Ring 5
Status: Independent hospital grounds
Law: Prison regime
Wealth: Not applicable

overview

Down the corridors, through cells, around corners, the wail of the klaxon filled the floor.

Booted feet crushed scuttling insects as they passed, leaving only damp marks, barely visible in the flickering light. Hapless inmates were kicked or thrown from the path of the onrushing guards. Screams issued from those dealt a blow by a truncheon or caught by a steel toecap.

The squadron of guards rounded the corner and slid to a halt in an enormous, steam filled room. The space was faced with dirty white tiles, cracked, worn and broken with age. Beige steam filled the air and through the steam were visible hundreds of naked inmates, scurrying to and fro, trying to batter down doors. A harassed, damp, scruffy man in what had once been a white coat popped up from behind a bath.

"Guard! Guard! Over here!"
"Doctor? What the fuckin' hell is going on here?"
"I'll be damned if I know. I was just checking on a cell down the way there and I heard this screaming. Think something's gone a bit wrong."
"A bit wrong, doctor? A bit wrong? There's a bloody riot happening. A bit wrong!"
The guard officer lashed out with his foot and caught the hapless doctor on the side of the head. As he fell, he bounced off the enamel iron bath, sending fragments of tooth skittering towards the plughole.
"Right, boys. Lets get this over with."

The guards moved into the steam, firing as they went. The screaming reached a new pitch of intensity, creating a counterpoint to the bass thumping of the guards' carbines. The mist went from beige to dirty red as the guards advanced into the bathroom, putting down the riot the only way they knew how.

A huge mental asylum and maximum-security prison. Inferno is co-operatively sponsored by five macrocorps (Nakamura, Hirplakker, GRID, Gorunna and Sideband) who contribute funds and resources in order to keep it running. This massive concrete cube is one of the most feared places in the entire city, renowned for the brutality of its regime and the harshness of its treatment.

Yet, despite the massive solidity of Inferno, something has happened in the past which has caused the building to be canted over to one side. Gigantic rents are apparent in the concrete, showing the rusting rebar which forms the internal skeleton of this looming monster.

Within, Inferno is split into numerous levels and sections, each housing patients, prisoners, wardens, nurses and doctors. The lower you go into the asylum, the darker and more dangerous it becomes. As you descend into the sub levels, you find the truly psychotic, psychopathic and evil. Some of the worst madmen and women in The City are incarcerated here, in concrete cells ten feet square. Suicides, murders and starvation are common. Inmates often become too violent to feed and are simply deprived of food until they lack the strength to fight or, as is most often the case, they die.

However, the worst is yet to come. Below sub-level 14, there is bare concrete blocking all the stairwells, all the lift shafts, all the service tunnels. For the staff, nothing exists below sub-level 14. Only the collective memory of an event so horrific that none dare speak about it. In the wards where the inmates are more lucid, they say that if you place your ear against the concrete, you can hear a faint tapping, as if from far away. Such talk must be kept quiet, as any inmates or prisoners mentioning sub-level 14 will be thrown into solitary confinement.

Physically, Inferno stinks. The sewerage system is unable to handle the thousands of inmates and staff. The power system is failing badly and contractors refuse to work in the place. Infestations are rife, insects and other far less pleasant creatures crawl over every surface, getting into food, beds, clothing and hair. The vast majority of inmates are allowed to wash, briefly, once every ten days. This is carried out in huge communal steam baths, spluttering brown water out of rusted, clogged nozzles. At all times, the guards and wardens will open fire at the least provocation; the walls of many corridors are stained red with blood as a reminder.

security/military presence?

Inferno swarms with guards, well paid to work in this monstrous place. The macrocorps provide training for the guards but refuse to provide any personnel from their own security arms. The asylum buys in weapons from the macrocorps at cheap rates, arming the guards and wardens to the hilt. Most of the doctors and nurses also carry weapons: night-sticks, knives, truncheons and pistols are common. Externally, Inferno is well defended against any possible jailbreak attempts. pillboxes, gun turrets and slit trenches surround the madhouse, ready to defend or to turn one hundred and eighty degrees and use their firepower against the inmates themselves. Escape attempts are actually few and far between, the inmates being too diseased and addled to come up with anything approaching a coherent plan.

By far the worst of these wings is number 3, serving the needs of life prisoners. With only one full time doctor and two nurses, the beds in the wing overflow with the ill and dying. Prisoners are crammed two or three to a bunk, those who die are often left beside their living compatriots for days on end. The toilets and washing facilities are continually blocked, overflowing into the corridors and wards, mingling with the smells of putrefaction and decay to create an almost unimaginable stench. Forced to crawl or hobble to these stinking cesspools, the inmates become even more infected and coated with ordure. Insects and parasites clamber over the bodies and the filth, burrowing their way into hapless, still living victims. The most recent evaluation of the wing discovered that ninety two percent of inmates in Medical Wing 3 died before being transferred back out.

Gangs from the slums surrounding Inferno sometimes use the external defences in their initiation rituals, daring new members to approach as close as they can to the flaring muzzles of the guns. So far, no group has been foolish enough to attempt a frontal attack on Inferno, but the troops remain vigilant, watchful, fearful. Some guards swear you can hear the screams and insane laughing of the inmates floating through the air over the trenches, others say that those propagating such tales are mad themselves.

highlighted location

medical wing 3

Description: Hospital facility

Within the horror that is Inferno, some places are worse than others. Inmates dread the inevitable sickness and injuries, for it means transfer to one of the medical wings. Lack of resources, staff apathy and years of neglect have turned these places of health into virulent pits of disease and infection. A full forty three percent of inmates transferred to a medical wing succumb to some form of infection or virus which is unrelated to their original condition. Even those who survive usually have some form of illness or affliction.

highlighted personality

susan jaeks

Age: 37
Height/Build: 5' 3"/Emaciated
Eye/Hair Colour: V.dark brown
Occupation: Inmate
Affiliations: None

An inmate on Sub-level 9, Jaeks is the semi-legendary Folly Hills Flayer. Incarcerated six years ago after a killing spree which lasted two years, she is quite genuinely mad, even more so after six years in Inferno. Psychologists have not yet got to the root of her problems or the reasons why she embarked on a rampage which cost the lives of twenty seven people, a rampage still talked about in hushed tones by the oppressed people of Folly Hills. Physically, she is small and unassuming, formerly a pretty woman before the rigours of life inside took their toll. Other inmates in Inferno speak guardedly about the method she used to dispatch her victims. Slowly flaying skin from their bodies and letting them die of shock and infection. These days, she speaks to no one, even the psychologists have admitted that she is now totally beyond help. She squats in her cell, silently staring at the door, her thoughts unknown and unknowable.

longshore university

Region: Lat 1, Ring 2
Status: Funded academic facility
Law: Strict
Wealth: High

overview

Dull smog obscured the towers of the University as Owens ambled his way to class. Wrapped tightly in his long coat, he whistled tunelessly to himself, unconcerned that he was already half an hour late for Doctor Laycocks' class. Brushing through the crowd of pamphleteers who constantly gathered around the main gates, he strolled towards the buildings of the Biological and Chemical Studies Faculty. Rushing towards him across the flagstones came a slight-

ly portly figure, puffing and panting as he came. Owens recognised him, Yaumer, one of the Portreeves.

"Mr Owens? A moment of your time!"

"What is it? Yaumer, isn't it? I must get to class."

"I bear a message for you. A message from Doctor Laycock." The Portreeve touched his cap even at the mere mention of the name.

"Oh, really! This is just too much! Hand it over then!"

His face clouding with anger, Yaumer passed across a scrap of rough paper, floridly embellished by Laycocks' archaic handwriting. The note was brief and to the point: "My rooms. As soon as you arrive. Laycock."

But surely the Doctor would be in class? Something must be afoot!

"You know Owens, this really has gone too far."

"What's gone too far, sir?" enquired Owens with all the boyish innocence he could muster.

"Dammit, lad! You know fine well what I mean! This constant lateness, absence from classes, not handing in work on time. It really won't do!"

"I'm terribly sorry sir, but I HAVE been making an effort."

"Effort? You call this an effort? You make me cancel a class, just to take the time to berate you, and you have the gall to say that you're making an effort? Outrageous!"

"Well, I don't know what else I can do."

"Well, then, perhaps I can ease the burden of decision for you. This very morning I received permission from the Head of the Faculty to make your life a little easier. Owens, this lax attitude must be stopped and, if you wish to continue to study at this university, then damn me, we'll stop it. As of tomorrow, all your classes are cancelled."

"But"

"No buts, boy. For the next six months, you're a porter in the faculty. Every morning, you shall report to the Head Porter and you most certainly will not go home until she tells you to."

"Well"

"SILENCE! You shall work, you shall be prompt in your arrival, you shall not slack off and you most certainly will not take days off to visit your sick grandmother! Should you be late once, just once, and you shall be expelled from this University. For ever!"

"I say"

"ENOUGH! I take it you possess enough intelligence to understand these orders?

"Yes, but"

"Now, GO!"

Owens crept out of the University, his face hot with embarrassment. He no longer ambled.

Premier place of learning within The City, Longshore is funded primarily by the TCMAA, with some funding coming from the macrocorps and other large companies and organisations.

Rambling over many acres of land, the university (like many other structures in The City) is architecturally ponderous and imposing. Every day, students flood in from lodgings in surrounding areas and from the student halls which lie on the university grounds. At any one time, there can be up to twenty five thousand students enrolled for courses, ranging from historical studies to analysis of The Shift. In fact, Longshore represents the largest repository of knowledge on The Shifted and Shifted beings. The heavily guarded wing housing the Shift Studies Faculty (known amongst students as 'The Rubber Room') emits a multitude of strange noises, smells and lights.

Gaining entrance to the university is not easy. Examinations and interviews are held on a regular basis to screen applicants (of which there are many) for their intellectual standing and suitability. A large proportion of applicants merely wish to become a student in order to have access to somewhere relatively clean and secure to live. Entrance standards are high and the Admissions Board is stringent in its application of university by-laws.

The main departments of Longshore University are as follows:

Shift Studies Faculty

Most guarded and mysterious of the five major faculties, the SSF is also the smallest and most elite. Only the finest researchers and students are even considered for positions within the SSF, a department surrounded by rumour and superstition. Within its halls, scientists probe the very fabric of reality, attempting to discern the very nature of The Shift.

Physical Sciences & Engineering Faculty

Regarded by many as the most worthy and worthwhile of all the faculties within the university, the PSEF receives the vast majority of funding from external bodies such as the macrocorporates. Quality graduates are almost always snapped up by the big companies and thrust into research positions, the nature of which varies from company to company. Students will often tailor their studies with a view to gaining employment with a particular corporation.

Biological & Chemical Studies Faculty

Despite the best scientific intentions, the BCSF is a chaotic, disorganised department, both mentally and physically. Plants crowd the corridors, homunculi chitter in their cages and the air is heavy with the smell of organic life and death. Chemists are continually poisoning, incinerating and exploding themselves as they carry out their nefarious experiments. The biologists frequently die at the hands of their creations, pass away through the effects of various venoms or succumb to a mysterious ague.

Faculty of Aesthetics

Dedicated to the arts, languages and culture, the Faculty of Aesthetics is primarily funded by donations from Sideband Media. Sideband sees the Faculty as an ideal recruiting ground for talented individuals. Faculty staff are pleased to have substantial funding (which even exceeds that of the Biological and Chemical Studies Faculty) which allows them to maintain good standing within Longshore.

Historical Research Faculty

Devoted to the study of the history of The City, the social character of it's society and the many subjects which link in to this complex topic, the HRF is viewed with something bordering on derision by the more scientifically inclined departments. In truth, the HRF carries out a sterling job in attempting to piece together the nature of The City, how it came to be and what life was like prior to The Shift and The Bombardment. Consequently, the HRF often works in close co-operation with the Shift Studies Faculty.

security/military presence?

The security of the university is attended to by the stern and unbending Portreeves. Clad in their baggy brown uniforms, they all carry extensive sets of huge iron keys which serve as both a badge of office and as a weapon. Many a drunken student, reeling back to his or her halls after an evening of debauchery has received a stern lesson in discipline from the bludgeoning keys of the Portreeves.

highlighted location

the shift studies faculty

Description: Heavily guarded, secure wing of the University

Housed in one of the oldest wings of the university and shut off from the rest of the student body, the SSF probes the very fabric of space and time itself. Outside the ivory towers of academia, many of the researchers here would be considered eccentric at best, hopelessly insane at worst.

Entrance is only granted to a favoured few students, those who show the most promise in a wide variety of disciplines. Approaches are made to members of other departments who display the right aptitudes; but these approaches are always covert and subtle in nature.

All windows in the faculty are shut off by thick iron sheets and most of the doors welded and riveted shut. Strange noises and fearsome lights can occasionally be seen creeping through the cracks. Some say that the SSF holds Shifted beings captive. Others say that they are actively gaining help from The Shifted, for reasons known only to themselves. Suffice to say, the Shift Studies Faculty of Longshore University is one of the most secure places in The City.

highlighted personality

professor elias fairweather

Age: 65
Height/Build: 5'7"/Thin
Eye/Hair Colour: Blue/White
Occupation: Faculty Head, Physical Sciences and Engineering Faculty, Longshore University
Affiliations: Longshore University

Head of the Physical Sciences & Engineering Faculty, Fairweather is a most level headed and serious man. Apart from one thing: ekranoplan racing. Unknown to his staff and peers at the University, he harbours an intense interest in The City's biggest sport. Not just watching it, oh no, he builds ekranoplans as well. Assisted by chosen students, sworn to secrecy, he constructs racers in a long forgotten cellar at Longshore, towing them out to the canal in the dead of night to test their abilities. Several times he has come close to discovery, but thanks to the efforts of his loyal students, he has so far remained undiscovered. At first glance, Elias appears to be your typical academic. With a shock of white hair, thick glasses and perennially clad in an oil stained cardigan, most think of him as dedicated to his subject and to Longshore. However, he only maintains his position in order to have the funds and facilities to indulge his secret passion.

Other areas

Some places in The City defy classification, being so different or outlandish that they are not easily defined. The waving fronds of The Brackens, the humidly verdant Forrest and the depressingly foetid Smokey Mountain all have strange, unique properties which set them apart from other areas.

the brackens

Region: Lat 1/2, Ring 6/7
Status: Uninhabited area
Law: None
Wealth: None

overview

A cold wind stirred the foliage. The fronds seemed to whisper to The City, challenging the might of its brick and concrete. Shadows flickered across the surface of the plants, here one second, gone the next. In a place where The Sound was ever present, here was an oasis of calm and quiet.

Rain began to patter down onto the leaves. Thick, brown and oily, it ran from their slick surface as if attempting to escape, for here was a place where none dared venture. Those who did, and survived, were rendered mindless by whatever inhabited the rolling acres of green verdure. Nowadays, The Brackens lay undisturbed, feared by all.

The wind whipped through the plants, turning the droplets of rain into a mist, causing the serried ranks of green to undulate as if alive with vital force. In the buildings nearest to the edge of The Brackens, residents pulled their curtains tighter, shutting out that which they feared the most. Night was falling. Soon the green would turn to black and parents would warn their children. Beg them never to go playing in the inviting sea of lush growth.

The Brackens hold a secret. And everyone wishes it would remain that way.

One of the few places in The City where it can truly be said that no one lives, The Brackens are a wide expanse of green within the urban sprawl. Folk legend has it that The Brackens are a remnant of life before The Shift, an area that was somehow untouched by the horrors of one thousand years ago. More educated citizens see things with a different slant. Diligent researches by various departments of Longshore University have uncovered the true nature of The Brackens: they are a legacy of The Bombardment. While precise facts about the area are still scant, what is known is that the green splash of The Brackens sprang up after The Bombardment, seemingly of its own accord. What had once been housing, parks and factories became a rolling, verdant wilderness. Samples taken from around the edge of the area, analysed in the laboratories of Longshore University have revealed that the flora which grows in The Brackens is totally unlike anything else found in The City.

The rolling, softly undulating landscape which The Brackens present is the result of centuries of growth, plants cracking the rubble which they live upon, making mounds of pulverised brick appear as gentle knolls. The plants also seem to be remarkably hardy, weathering the worst of the pollution, acid rain and toxic waste which The City can throw at them. The plants even seem resistant to fire, a fact which has not gone unnoticed amongst those wishing to develop the area for living or factory space. It seems as if the plants are invincible, that in their domain, they are kings. Such is the fear and superstition which surrounds the area, nobody save a scant handful of hermits and lunatics live within half a mile of the tangled undergrowth. There is something within the foliage which brings death to almost all who enter. Heavily armed teams have been sent in by the macrocorps; after days without contact, solitary individuals would stagger out, raving incessantly, gibbering nonsense, their minds destroyed by whatever lurks within the green.

In recent decades, attempts to tame The Brackens have tailed off. The macrocorporate now leave the area firmly alone and those who live in the regions surrounding The Brackens sleep uneasily at night, fearful of the waving sea of fronds.

security/military presence?

There is no security or military presence within The Brackens. Some organisations occasionally send troops into The Brackens. Few soldiers ever return.

highlighted location

Who know what lies within The Brackens? Certainly, no one who has ventured into the area and come out again has ever been in any kind of fit state to relate details about anything they found.

highlighted personality

As no one lives within The Brackens, allegedly, there is no personality to highlight.

the contested grounds

Region: Lat 7, Ring 4
Status: Warzone
Law: None
Wealth: High

overview

"It was a terrible, exhausting battle above and below the ground, in ruins, cellars and factory sewers. Our warcrawls climbed heaps of rubble and tangles of iron, and crept screeching through chaotically destroyed workshops and fired at point-blank range in the narrow railyards.

Many of the warcrawls were shaken apart or exploded from the force of an exploding Hirplakker mine. Or, it could have been one of our mines. Such is the nature of war in this place, the battle swinging back and forth so quickly, that we are constantly being strafed by our own mikefighters and wandering into our own minefields.

I cannot understand how men can survive in such a hell as this, yet the Hirplakkers sit tight in the ruins, and foxholes and cellars, and a chaos of steel skeletons which used to be factories.

No one can tell me this war means anything any more. We are all just meat for the cannon, pawns in a game none of us understand."

Force Commander Eric Danzig, 2nd Battalion, Brigade of Light.

Formerly a vast industrial and railhead area controlled by Hirplakker, the Contested Grounds bore the brunt of the Hundred Block War and still remain a festering sore on the face of The City. While Hirplakker admitted defeat, no formal surrender was ever organised between them and Arclight. Hence, the war drags on in a low-level manner, each side desperately wanting to pull out, yet unable to concede.

The Contested Grounds lie alongside the Black Canal, on the northern bank. Because of the ongoing conflict, their periphery has become a haven for smugglers, traders, scavengers and thieves. Small settlements housing prostitutes, drug dealers and gambling dens have sprung up along the water's edge, taking advantage of soldiers who have gained a few hours respite from the constant pressure of the Grounds. These settlements are interspersed with the camps of both sides, areas of unspoken truce where supplies are offloaded and the wounded taken out. Noise is constant, with boats coming and going, mikefighters and aerostats droning overhead and the intermittent thump of artillery and heavy weapons fire. The heaviest fighting takes place around the Flak Towers, massive concrete fortifications constructed decades ago by Hirplakker for just such an eventuality.

The opportunities presented by the Contested Grounds are many, hence the fact that large numbers of scavengers and mercenaries come to probe the ruins for hitech military equipment. Discarded weapons are quietly removed and find their way onto the black market. Stores are liberated and sometime small units of fighting troops are attacked in order to steal their gear.

However, of all the inhabitants of the Grounds, most hated are the snipers. Concealed in ruined towers and in camouflaged trenches, they strike without warning. Snipers from either side are shot if caught, an end usually accompanied by brutal, inhuman tortures. The pain and suffering of the 'Grounds draws The Shifted in as well as the scavengers and mercenaries. Simils sell their services to the highest bidder, clanking through the ruins, hunting for their prey. Reports abound of strange sightings within the Grounds; visions best-left unseen and sounds best left unheard.

Security/Military Presence?

Large numbers of troops from both sides occupy the Contested Grounds, making it the most heavily militarised region in The City. Add this to the hundreds of mercenaries, scavengers, prostitutes, and peddlers which occupy the Grounds and their borders, then you have a fairly sizeable population. At any one time, it is estimated that there will be ten thousand troops from both sides fighting in and around the Contested Grounds.

highlighted location

the flak towers

Description: Weapons emplacements/fortifications

Constructed decades ago by Hirplakker for just such an eventuality, the Flak Towers have become the bastions of the Contested Grounds. Concrete towers five stories tall, with reinforced walls five metres thick, the eight towers are virtually impregnable. Bad planning on Hirplakker's part caused four of the towers to be captured during the Hundred Block War. Never really expecting that such a conflict would take place, the towers were kept poorly supplied and badly equipment. When the war kicked off, the Hirplakker troopers found themselves sealed inside with precious little food and dwindling ammunition supplies. Unwilling to surrender, the troops starved, some turning to cannibalism in a vain attempt to survive. When the last, emaciated, half-mad soldiers finally opened the portals, they were summarily shot by Brigade of Light troops, disgusted at what they found within. Arclight now controls three towers, Hirplakker four and one acts as a base-cum-meeting ground for scavengers, guffers and assorted camp followers.

Each tower can hold up to two thousand soldiers and enough food and ammunition to keep them fighting for two hundred days. The roofs are studded with anti-aircraft artillery which is in constant use, shooting down mikefighters and aerostats from both sides. Hirplakker concentrates its fight on the towers, preferring to occupy solid defensive positions rather than adopt a more attacking style. Arclight on the other hand uses the towers as supply bases for its more fluid form of fighting, striking out at the enemy, then retreating for re-supply. No weapon has yet been developed that can breach the walls of the towers, although the Brigade are known to have in place something known as Unit 731 which, it is alleged, may give them a decisive edge in the battle for the towers.

highlighted personality

sergeant gerald green

Age: 30
Height/Build: 5' 10"/Stocky
Eye/Hair Colour: Grey/Grey
Occupation: NCO commanding, 3rd Platoon, 'C' Company, 31st Infantry Regiment, Hirplakker Cadre
Affiliations: Hirplakker

Green has served in the Contested Grounds for two years and doesn't want to leave. Every time he goes on leave he feels dislocated, disjointed. The hell of the Grounds has become normality for him, without them, nothing seems right. He can no longer relate to civilians, preferring the company of soldiers. Three times he has been assigned other duties within Hirplakker's military forces, three times he has demanded reassignment to the Contested Grounds. His commanders have resigned themselves to the fact that Green will live out the rest of his days there. Some discount him as a madman, others see him as the harbinger of a new race, a new breed of man evolved for fighting in this wasted landscape. Whatever their opinions, he remains, crouching in the rubble, cradling his rifle, praying that he will remain here forever.

the forest

Region: Lat 8, Ring 3
Status: Private gardens and food production area
Law: Strictly enforced by-laws
Wealth: High

overview

Edrich Grosbart stood up from his toils, placed his filthy hands in the small of his back and groaned. As the years progressed, his bones ached even more and his muscles protested with enhanced vigour. Behind him, gravel crunched softly.

"Grandfather?"

He tuned to see the girl who had addressed him. She was slim and willowy with a radiant, open face and dancing eyes. His pride and joy, his granddaughter Edrica.

"Ah, my dear! How are you keeping today?"

"Very well grandfather. And you?"

"Oh, you know, the usual aches and pains. Old age does not come alone, as they say."

"Grandfather, I must speak with you."

"Hush for a moment, child. Take tea with me and let us talk of simple things."

"As you wish grandfather."

"Now, my precious, what can I do for you?"

"The gardeners have caught a man."

Grosbart raised an eyebrow and looked quizzically at Edrica.

"Caught a man? Surely you don't come all this way to bring me that simple news?"

"He was a very bad man, a wicked man."

Edrica gazed at the gravelled ground, unwilling to meet the piercing gaze of the head of her family.

"And what, perchance, did this wicked man do?"

"He destroyed a shrub, grandfather."

"Did he indeed? Well, that is bad news. And what, do you think, should be his punishment?"

"I don't know, that is why I came to you."

"Ah. Very well then, I shall give you my judgement. Execute him. Hang him from a limb of the tallest tree in the main public dome. Let he who has destroyed beauty serve as a warning to others."

"Yes grandfather, I shall inform the gardeners."

The girl rose as if to leave.

"My child. I would advise you to watch the proceedings. Let it serve as an education to you."

Silently, the girl turned a walked swiftly away down the gravel path, her footsteps crunching into the distance. A zephyr stirred the air. Edrich Grosbart pulled his coat on tighter and gazed into the depths of his tea.

Grosbart took his granddaughter by the hand and led her down a winding gravel path, though shrubs alive with the sound of insects and small animals. Before them stood a mighty tree, its branches shining like polished bronze, its limbs curving gently to form a secluded bower. Within the bower, Grosbart went through the motions of firing up the small charcoal burner and boiling water. Just as the liquid came to the boil, he sprinkled in a selection of herbs from sealed flasks resting on a flattened limb. Above the smell of organic life, a sweet, aromatic odour arose.

"Tea?"

"Yes please grandfather."

Taking two fine cups, he poured the steaming brew into their white perfection, the yellow liquid splashing gently over their rims. Clasping his cup in both hands, he eased himself into a padded armchair and extended his long legs.

A massive hydroponic garden, The Forest serves two purposes. One, it provides a steady supply of fresh fruit and vegetables, second, it provides employment to a great many citizens in the Eastern area of the TCMA. Small sections are also maintained as parks and botanic gardens for the pleasure of local taxpayers.

Owned and operated by the Grosbart family, The Forest is a huge and rambling collection of domes and sheds. Some of the domes are very old indeed, constructed of black iron and glass, pale light filtering down upon a morass of plants. From towering trees to fruit bearing bushes, all manner of flora is collected here. It is perhaps the largest repository of plant life in The City, a great storehouse of pre-Shift life. Many plants have also been bred and modified over the decades to be hardier, more succulent or just more beautiful. The heavy, organic smell of the garden is a marked change from the polluted stink of The City. Complex systems of filters and airlocks prevent any hint of taint from entering the fragile domes.

To the majority of those who are aware of the existence of The Forest, it is a place of wonderment. The sections open to the public are far more wild and lush than anywhere else, housing greenery which astounds the casual observer. The gardeners who maintain The Forest are the subject of almost religious awe and envy, being the guardians of rare skills and arcane knowledge. Most of the gardeners live in the areas surrounding The Forest, living in luxury when compared to their neighbours and friends.

Every year, a new intake of gardeners is taken on to replace those who have retired or died in the line of duty. Competition for the places is fierce; murder and sabotage are common in desperate attempts to be granted the privilege of a job. Only a select few are taken on.

security/military presence?

The gardeners themselves ensure the security of The Forest, defending their place of work with a devotion which borders on fanaticism. Those who break the rules (such as walking on the grass, picking the flowers or stealing fruit) are subject to harsh punishments. Even the TCMAA seems unwilling to incur the wrath of the gardeners and the Grosbart family. Perhaps the most dreaded of punishments is being banned from The Forest. Those who are banned are scrupulously denied access to the area and can only gaze longingly through the steamed up windows.

While the gardeners do not carry firearms, they are adept at using the simple, innocent tools of their trade for violent purposes. However, some do carry small, easily concealed crossbows, all the better for silently taking down fleeing transgressors.

highlighted location

the grosbart residence
Description: Hydroponic dome/family home

Nestled at the centre of The Forest is a small, unassuming dome with a single entrance. Within this dome lives the extended Grosbart family, owners and operators of the wonder which is The Forest. They eschew the normal accou-

trements of life in The City, preferring to live amongst the trees, flowers and shrubs of their amazing creation. Four generations of the family make their home here, residing within carefully manipulated and altered trees whose trunks have been warped over the decades to created wondrous organic living spaces.

Senior member of the family is Edrich Grosbart; a haughty, overly dignified man of advanced years. Never leaving the family dome, he sends his children, grandchildren and great-grandchildren out to do his bidding. Edrich prefers to spend his time tending his flower-beds and splicing hybrids in his small but well equipped laboratory. Only the most senior and well respected gardeners are granted an audience with the senior Grosbart, and even then only in times of great urgency.

Members of the public never see the interior of the Grosbart residence; they can only stare at the misted walls as they are shepherded to the public areas. They can only dream of living in that wonderful place, surrounded by healthy, clean plants, the air misted with unpolluted water and filled with the sound of babbling streams.

highlighted personality

deaf jim
Age: 47
Height/Build: 6'/wiry
Eye/Hair Colour: Blue/black
Occupation: Gardener
Affiliations: The Forest and the Grosbart family

Well respected by his peers, Deaf Jim lost both of his ears in a horrific gardening accident some years ago. Scarred lumps of flesh protruding from his tangled hair show where his ears once were. Despite his name, Deaf Jim is not in fact deaf. People just assume that because he has no ears, he cannot hear.

He tends the plants of Public Dome 4 with a quiet pride, taking the utmost pleasure in the beauty which his callused hands can create. Visitors to the dome can feel his eyes watching them from the shrubs, monitoring their every move, waiting for someone to disturb the tranquillity of the garden.

At a little over six feet tall, he is not an exceptionally big man, but years of back-breaking labour have endowed him with a strong physique and powerful grip. In his modest flat next to the southern edge of The Forest, he maintains his own private gardens, carefully tending tiny trees and spectacular blooms. The Grosbarts tolerate his freelance gardening, as they know a devoted and hard-working employee when they see one.

Smokey Mountain

Region: Lat 7, Ring 7
Status: Ungoverned, waste disposal area
Law: None (see below)
Wealth: None

One of the many vast rubbish tips scattered across The City, Smokey Mountain. Many thousands live within the heaps of the Mountain and the entire dumpzone is ringed with barrios and slum housing. The area gets its name from the smoke which is continually given off due to combustion deep within the rubbish piles. Methane gas explosions and toxic waste contamination are not uncommon.

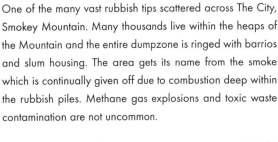

Overview

KAAAAAFRAAAP.
CRUNCH.
TICK.
TIS.
A hail of rubbish settled on the uneven surface of the dump. The crater created by the gas explosion was hidden behind a thick pall of smoke. Somewhere, a child screamed in agony. Shouts drifted through the smoke: fathers and mothers howling for children.

Holschweg gradually crawled out from the rusting steel tank in which he made his home. "Well, that's an exciting start to the day" he mused. A massive dirty yellow circle drifted, droning, overhead. Another cargo aerostat preparing to drop it's weighty load, probably on some unfortunate individual (or most likely, individuals, betting amongst the pilots being what it was).

This had to be the worst assignment ever. As a respected reporter for Sideband Media, living in the most awful dump in The City was not his idea of a good time. Just because some twat in The Cathedral had paid a thousand quid to an alleged contact to find out that, possibly, Hirplakker was, allegedly, using (maybe) Smokey Mountain to recruit new workers (why?) and then using them as experimental test subjects. That had to be the craziest, most ludicrous rumour that Holschweg has heard in his ten-year career with the company.

"Only ten days to go, then Catkins takes over." he mumbled to himself. Swearing softly, he turned back into the tank. Some git had stolen his food supplied the day before; he was reduced to eating what he could scavenge. "Ah, fishheads. Mmmmm." Someone was going to pay for this.

The most wretched of the poor and homeless live within the vast rotting pile that is the rubbish tip. They drift in from other areas of The City, unable to find even the most dilapidated housing or sheltered doorway. Riddled with tunnels and chambers, hundreds die each day inside its sweltering body, dying through starvation, poisoning or being crushed under tons of waste. During the lighter hours, countless numbers of people swarm across the dumps acres of surface area, through artificial valleys and across man made chasms.

Most populous are the huge concrete dumping ramps, where barges and trains and the occasional truck unloads its stinking cargo. Violent outbursts are common here, as the destitute fight like rats for the choicest scraps, killing with home-made weapons and their own blackened hands. Most unfortunate are those killed by falling debris from the hovering macrocorporate aerostats which drop their loads anywhere over the site. Pilots care little for lives of the tip dwellers; many run informal sweepstakes on who can hit the greatest number of unfortunates.

Smokey Mountain represents the lowest form of existence in The City, there is no where else to go. Even the slum dwellers of Dreamingspires and Mire End have a better life (despite what they think). In a place populated by the poor, the insane and the evil, this is the final depth of degradation and despair. Rumour has it that corporations trawl the dump for experimental subjects, as even in the slums, people have friends. Here, nobody cares. Death is so commonplace that the denizens have become inured to the carnage which surrounds them. Even the soldiers in the Contested Grounds are less tolerant of casual death and grievous injury.

Security/Military presence?

The only security presence is that which surrounds the gates to the dumping ramps. This is essentially to prevent hordes spilling onto the streets and attacking the vehicles, demented in their desire to get to the scraps first. The security troops (the vast majority of whom are contracted from Trilhoeven) shoot to kill, without question and without mercy. Each massive gate will have upwards of one hundred troops on standby at any one time, heavily armed and well prepared.

highlighted location

dumping ramp one

Description: Canalside rubbish offloading point

The main offloading point for rubbish being brought up or down the Black Canal from the industrial and residential zones, DR1 swarms with sanitation workers, security troopers and scavengers.

Whatever the weather, a massive cloud of insects hangs over the area, stinging, biting, spreading disease and infection. The luckier transfer workers have sealed suits and gas masks to protect them from the stinking chaos that surrounds them. The more expendable, mass labour force has no such luxury. They toil with rags round their mouths and noses, hauling boxes, bags and bins full of ordure and filth. Cranes and lifters carry the larger items of refuse to the dump gate itself and load them onto the massive tracked carriers which take the trash out to be finally dumped. Scavengers and dump dwellers swarm thickly over these carriers as they emerge from the gates, shots ring out to prevent them getting too close to the gates themselves. Sealed in their armoured, air conditioned cabins, the drivers only worry is that a foolish aerostat pilot will drop a particularly heavy load right on to of the dirty, mucky carrier. Pitted, moss encrusted, slimy concrete walls enclose DR1, making it feel more like some hellish prison than a place of work.

highlighted personality

erika goreshiny

Age: 22
Height/Build: 5' 6"/Wiry
Eye/Hair Colour: Dull blue/Matted, dirty blond
Occupation: Sanitation worker (unskilled)
Affiliations: TRH Haulage (employer), Third Church of God the Architect (member of)

Every day, Erika travels many miles up the Black Canal from her home in Hangside to work a twelve-hour shift at DR1. Wracked with illness from the horrific conditions, limping from infections in her right leg, she continues to work for two reasons. Firstly, she needs the money to survive. Secondly, as a faithful member of the Third Church of God the Architect, she firmly believes that her unceasing and uncomplaining toil will gain her entrance to His mighty Heavenly City. Her eyes have the steely glint of a fanatic and she has few, if any, friends at her place of work. On her breaks, she sits and reads scriptures from the Holy Writ, finding passages to comfort her in her suffering. She knows that her time cannot be far off. A time when she will have passed the testing and will be admitted into that most glorious of places.

"Those people down there don't have a clue. You think they matter, the scum, the plebs, the huddled masses? All they want is violence, pornography, booze and blissful ignorance. None of them matter. Drones, nothing but a resource, Their blood lubricating the machines of society. Why? Because it's the cheapest thing there is. From here I can see farther than any of them have been in their lives. None of them can comprehend, none of them understand. We built this company, we sit on top of a timebomb, waiting for the final second to come. They will not be the cause of our downfall. Not while I still have one breath left in me."

Matt Kenzie, Senior President, Arclight Macrocorporation.

the power

Who cares?

The pen scratched across the rough surface of the ledger. In a corner of the ill-lit room, a dingin clanked and whirred, taking it's own lazy time to execute its program. Wind whistled through cracks in the wall, stirring up miniature dust devils on the bare concrete floor. Scrivener set down the pen and pumped the reservoir of the fishoil lamp which cowered in a corner of the desk not occupied by the massive ledger and assorted documents. Outside the lonely window, the people of Folly Hills bustled about on their eveningtime business. The wind rattled the thin iron sign hanging from the wall "Scrivener & Daughter, Accountants & Documentarians. Rates Negotiable". Few people round here needed such services these days, most were concerned with where the next pound was coming from, rather than keeping track of the pounds which had gone before. Eastern Folly Hills was deprived and downtrodden, yet it was a community fiercely proud of its suffering, it's very humbleness.

•

Sighing, Scrivener arched her back and tried to ease the cramped, bunched muscles. Days, weeks and years spent bent over a low desk were not a recipe for good health, even if it was indoors out of the cold and rain. A bell rang and the dingin lapsed into silence. A wafer thin sheet of punched metal had been deposited into its output tray. The sheet detailed the complex financial arrangements of one of Scriveners more dubious clients, a lady with an alarming number of wealthy male friends who visited at odd hours of the day. Still, it wasn't her place to comment on how people made their money, merely to record, calculate and tabulate. Unwrapping a foil package, she withdrew the last few crumbs of the baked fish that had been her lunch and nibbled absent-mindedly at them. Tea, that was what was needed. A nice cup of tea would help things along.

•

As she stood up and ambled over to the corner table, Scrivener glanced at the ceiling as the noises from the tenement above began to filter down. The labourers were coming home from work, coming back to their cramped rooms and squealing families. Meals would be prepared and clothes darned, the simple chores of family life. Reaching for the spigot of the battered cistern, she drew a cup of water and balanced it on top of the fishoil lamp. Sprinkling in a few leaves from her tea pouch, she sat back and waited for the water to boil. One of the few pleasures of life, a nice cup of tea.

•

Tea. It was habit that had lead to her father's unfortunate disappearance, that cold, windy night in Mire End. Attempting to find a shop selling a particular specimen of leaf, he ambled down the wrong alley and was never seen again. The Provosts were sympathetic, but could do little. Mire End was out of their jurisdiction. People from the Three Canals went there at their own risk, they said. Unsavoury types, not the sort of people you'd want to consort with at all.

•

With alarming force, the rickety door was flung aside, admitting wind, rain and a young man who seemed to be the inhabitant of an oversized dogskin coat in an alarming shade of russet. He stared out from under a dark headscarf, then slammed the door behind him and commenced an agitated fumbling with the lock.
"Er, excuse me? Do you mind if I ask what you're doing in my office?"
The man twisted his head and fixed Scrivener with a baleful glare. He then turned back and recommenced his fumbling with the key.
Scrivener cleared her throat. "I don't wish to appear rude, but I'd really like to know what you're doing."
For the second time, the man with the baleful glare turned, this time, he drew a long, pointed dagger from the recesses of his alarming coat. At this, he found himself in the unexpected position of having a cup of near-boiling tea flung in to his face. Screaming wildly, he dropped the dagger, clutched at his rapidly reddening visage and ripped his headscarf off.
"Bloody hellfire missus, there was no need for that!"
"I think there was every need for that, you hooligan! Coming in to my place and waving a knife about. And it»s not missus, it's Miss, for your information!"
In between pained grimaces, the would-be assailant looked up "Sorry miss, didn't me to cause you any fright, just looking for somewhere to hide is all."

•

Removing her half moon spectacles, Scrivener took a longer look at the man. Young, fairly handsome in a rough-hewn, scruffy kind of way. He had a roguish, raffish quality that must appeal to the tarts and dollymops of Folly Hills.

"Well, you can flipping well find somewhere else to hide! And who you hiding from anyway?"

"The Provosts, 'int I? They been chasing me all the way from Brookmyre Walk. Bloody nonces!"

"Provosts, eh? Well, you're in luck. They were the ones who did nothing for my old dad, I've no love for them. Quick, get yourself through this hatch."

Scrivener began hauling the heavy dingin aside to reveal a small trapdoor in the floor. It creaked open to reveal a foetid, dank cellar echoing to the rumblings and clankings of sewage pipes. "Down you go." The young man looked highly dubious about the entire enterprise, but bundled himself through the hatch anyway. No sooner had the dingin been shoved, accompanied by a reasonable amount of rather unladylike curses, back over the trapdoor, than there was a rattling from the door and cries to open in the name of the law.

•

"Yes Constable, how may I be of assistance this rather inclement evening?"

The Provost on the doorstep seemed rather taken aback. His colleagues shuffled their feet nervously and stared at the damp pavement.

"Well, you see madam, a miscreant has been seen in this vicinity. In fact, we've been chasing him a right long distance. A right bad'un he is, stolen some very valuable property. Official documents, you see. We suspected he might have entered one of these here buildings."

"And as a lady on my own, do you not think I'd be somewhat alarmed if a rogue of some sort tried to gain entrance to my place of work?"

"Well, you see, we have to make enquiries..."

"Constable, you may have time to waste, but sadly I do not. I have the accounts of several important clients to complete and some documents to draft, perhaps you could return at a more convenient time?"

"Umm...ahhh...yes, no problem, of course. Sorry to have disturbed your business madam, we'll be proceeding on our way."

The Provost tipped his cap, glared at his quietly sniggering colleagues and marched off down the street, swatting pedestrians out of the way in a disgruntled fashion.

•

Treacly rain spattered down on the gabled roofs and tacked-on shanties of western Folly Hills. Two figures wan-

dered nervously through the crowding darkness, occasionally lit by the cones of light from ineffectual and rare gas lamps. To an outside observer, they seemed to follow a deliberately random path, wandering and skittering down alleys, ducking into closes and skirting round the edges of courtyards and quadrangles. They eventually arrived at an unprepossessing, slightly decayed, four storey tenement, it's exterior patched with fungus and the staining of decades of rain. The unlit close and stairwell echoed to the sound of dripping water, the scratching of scurts and muffled noises of numerous families going about their business. Despite it all, the close was freshly swept and the rubbish was arranged in neat piles, ready to be collected by neighbourhood recyclers.

•

Scriveners' rooms were arranged shotgun-style from the front door, three shabby apartments, high ceilinged and bare floored. Blankets tacked to the filthy windows blocked most of the light as Scrivener fumbled with a lamp, eventually sparking it into smoky life with an audible grunt. The room in which they stood was piled high with mouldering documents and disintegrating ledgers. Waxy punched cards for a dingin lay in card boxes or scattered randomly about the floor.

"Nice place you got here, Miss Scrivener."

"Thanks, it does for me. Er, what was your name again?"

"September, Jed September."

"What an unusual name, September. Where does it come from?"

"Haven't a clue, old name apparently. Me mam said it»s been in the family for centuries. 'Course, she talked a lot of rot did me mam. Was the drink, you see?"

"Right, I see. Tea?"

"Yeah, cheers. That'd be grand."

Wandering through to the next room, Scrivener absent-mindedly picked up a few scraps of clothing, patted piles of papers and wondered what in the name of everything sane she was doing inviting a young, albeit relatively handsome, stranger into her home. And a potential criminal to boot! Mad, quite mad. The gas ring sparked into life, its weak flame eventually boiling the kettle, its shrill whistle echoing forlornly through the rooms.

•

"So, if you don't mind me asking, why are the Provosts chasing you about the place?" She fixed him with a pointed stare, looking out over the cracked rim of the teacup.

"Well, I can't say too much. They just don't like people like me. Like us. Just where I come from, is all."

"And where would that be?"

"Mire End."

"Right, I see your point. So they were giving you grief just 'cos you come from Mire End?"

"Not quite, more because of what I nicked. Kind of got my hands on some stuff some folks would rather didn't get out. Kind of secret stuff, you know?"

"No, I don't know. Pray tell me more."

"Well, I can't like. Got an idea what it is, just can't make head nor tale of it. Trouble is, can't read very well, can I. Me mam didn't believe in all that reading stuff, said we had better things to do with our time."

"Well, would you like me to take a look at whatever it is you've got?"

"Dunno. Dunno if I can trust you, you know how it is."

Scrivener's brow crumpled "Look, I let you hide in my place, brought you home, gave you tea for Gods sake! Now, unless you want me to march across the road, call the Provosts and have you arrested, you better give me a bloody good reason not to!"

"Alright, alright! Fair's fair. Just don't say I didn't warn you, that's all."

He withdrew a small package wrapped in greasy brown oilcloth from the noisome interior pockets of his coat and laid it carefully on the table. As Scrivener unwrapped it, she saw within a sheaf of folded yellow papers and a plain, unadorned box. The box contained perfectly ordinary punch cards for a dingin, thin plates of iron shot through with tens of tiny rectangular gaps. The papers were covered in a crabbed handwriting and columns of closely spaced figures. Rubbing her temples, she examined the papers under the sickly light of the lamp. As she read through the notes, figures arranged themselves in her head, sums added up and equations formed.

"Shit! You know what this is?"

"What?"

"Well, looks like someone in the TCMAA has come to some sort of deal with the Fulgurators. Seems like your burgh is about to be sold out big time."

"WHAT? The bastards! They can't do that! What they up to?"

"Re-opening the old Mire End Branch Line of the railway for one thing, building some sort of yard in the East End. Hmmm...wonder what the dingin cards are for?"

"Bugger the damned dingin cards, we've got to...did you hear something?"

"No, what? It's just the scurts, this place is riddled with the little bastards."

Sideways, September moved across the room and twitched a blanket aside.

"Don't know nuthin' about scurts, but there's about ten Provosts down there goin' in and out of closes. And they ain't yer normal lookin' Provosts, neither. These guys look serious."

"Great. Wonderful. Now I'm really in it. Thanks a lot September, now I'm going to get arrested!"

"No you're not. Just need you to do one thing: keep the stuff, hide it, get it to some people, get this out. You want hundreds of people to lose what little they've got? You want kiddies tipped out on to the streets? Do it for them."

There was almost a note of pleading in his voice, desperation for his wishes to be carried out. As he stood there, he drew two ugly black sparklock pistols from his coat. Clockwork mechanisms whirred and clicked into life as he flicked the safety catches off. "I'll get them away from here, no worries."

"But, what? How? They'll..."

"Don't you worry 'bout me, I can take care of myself. Been doin' this a while now, me and my mates here'll sort things out. Just get the word out, let the people know."

"Right. I'll try my best."

For a brief moment, in the pale light, he appeared almost a dashing figure, clad in his voluminous coat, weapons at the ready, ready to take on all-comers, to fight for what was good. At the door, he turned: "Goodbye, Miss Scrivener."

"Goodbye, Mr September. See you again."

In her rooms full of papers and books, Scrivener clamped a cushion over her head and tried not to hear what was going to happen. She heard nothing. It never happened. September had gone, as if he'd never been at all. Only the sheaf of papers and a box of cards were left. Donning her warmest coat and stashing the papers and cards at the bottom of her satchel, she prepared to go out into the night. As to where she was going, she'd work it out eventually.

Criminal organisations

the 3rd Syndicate

Status: Criminal organisation
Headquarters: Unknown
Membership: Not quantified, but supposed to be at least ten thousand
Areas Of Operation: Narcotics, hitech weapons procurement, kidnapping, extortion

overview

Most massive and widespread of the criminal groups in The City, the 3rd Syndicate wields enormous power and exerts influence over the lives of a vast number of inhabitants. Notoriously violent, individual assemblies (as the sub-organisations are known) can control entire burghs and parishes in the more lawless parts of The City. They are particularly active in the TCMA, where they are a continual thorn in the side of the Provosts.

Persuasive rumours circulate that the leaders of the 3rds have powerful, influential contacts within the Council and the macrcorps. Although never proven, they do seem to have access to large amounts of hitech weaponry and equipment. Another persistent rumour is that back in the mists of history, the 3rds were allied to one or more of the macrocorps. However, any media service even mentioning this rumour (indeed, any rumour about the syndicate) suddenly find themselves the target of threats, escalating into violence. Another feature of the 3rd Syndicate is its almost pathological hatred of the Hohler Gang. The most obvious expression of this is the continual gang warfare around the Long Pond area of the TCMA. The Provosts are at a loss to prevent the continual round of killings, bombings, reprisals and kidnappings which this conflict has given rise to. The citizens of Long Pond have become inured to this over the years, seeing collateral casualties as just another hazard of living in The City.

organisation

The 3rd Syndicate is made up of many assemblies, individual cells numbering from ten to two hundred gang members. Only the most trusted of the assembly leaders are aware of the identities of the Syndicate leaders, and even they do not know the exact location of the groups headquarters. What is known is that there are three people who exercise overall control, criminal masterminds of unparalleled sophistication and brutality. Each assembly has strict instructions to avoid treading on the toes of others, transgressions of this rule being punished in the most severe way.

highlighted personality

carpenter halstead

Age: 25
Height/Build: 5' 8"/Stocky
Eye/Hair Colour: Grey/Blond, shaven
Occupation: Assembly leader (Long Pond)
Affiliations: 3rd Syndicate.

Weak willed is a description which could never be applied to Carpenter Halstead. Exceptionally young to be in charge of a major 3rd Syndicate assembly, he is extraordinarily young to be in charge of one of the most important assemblies in The City. Long Pond is the scene of constant fighting between the 3rds and the Hohler Gang, a war which has been carried on over many years.

Murder and deception come easily to this young man, a fact which has only endeared him to his superiors. Hating the Hohlers with a passion which seems routed in his very soul, he persecutes the 3rd Syndicate's aims with unabashed vigour. It is an immense source of pride for both him and his assembly that he ranks among the top ten most wanted individuals in the TCMA.

daylight

Status: Criminal organisation
Headquarters: Unknown
Membership: Unknown, rumoured to be at least two thousand individuals
Areas Of Operation: Narcotics, prostitution, kidnapping, extortion, assassination

overview

Daylight are a continual thorn in the side of both the 3rd Syndicate and the Hohler Gang. They operate with such a level of ferocity that even hardened criminals are taken aback by the sheer violence of their methods. Where some gangs would, in conflict with another gang, start with some small scale intimidation and a few beatings, Daylight starts by firebombing or shooting their intended targets. They seem to know no restraint, turning to violence as a first and only resort for the resolution of problems.

Daylight seemingly grew out of a coalition of smaller street-gangs in the Fogwarren area, coming into being a couple of decades ago. Since then, the group has grown in size, strength and wealth, yet still keeps true to its roots on the street. Internal disputes are settled not through assassination or backstabbing, but through organised knife fights. Rules are laid down and challenges are issued if it is felt that a slight has been done or wrong has occurred. All in all, the internal politics of the gang are extremely honourable, with every member adhering to the rules or finding themselves subject to the harshest possible discipline. This sense of honour, however, does not extend to their dealings with the outside world. While the 3rds and the Hohlers will (most of the time) attempt to ensure that bystanders are not harmed by their squabbles, streetfights and bombings, Daylight could not care less about the lives of 'civilians'. Innocents, including women and children, are regularly caught up in their bitter, twisted aggression against other gangs and syndicates. So, while groups like the 3rds have attained a strange sort of 'hero' status amongst many ordinary citizens, Daylight is viewed as nothing but a force for evil and destruction.

For some unknown reason, Daylight also seems to have a big issue with the armed forces of the Red Canal Collectivist Republic. Where this enmity came from, observers are at a loss to explain, yet it demonstrably does exist. Daylight members will go out of their way to antagonise the RCCR, even going so far as to launch attacks against warcrawl patrols. Needless to say, the RCCR is absolutely baffled by the behaviour and has ordered it's military forces to respond in kind against such provocation. Rumours has it that Special Department teams have been assigned to the task of hunting down and eliminating the Daylight leadership.

In terms of their criminal activities, Daylight are seriously into drugs. This is their main source of revenue and power, filtering narcotics down to the streets through their distribution and dealer networks. Their tendrils stretch into all areas of city life, even extending into wealthy areas such as Lucent Heights and Coldbath Fell. As something of a sideline to their drug dealing activities, they are also in charge of large numbers of prostitutes and brothels, dealing in sexual proclivities ranging from the mundane to the bizarre and outlandish.

organisation

Daylight operations in a particular area come under the control of senior gang leaders know as 'walkers'. The walkers can be in charge of up to one hundred individual gang members and have carte blanche to carry on their criminal activities as they see fit. Unlike some other criminal organisations in The City, the Daylighters have no particular mode of dress or identifying features, tending to dress fairly inconspivously. As for the structure of Daylight above the walkers, nobody has ever pentrated the organisation to this level. Daylight seem particularly adept at sniffing out traitors, undercover agents and sting operations, a factor which has caused extreme annoyance to more than one security agency.

highlighted personality

nathaly shivers

Age: 33
Height/Build: 5' 6"/slight
Eye/Hair Colour: Pale brown/black
Occupation: Assassin
Affiliations: Daylight

A curious part of the Daylight organisation, Shivers stands apart from the rest of the gang in Shore Ditch Warrens. The reason for her status is her skill as an assassin. Formerly a trooper with Trilhoeven, she honed her sharpshooting skills during inumerable small conflicts, police actions and internal disturbances. She left the employ of the macrocorp in dubious circumstances, taking a sizeable amount of military hardware with her. Within weeks of decamping from Trilhoeven, she had been taken under the wing of Trudi Serov, the Daylight walker in charge of operations in Shore Ditch Warrens. Recognising that she had a useful, valuable asset on her hands, she immediately notified her superiors. Ever since then, Shivers has worked for Daylight, eliminating rivals, disposing of traitors and generally being ruthlessly efficient at her job. She talks to the walkers as equals and rumour has it that she is very much in favour with the mysterious, shadowy leaders of the syndicate. Personality wise, she is a cheerful, outgoing, fun-loving woman who can quite often be seen living it up in the bars and clubs of Shore Ditch. However, this does not remove the fact that she is a ruthless, calculating killer. When working, her stock in trade is being unobtrusive, quiet and nondescript. Dressed in dull workers clothes, her only distinguishing feature is the long dogskin bag, similar to those carried by mechanics and toolmakers. Her bag, however, contains a far more deadly implement: the sniper rifle she took when she left Trilhoeven all those years ago.

the hohler gang

Status: Criminal organisation
Headquarters: Unknown
Membership: Unknown
Areas Of Operation: Prostitution, drug dealing, extrotion and almost every other known form of criminal activity.

overview

With a finger in almost every, metaphorical, pie, in a few short decades, the Hohler Gang have gone from being a rag-tag bunch of back alley muggers, peddlers and pimps to become one of the pre-eminent criminal syndicates in The City. Indeed, their only real competitors are the 3rd Syndicate, with whom they have an ongoing, singularly vicious conflict.

The founder of the gang, Lorentz Hohler, still presides over the activities of his criminal empire, although at ninety three years of age, he is a wizened, twisted figure confined to his baroque iron wheelchair. Despite his physical disability, he maintains a grip of steel over his younger lieutenants, working through a legion of absolutely loyal confidants who obey his every word. Living in luxury in his Lucent Heights mansion, Hohler receives visitors from a disparate collection of organisations, from the Provosts to Trilhoeven executives, from Bishops of the Third Church of God The Architect to impoverished canal traders.

The gang itself is composed of an unknown number of members operating throughout The City. Arms dealing, extortion and prostitution are the mainstays of Hohler Gang income, with arms dealing being their single most profitable enterprise. If you need a particular weapon, the Hohler gang will be able to get it for you, at a price. Most higher level gang members carry a dazzling array of hitech weaponry,

with magnetic repeaters being particularly favoured symbols of authority. In higher class burghs of The City, such as Coldbath Fell and Lucent Heights, the gang runs a series of brothels catering for the tastes of more 'refined' customers. Through intimidation, bribery and assorted kickbacks, local security and police organisations overlook these establishments, preferring to look the other way and ignore the curious sexual proclivities of the wealthy patrons. These brothels are identified by a simple white plate fixed to the door of what often appears to be a regular apartment or house.

organisation

The gang is tightly controlled from the very top on down, each level of 'management' making sure that their subordinates follow orders to the letter. The smallest unit of the gang is the cell, which can be anything from ten to over one hundred gang members strong. Cells are made up around a core of one or two experienced gang members assigned to an area by the higher levels of the organisation. These individuals are responsible for the activities of the cells, even down to the actions of individual members. Consequently, discipline is tough and standards uncompromising. Failing to follow orders, not bringing in enough profit or disrespecting more senior gang members are all offences which are punished severely. Above the cells are lieutenants responsible for a particular burgh

highlighted personality

ilya sung
Age: 34
Height/Build: 5'11"/Wiry
Eye/Hair Colour: Grey/Black
Occupation: Hohler Gang cell leader
Affiliations: Hohler Gang

The vital thing to remember about Ilya Sung is that he is a very dangerous psychopath. This man would kill his own mother if he thought it would benefit his position. He is currently head of the Hohler Gang cell operating in Merryhell.

His sparse, wiry build comes from practising often in the gym, honing his skills knife fighting. He came to Merryhell from Long Pond five years ago and has been in control of the cell ever since, keeping his minions in a constant grip of fear. His dapper style and elegant looks belie the fact that he is a very dangerous individual, whose threats should not be taken lightly.

Local governments

the red canal collectivist republic (RCCR)

Wealth: Expenditure not disclosed
Areas of Operation: RCCR controlled zone (see map)
Military Capability?: Army of the RCCR, Special Department of the RCCR (secret police)

"Mornin', komrade." Ursen was always irritatingly cheery at this time of the day, thought Ignatz, always smiling and happy. Not right for a man getting up at this hour.

"Good morning to you, komrade. Another day doing good for the people, eh?" The false cheer made Ignatz wince, going around with this mask of komradely friendship thirteen hours a day was getting wearing.

"Indeed komrade, indeed." Ursen cracked the knuckles of his chubby hands and pulled the tight fitting helmet down over his head. He plugged the snaking wire of the commo system into the jack on his control board and settled back into his seat. Dingins rattled and clicked in their armoured casings as the systems of the warcrawl came to life. Pixels on flat screens rearranged themselves into meaningful symbols, lines of data, streams of code. Ignatz settled his own helmet on a tightly shaven head and squirmed into the gunners chair. The dingins began running the gunnery programmes, bringing up ammunition status readouts, air density, threat levels.

"You think we'll see action today, komrade?"

"Not sure, maybe. Insurgents might try to breach the factories on the north edge again. Never can tell. Still, the will of the people drives us on, eh komrade?" Ignatz could scarcely believe what had just said, komradely platitudes direct from the Collective. Fake. Liar.

"That's the spirit, well said komrade!" Ursen twisted in his seat and grinned with broken teeth.

The warcrawl trundled down the street, it's wide tracks crashing and thundering on the road surface. Komrades on the streets cheered as the dull grey machine roared by, the blue circle insignia of the RCCR emblazoned on it's flanks. Small children ran alongside, attempting to touch the vibrating steel surface of the ugly, battered fighting vehicle. Ignatz swung the main turret and elevated the gun tube in mock salute to the crowds. They swung ninety degrees onto a street sloping down to the Red Canal, then ninety again to run alongside the great waterway. On the opposite bank, people stared and made rude gestures as the warcrawl accelerated.

"Maybe you should fire off a couple, just to show them. Eh?"

"No, komrade. I think not. Besides, it would be wasteful to expend ammunition. They are not Insurgents."

"Very well, Komrade. Very well." Ignatz could feel Ursens desire radiating up from inside the warcrawl, his desire to do damage. Maybe that's why he was a driver rather than a gunner, too unstable to be put in charge of weapons. The armoured hulk scuttled beneath giant murals painted on the sides of buildings, murals designed to put the wind up the TCMA. Cheap propaganda. The comm set whistled, incoming tight beam from a booster on top of one of the buildings.

"Komrade Ignatz? Komrade Ursen?"

"Yes, Komrade Commander, how can we serve the will of the people today?" Ignatx felt his gorge rise as he spoke the words.

"Insurgents, up the canal. Meet up with other units and take action." The instructions were perfunctory and totally lacking in detail. As usual.

"Thank you, Komrade. Proceeding with all due speed."

Ursen gunned the engine eagerly as Ignatz readied his weapons. More chasing after phantoms. More pointless flitting about. Fake, all fake. Lies and smoke.

overview

The only other independent authority even approaching the size and power of the TCMAA, the Red Canal Collectivist Republic covers a wide stretch of The City between the Red and Black canals. All citizens of the RCCR are followers of a political doctrine known as 'collectivism'. Broadly, collectivism states that there are no individual possessions and that everything is owned collectively by the mass off the citizenry. Everyone is welcome to join the RCCR, provided they do their utmost to contribute as much as they can to the collective good of the Republic. In exchange for such services, the Republic provides housing, food , transport, entertainment and all the other need of the citizenry.

Some say that the basic tenets of collectivism are truly ancient, going back far into the unknown mists of time. However, most citizens of the Republic firmly believe that the fundamental principles of collectivism were set down just over two hundred years ago by a poet, philosopher and politician named Konrad Earle. Earle, so folklore has it, worked hard as a burgess on the council of a small burgh in between the Red and Black canals. He grew tired of the corruption, backstabbing and duplicity of his political colleagues and decided to start a new political movement to give power back to the people. In the beginning, the collectivist movement had few adherents, yet as it's advantages became plain, more and more flocked to join the movement. After five short years, the collectivists were in control of two burghs, running them according to strict political principals. Earle died shortly after, but his political legacy lived on, with the collectivist influence spreading further afield. Being pragmatic as well as political, the collectivists struck deals with several macrocorps, promising to subdue and take over certain troublesome areas if, in return, the macrocorps would arm and quip their growing paramilitary forces. It was then that the gaggle of collectivist burghs formed the RCCR and declared that any follower who wished to live in the true heartland of the collectivist cause would be welcome to come and join them in their workers paradise. The RCCR was born.

The road to the RCCR's current powerful state has not been an easy one. Some burghs objected to being collectivised and fought back with savagery. Still, the macrocorp equipped Republicans carried out their campaigns with skill and cunning, ruthlessly destroying areas, throwing men into combat with little care for their lives. Many heroic stories come from these times, stories of komrades singlehandedly taking on houses full of the enemy, of dying soldiers throwing themselves into canals to provide bridges of bodies for their komrades to cross. These tales permeate the consciousness of the Republic, huge posters display the smiling visages of fallen heroes, lumbering warcrawls bear the names of great soldiers.

Structure

Overseeing the good order of the RCCR is the Peoples Council, a hundred strong group which collectively decides policy for the Republic. Representatives are elected by the agreement of all komrades and serve for three years. The Peoples Council makes decisions on behalf of the people on all matters relating to internal and external policy. However, the activities of the Peoples Council are not entirely without oversight. Sections of the Special Department, the shadowy paramilitary police force of the RCCR, maintain a watch over the representatives, noting their every word, watching their movements, looking for one solitary sign of treachery.

Military forces

Due to the fact that many other organisations and whole areas of the city hate the RCCR, the Republic spends a truly vast amount of money on its military forces. The ties it once had with the macrocorps are long gone and it is now pretty much self sufficient in terms of arms production. All komrades must serve at least a year in the armed forces at some time in their lives, but they can also join up on a permanent basis, becoming full time soldiers in the service of the people. At any one time, the standing army is over twenty thousand strong, organised into ten divisions of approximately similar numbers. Of these divisions, the 1st Guards Infantry Division is the most prestigious, tracing its ancestry right back to the komrades who fought to establish the RCCR. All members of

the 1st are full time soldiers, fanatically dedicated to the collectivist cause. 2nd and 7th Armoured Divisions are the iron fist of the Republic, containing almost all the warcrawls in the army. 3rd, 4th, 5th and 9th are infantry divisions while 6th and 8th provide the airpower of the army. 10th Support Division is a mixed formation, combining specialist troops such as sappers, combat engineers and waterborne units. All in all, the army of the RCCR is an incredibly powerful force, a fact which has not gone unnoticed by the macrocorps, the TCMAA and various other vested interests.

In addition to the army, there is also the previously mentioned Special Department, which serves as police force, intelligence agency and espionage network all in one. Clad in their black coats and wide-brimmed hats, Special Department officers have wide-ranging powers of investigation and detention. No komrade is above their suspicion, even decorated heroes have been known to be dragged off to their chilly grey prisons and asylums. Ordinary citizens both fear and respect the Special Department, afraid of their intrusive investigations and seemingly limitless power and deeply impressed by the thoroughness of their actions against internal and external threats.

highlighted personality

Oliver Telegin

Age: 29
Height/Build: 5' 8"/Average
Eye/Hair Colour: Blue/Light brown
Occupation: Street sweeper/Special Department informer
Affiliations: RCCR, Special Department of the RCCR

On the surface, Oliver Telegin is your everyday, solid citizen of the RCCR. He works hard in his job as a street sweeper, he helps maintain the tenement in which he lives and attends as many community sings as he can. A productive, worthwhile member of society. Beneath this veneer of komradely devotion is a complex skien of lies, double-dealing and treachery. Telegin is an informer for the Special Department, keeping tabs on his neighbours and work colleagues, noting transgressions and divulging traitorous activity. That having been said, Telegin is himself a traitor. Certain elements within the TCMAA use him for information gathering purposes, utilising his position of trust for their own ends. He now finds that his involvement with the Special Department and the TCMAA runs so deep that he has absolutely no hope of successfully extricating himself from the grasp of either organisation. He nervously waits for the day when the Special Department discovers his treachery or for when the TCMAA, no longer needing his services, decide to tip the Department off themselves.

three canals metropolitan area authority (tcmaa)

Numerical Strength: 56,000 personnel directly employed by the authority.
Wealth: Expenditure of approx. £234,000,000.00 per annum.
Areas of Operation: Three Canals Metropolitan Area and surrounding border areas (see map).
Military Capability?: TCMAA Provosts (police service).

overview

Seen by many as an oasis of order within the chaos that is The City, the Three Canals Metropolitan Area (TCMA) is a sprawling mass wedged between the Green and Red canals. Running straight through the heart of the region is the Grand Canal, mightiest of waterways within The City. Incorporating diverse areas such as Folly Hills, Bankside, Lucent Heights and Clearwater Break, the TCMA is a study in contrast. From abysmal poverty to enormous wealth, it is a microcosm of The City itself.

Exercising control over the teeming masses which inhabit the area is a phenomenal task, a task overseen by the Authority. Here, bureaucracy is taken to the highest level, as civil servants strive to make sense out of the labyrinth of streets and canals which surround them. Monitoring this hydra is the Chief Burgess, Markus Heilige. Heilige rules with an iron fist concealed within an iron glove. He is not averse to making deals with the Shifted or criminal organisations such as the 3rd Syndicate in order to ensure the smooth running of his Authority. It is, for example, well know that he let the Hohler Gang have Mire End, lying just across the Green Canal from Folly Hills, if they guaranteed not to encroach into Folly Hills, Fogwarren and Bankside. It is this kind of manipulation and bargaining, which have made Heilige such a force within the Authority.

Heilige manipulates public opinion through the august office of the Mayor. The current incumbent is Owin Hardgadley, an easily lead dupe from the Authority who is little more than a figurehead for Heilige's machinations.

Ruling from the enormous, rambling pile that is Breaken Hall, there are two forces within the Authority which vie for supremacy: the Community Service Board and the Provosts. the Community Service Board is in absolute charge of welfare, housing, healthcare and the provision of residency permits, whilst the Provosts have ultimate control over law enforcement within the TCMA.

the community service board

Dear Mr Jorgensen,

It has come to our attention that you have been resident within the TCMA for nineteen years, within which time you have been employed for a total of seventeen days. The TCMA values each and every one of its citizens, which is why your situation concerns us. It would therefore be appreciated if you could attend Community Service Board Office 26 (Lake Boulevard, Folly Hills) for an informal interview. Please bring your residency permit, birth certificate, Council Tax certificate, water and sewerage tax certificate and a two thousand-word essay on why you should continue to be a citizen of the TCMA.

Yours sincerely,
Rolf Garner
pp Islera Koretz

Both fearsomely complex and fearsomely harsh, the Community Service board is the most powerful and influential (outranking even the Provosts) part of the TCMAA. They provide unemployment benefit, citizenship permits, business permits, tax collection, health services and also (by some long forgotten ancient ruling) water, power and sewerage.

Every citizen lives in fear of the Board, dreading the day when a message inviting them to attend an informal interview lands in their lap. The working lower and middle classes are terrified of losing their jobs, as this entails a huge round of interviews and tests to see if they will be allowed to remain a resident. In a stark contrast to this, the Board seems to take precious little interest in the unfortunate slum dwellers of Dreamingspires and other run-down regions. They prefer to husband their resources, dolling them out to those who they deem most worthy.

The CSB has one hundred and three sub-offices scattered about the TCMA, each with their complement of assiduous, tenacious CSB staff. Externally, the offices are surprisingly like Provost bunkers, a fact which has not gone unnoticed among the citizenry. Working for the Board is a guarantee of a job for life and good treatment for ones immediate family. Competition to join (especially amongst those in more tenuous employment) is unsurprisingly fierce, despite the revulsion which the majority of the population feels towards the Board.

the provosts

Sideband Newsline

> Subject: CATCH Team Kills 43 In Raid
> Stringer: Anon

"Tonight, the neighbourhood of Crush Street bore witness to one of the most bloody police actions in the history of the TCMA. An eight man Provost CATCH team raided a tenement block in which it was suspected that members of the 3rd Syndicate were operating a drugs factory. '

'In the ensuing violence, 43 people, men, women and children are known to have been killed and many more injured. The CATCH Team suffered no injuries.'

'Local burgess Francois Hoysek stated: "Seldom have I seen such brutality and casual disregard for the wellbeing of the very citizens whom the Provosts are sworn to protect. I shall be taking this matter to the highest level"

'Commander of Provost Assault Division, Captain Adam Micdevitt gave the following statement to the press: "Fuck off."

Maintaining law and order within any portion of the City is an arduous task, a task that is no easier within the boundaries of the TCMAA. Since the TCMAAs' inception, one of the prime concerns of the authority has been to provide safety and security for its citizens. Consequently, one of the earliest programs set up by the fledgling authority was to train and equip a professional police force.

In the one hundred and eighty years since then, the Provosts have grown to a force of 9,000 men and women. Although they nominally answer to the TCMAA Council, the Provosts are commanded by Provost Marshal Graeme, an officer with thirty-eight years of service behind him. Graeme oversees the workings of the five Provost Divisions (Patrol, Support, Assault, Investigation and Internal Affairs) and represents the interests of the force on the council.

Broadly speaking, the Provosts are well respected by the citizens of the Three Canals and the job brings with it no small measure of pride, responsibility and remuneration. It is well known that the Provosts receive a handsome paycheck for carrying out what is an admittedly difficult job. In terms of manpower, the largest of the five divisions is Patrol, which carries out the role of general policing. Second to Patrol is Support, which is home to pilots, mechanics and vehicle crew as well as other ancillary staff. All vehicles used by the Provosts are maintained by support and all vehicles are piloted by Support officers. Compared with Patrol and Support, the other three divisions are very small, scarcely having one thousand officers between them. Least liked is Internal Affairs (not surprisingly). Made up of dedicated officers with no families or strong ties, IA watches not only the activities of the provosts but also covertly spies on the goings on within the TCMAA Council. Investigation Division carries out the work of investigation into Category A crimes (murder, rape, industrial espionage etc.) and is a strictly plain-clothes division. Lastly, Assault carries responsibility for riot control, hostage rescue and tactical response. For this purpose, it has three sections to call on: the Rapids, the Tacticals and CATCH. The Rapids are fast response SWAT units and are often the first on the scene of a violent disturbance. They are lightly armed and equipped. The Tacticals are the heavier counterpart to the Rapids, carrying heavier weaponry and wearing far more substantial armour. Last of the Provost units are the CATCH Teams. When the toughest criminal hideouts have to be raided, or a crazed serial killer is cornered, it's CATCH who are called in. Other Provosts reckon that the CATCH team members are borderline psychotic themselves and tend to steer clear of these very heavily armed, very well equipped but very unpredictable officers.

highlighted personalities

Lieutenant Myles Harking

Age: 29
Height/Build: 6'/Strong
Eye/Hair Colour: Hazel/Black
Occupation: Police officer
Affiliations: TCMA Provosts

First and foremost, Myles Harking is reckoned by most that are in the know to be one of the few good cops left in The Provosts. Saying that is quite something, as he is commander of the Assault Section officers of the 87th Street Patrol Area. His gritty determination and an iron will in the face of adversity have got him where he is today. He is known to react with disgust to dishonesty within the police force and has had many officers under his command transferred or dismissed. Rumour has it that he is being groomed to take over one of the top spots in the Provosts, possibly as head of Assault when Adam Micdevitt retires (although the likelihood of that happening in the future is minimal).

Physically, he is an imposing figure at 6'1" tall and of strong build. His dour visage masks a keen sense of humour and a sharp mind.

deputy assistant chief community service officer islera koretz

Age: 37
Height/Build: 5' 9"/Average
Eye/Hair Colour: Blue/Blond
Occupation: TCMA CSB
Affiliations: TCMAA

Koretz is a stern woman, and is most certainly on her way to the top. It is no secret that she has ambitions of eventually inheriting Markus Heilige's job, a position which she has been manoeuvring for over a period of years. Her talents for sniffing out fraud and keeping a tight reign on expenses have achieved almost legendary status. What is less well known is her background.

Growing up in Dreamingspires provided the hardest of possible educations. Life amongst the most wretched citizens of the TCMA was a lesson in survival. Through her own choice, she begged for entrance into one of the Third Church of God the Architect orphanages dotted about the TCMA and when she came of age, was eligible for TCMA citizenship. Determined to make the best out of her like, she joined the CSB as soon as she was able and since then her steely determination and killer instinct have taken her almost to the top of the most complex organ in what is a diabolically labyrinthine bureaucracy.

captain adam micdevitt

Age: 42
Height/Build: 5' 10"/Wiry
Eye/Hair Colour: Pale grey/Black, greying at the temples
Occupation: Police officer
Affiliations: TCMAA Provosts

Well known throughout the TCMA and further afield, Micdevitt is the hard-hitting commander of the Provost Assault Division, with personal command of the feared CATCH Teams. Leading from the front and providing an example for his men are two of the features which have endeared him to the personnel under his command.

A fairly unremarkable figure at first sight, Adam Micdevitt is wiry and of average height, not at all looking like the public image of an ex-Brigade of Light man. On duty he is tough and at times brusque, off duty he can be pleasant and mild mannered. Unknown to anyone but himself he regularly makes large donations to various charities helping the vast numbers of homeless in the TCMA.

superintendent julia whitelaw

Age: 44
Height/Build: 5' 6"/Trim, well muscled
Eye/Hair Colour: Dark brown/Strawberry blond
Occupation: Police officer
Affiliations: TCMAA Provosts

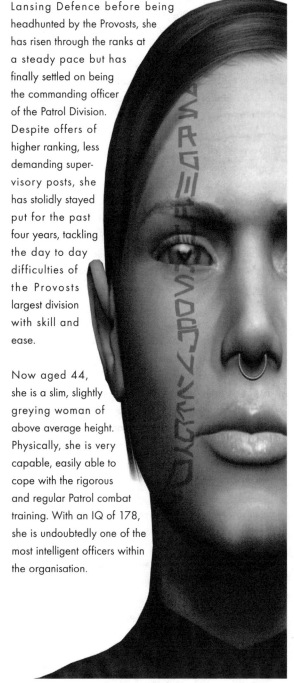

The highest-ranking female officer in the Provosts, Julia Whitelaw has proved to be an exceptionally gifted and talented senior officer. An Inspector with Lansing Defence before being headhunted by the Provosts, she has risen through the ranks at a steady pace but has finally settled on being the commanding officer of the Patrol Division. Despite offers of higher ranking, less demanding supervisory posts, she has stolidly stayed put for the past four years, tackling the day to day difficulties of the Provosts largest division with skill and ease.

Now aged 44, she is a slim, slightly greying woman of above average height. Physically, she is very capable, easily able to cope with the rigorous and regular Patrol combat training. With an IQ of 178, she is undoubtedly one of the most intelligent officers within the organisation.

Macrocorps

not one step back: the hundred block war

An Analysis, by Grigori Kircher, historiographic cliometrician, Longshore University

From a political, historical and cultural perspective, the so-called 'Hundred Block War' was one of the most interesting events of recent decades. It's impact is still felt, most of all by the two main protagonists: Arclight and Hirplakker. The echoes of the conflict still haunt parts of The City and have lead to a series of topographical, political, cultural and societal changes.

Reasons: Arclight

Arclight had one bold aim in attacking Hirplakker: the acquisition of resources. Arclight had gown, over a very short space of time, from being a middle-rank company in The City to challenging the might of an industrial giant such as Hirplakker. The sudden change in company focus, the cancellation of GRID contracts and the turning over of production to armaments manufacture is well documented and need not be covered here.

The reasons for this sudden turnaround in activity have yet to be disclosed. Fronsac, in his paper entitled "Sudden Light: The Ascendancy of Arclight" argued that the company had made a rather sudden and remarkable scientific advance in areas not dominated by the other macrocorps. Fronsac argued that in order to realise the full potential of these advances, they would need to have access to resources in the manner of a macrocorp. While the quality of Fronsacs scholarship cannot be questioned, the nature of his conclusions is somewhat suspect.

Arclight saw Hirplakker as an easy target. Fat, bloated, complacent and engorged on its own power, it was unprepared for hostile action, despite it's impressive and much vaunted armed forces. Arclight desperately wanted to ascend to macrocorporate status and the riches that such a status bestowed. It was for this sole reason that it set off down the path to war.

Reasons: Hirplakker

Hirplakker's reasons were far more prosaic than those of Arclight. Hirplakker was fighting a war simply to survive. It's

initial encounters with Arclight were viewed as more of a nuisance than a credible threat. Yet, as the attacks grew in number and scale, the company gradually brought itself onto a war footing, ramping up arms production and preparing its substantial armed forces for conflict. The controlling intellects behind Hirplakker were slow to realise the significant threat that was posed to them. When the penny finally dropped, it was too late to fight anything but a war for survival. Hirplakker had no reason to fight other than the desire for continued existence.

The Conduct of the War

The actual fighting can be characterised by the markedly differing strategies employed by both sides. On one side, there was Hirplakker, a rigidly stratified command structure depending entirely on its controlling intellects for strategic insight. Officers were hidebound by centuries of tradition, soldiers cowed to the point of acquiescence. Arclight demonstrated the opposite end of the military spectrum, employing a loose structure, unfettered by outdated doctrine and obsessions of rank. The largest single unit ever fielded by Arclight during the war was fifty men. The largest single unit fielded by Hirplakker was one thousand men. The flexibility of the Brigade of Light structure and the space for individual initiative afforded to unit commanders was the key to early Arclight success.

Both sides, however, have been heavily criticised for their treatment of non-combatants and prisoners of war. Hirplakker's cynical exploitation of Mire End and the Brigade of Light attack on their (false) staging post still ranks as one of the most appalling military actions in the recent history of The City. The loss of life in Mire End has never been fully tabulated, but it has been estimated to be in excess of two hundred souls. The continuing detention of prisoners on both sides has been a thorn in the side of both companies ever since the semi-official 'conclusion' of the war.

The other continuing aspect of the war is the refusal of both sides to give any ground in the ongoing low-level conflict in what have become known as The Contested Grounds. This former area of storage facilities and railheads was one of the major Arclight objectives during the war, yet was comprehensively wrecked by both sides, it has become nothing more than a wasteland occupied by hundreds of troops. It is symbolic of the pride of the two combatants that they continue to fight on in The Contested Grounds, even after officially coming to peace terms. It seems that neither is willing to give up what has become an entirely pointless struggle, a struggle which will continue, it seems, for a log time to come.

arclight

The Opposing Sides: Arclight

Prior to the Hundred Block War, Arclight was known to have maintained a small, regimental size, combat unit for the purposes of facility defence. What was not known was that this unit was, in fact, far larger and far better equipped than anyone could have imagined. The so-called Brigade of Light proved itself to be a highly effective, flexible, dynamic fighting force, easily capable of taking on Hirplakker on even terms. Their main strength lay in the strategic and tactical abilities of their commander, General Katarina van den Haas and in the individual initiative shown by commanders in the field. The Brigade demonstrated a remarkable lack of reliance on one single type of force or any single type of tactical doctrine. They struck swiftly and effectively against the lumbering Hirplakker formations, making good use of local knowledge acquired by spies, scouts and informants on the ground.

The Opposing Sides: Hirplakker

Hirplakker had, to all intents and purposes, become complacent. The last thing it expected was an attack from an apparently smaller and weaker opponent. Their main fighting capability was based around their much vaunted GenePool Troopers. Rigidly controlled, strictly organised and badly deployed, the Troopers were decimated by the lightning strikes of the Brigade of Light. A series of immense tactical and strategic blunders by Hirplakker practically gifted victory to Arclight. The decisions taken by the larger company were, to most observers, idiosyncratic and at times positively insane.

Conclusions

If one conclusion is to be drawn it is that Hirplakker was roundly defeated in what was the first major conflict in The City for nigh on two hundred years. Severely shaken by massive, unsustainable losses, Hirplakker aquiesed to the demands made by Arclight, gifting them the access to the resources which they so greedily desired. It is a defeat from which Hirplakker has yet to recover. The company seems to be caught in a malaise, unwilling to acknowledge the reasons for its defeat. The massive purges which followed the conclusion of hostilities only demonstrated further the lack of understanding in the high command.

On the winning side, there was nothing but rejoicing. For relatively little cost, Arclight had gained macrocorporate status, elevating itself to the exalted ranks of Trilhoeven, Gorunna and the rest. Yet, the bleeding wound that is The Contested Grounds continues to trouble both sides. It is a horrific reminder of defeat, sacrifice and pain, a bubbling cauldron of misery and self-doubt. Whether or not either side will have enough courage to lose face by pulling out of The Contested Grounds remains to be seen.

Status: Territory owning macrocorp
Headquarters: Luminosity Tower
Product(s)/Service(s): Advanced armaments, aircraft, communications systems, personal electronics, powered personal armour.

overview

A stern challenger to the might of Trilhoeven in the field of advanced armaments, until a few years ago Arclight were considered outsiders in the macrocorporate world. Indeed, it was the opinion of the other seven macrocorps that Arclight were merely a very large company trying to create waves in The City by attempting to gain control of resource facilities.

However, Arclight asserted their macrocorp status during the Hundred Block War three years ago when they defeated the massive Hirplakker Combine in a dispute over trade and exploitation rights to several highly lucrative regions of The City. Arclight are now firmly ensconced as the eighth macrocorp while the tail end of the Hundred Block War rumbles on in the Contested Grounds.

Arclight rules its corporate empire from the astonishing Luminosity Tower, built entirely since the Hundred Block War. No citizen can fail to be impressed by the elegance and might of the tower. From here, the leaders of the corporation control their business dealings, watching the thousands who labour for Arclight live out their lives.

organisation

Controlled by five families, the van den Haas', the McKenzies', the Singhs', the Grays' and the Spitzers, Arclight's business organisation is somewhat idiosyncratic and not a little nepotistic. Infighting, assassination and sometimes war are not uncommon within Arclight. Currently, the Grays' hold the upper hand, with seven out of the twenty-three seats on the board.

security forces

The Hundred Block War revealed that Arclight had managed to construct one of the best equipped and best trained security forces anywhere in The City. The military heart of these forces lies in the Brigade of Light, a 15,000 strong force of elite soldiers. Complementing this military arm are the paramilitary Ruby and Sapphire Sections. Ruby Section deals with internal security matters, Sapphire with external matters.

The Brigade is made up of infantry with limited heavy armour support, a reasonably sized air wing and a large force of power armoured Tentenel troops. Their tactical ability and training are second to none, while their equipment is among the best, if not the best, in The City. Most troops are fanatically loyal to Arclight, more than ready to lay down their lives to defend both it and the honour of the Brigade.

highlighted personality

general katarina van den haas

Age: 67 (looks 30)
Height/Build: 5'7"/Slim
Eye/Hair Colour: Grey/Dark Brown
Occupation: Commander of the Brigade of Light
Affiliations: Arclight, all sections of the Brigade

General Katarina van den Haas, Commander-in-Chief of the Brigade of Light. Eldest daughter of the van den Haas family, one of the five families who control Arclight, Katarina is now sixty-seven years old but thanks to her genetically enhanced background and limitless medical treatment, she hardly looks a day over thirty. This has lead to more than a few embarrassing situations with young suitors apparently unaware that she is old enough to be their grandmother.

A strong willed woman, it was she who masterminded Arclight's victory over Hirplakker during the Hundred Block War. She also turned the Brigade of Light from a merely good military machine into one of the most formidable fighting forces in The City. Her drive to ensure Arclight's pre-eminence saw the Brigade of Light go from strength to strength, increasing the number of armoured Tentenel troops and destroying the rigid, stratified, nepotistic chain of command which had been so endorsed by previous commanders.

gorunna logistics

Status: Territory owning macrocorp
Headquarters: Trenevier Compound
Product(s)/Service(s): Armaments, communications systems, transportation systems and services.

All Gorunna products, from powered assault suits to communicators, are rugged, dependable items. While not scaling the heights of technological advancement like Arclight or Trilhoeven, Gorunna products are ideally suited to life in The City. Because of their powerbase in heavy engineering, Gorunna produces most of the really heavy equipment (such as cargo aerostats) used in The City and as such, Gorunna manufactured construction equipment is used citywide, even by rival macrocorps.

organisation

Overall control of the company is exercised by the Board: a fifteen-person group of directors headed by the Chief Logistics Officer (CLO). Current CLO is Martain Geriss. Next in line to the board are the Co-ordinators, each one being responsible for the efficient running of Gorunna operations in a single area of production. The corporation itself is divided in to a number of departments, each handling their own area of expertise but there is a certain amount of cross-fertilisation of ideas between the departments.

security forces

The majority of the company's security forces are directed towards preventing internal dissent and worker insurrection. They drive their employees hard in places such as the Deepdown mining zone (see 'The Place'). Consequently, passions often run high amongst a workforce that feels (with some justification) that it is being used and abused. Green clad Internal Order Cadre (IOC) officers constantly patrol the factories, mines and powerplants, rooting out revolution and anarchy.

In comparison, the External Order Cadre (EOC) is small and rather ill equipped. However, such is the value that other corporations place on Gorunna (and the fact that they are so huge), an attack or hostile take-over would be unthinkable.

highlighted personality

Stephane Almovar

Age: 33
Height/Build: 6' 5"/Slightly plump
Eye/Hair Colour: Auburn, short and businesslike
Occupation: Operations Controller, Gorunna Logistics Deepdown Minezone
Affiliations: Gorunna Logistics

Stephane Almovar is the current head of operations for the Deepdown minezone. A ruthless, efficiency minded bureaucrat, he has introduced conditions of virtual slavery in order to obtain better and better production figures. While this has gained him the admiration of his superiors, it has garnered the anger not only of the workforce but also from several citizens rights organisations.

Those who know him say that Almovar is on his way to a seat on the board, via the Co-ordinatorship of one of the major departments. Physically, he can be quite intimidating, being nearly six and a half feet in height and possessing remarkably piercing green eyes. A single man, he has no social life to speak of and spends most of his off duty time working out ways to increase productivity and reduce costs. He seems to be one of the few people who genuinely enjoys the minutiae of business administration. To protect himself from the spite of the workforce, he has built up both a cadre of loyal personal supporters and an extensive network of spies and informants within the mining zone and within the adjacent workers neighbourhoods. Industrial action or protest is usually stamped out before it ever begins, a fact which only serves to increase Almovars reputation for ruthlessness.

grid

Status: Territory owning macrocorp
Headquarters: The Powerhouse
Product(s)/Service(s): Power supplies, power production technology and personnel.

overview

Of all the macrocorps, GRID occupies an almost unique position of strength and security. For they have access to more raw power than any other group in The City. From their concrete fastness, the Powerhouse, they send out electricity through cables and conduits, packaged in batteries and superconductors. Deep beneath The City, they maintain their cyclopean reactors, centuries old fusion generators, patched, repaired, renewed, soldiering on through centuries of ceaseless toil. For large scale power requirements, most organisations within The City rely upon GRID and their massive power generating facilities. Whilst the other macrocorps maintain small reactors and power systems, none can match the sheer generating output of GRID. The only group that comes even close to their capabilities is The Ancient and Honourable Guild of Fulgurators. For centuries, the two organisations have glared at each other with seething, baleful animosity. Both know that GRID is the most powerful by a long way, and that the systems of the guild are falling apart, crumbling into ruin through lack of resources and skill.

GRID maintains its position by trading power for resources and manpower. The other macrocorps do the hard work of sending drones out into the Outlands and GRID buys what it needs in exchange for a percentage of its generating capacity. Other groups such as the Three Canals Metropolitan Area Authority buy GRID power, usually through monetary means or by offering certain concessions to GRID interests. Even individual tenements can strike a deal with GRID, hooking their houses up to the system, plugging in to light, warmth and comfort, according to GRID advertising at least. Others choose to adopt the cheaper but somewhat more sporadic and unreliable services of the Guild. That having been said, the service offered by GRID does not always meet expectations. Richer areas and the other macrocorps (political wrangles notwithstanding) can pretty much be assured of reliable service all of the time. Individual burghs and smaller companies which have chosen to buy power from GRID can often find themselves faced with brownouts, blackouts and other variations in service at the most unexpected times. This happens due to the company shifting supply to others areas as demand rises and falls.

organisation

GRID is, fundamentally, rigidly hierarchical in nature. The organisational layout offers little in the way of flexibility and has become weighed down with bureaucracy and inter-departmental acrimony. At the top of the tree are Maintenance, which comprises those who directly maintain the power systems and control supply. Below Maintenace comes (in order of precedence) Research, Facilities, Security and Administration. As you get lower down the hierarchy, the resources and facilites available become steadily worse. Administration, at the very bottom of the pile, get the worst offices, the most incompetent management, the most shiftless personnel and poorest pay. This is all despite the fact that they are fundamentally vital in keeping the tottering edifice that is GRID running.

security forces

Forming the paramilitary wing of GRID, the EyEwiRE Corps maintain defensive security at all GRID operations and perform a limited internal policing function. Unlike most of the other macrocorps, the Corps is not geared up or equipped for offensive operations. This is due to the company's self-image as something of a benefactor and vital component of life in The City. Whilst not reaching the levels of complacency and slackness achieved by the security forces of Gorunna, they are still fairly unprepared for any kind of serious operations. The Corps is very small, amounting to little more than 4,000 active personnel, backed up by reservists and part-time troops. They are, however, fairly liberally supplied with light weapons, mainly purchased from the likes of Trilhoeven. Although GRID produces small numbers of weapons, these are mainly special projects with limited application in the field.

highlighted personality

leo troeltsch

Age: 27
Height/Build: 5' 9"/Average
Eye/Hair Colour: Brown/Fair, centre parted
Occupation: Administration clerk, GRID
Affiliations: GRID

Dominated by the weight of demands, memos, invoices and queries which cover his desk, Leo Troeltsch makes a valiant effort to keep a small part of the mighty GRID operation running effectively. Clad in his threadbare, crumpled, coarse brown suit, he carries out his lowly administrative functions with all the outward appearance of joviality and good humour. Cramped into his tiny office, only a few feet square, wedged into an already crowded basement somewhere under the Powerhouse, he stamps, approves, questions and orders twelve hours a day with scarcely a complaint. And, strangely for someone in Administration, he is actually good at his job. The reason? Leo fundamentally cares about what he does. He genuinely and truly believes that in his own small way he's doing something to support GRID's position. When not at work, Leo enjoys many happy hours painting and drawing in his room scarcely bigger than his office. His artworks have become rather popular in the Powerhouse, eagerly being sought as gifts, bribes or for personal appreciation.

hirplakker combine

hirplakker

Status: Territory owning macrocorp
Headquarters: The Iron Bastion
Product(s)/Service(s): Armaments, communications systems, construction, food and beverage products, personal electronics, powered personal armour, security services, vehicles.

overview

A massively widespread and diversified macrocorp, Hirplakker provides more services and has a wider client/product base than any other macrocorp. Unfortunately, they are still licking their wounds after their defeat at the hands of Arclight in the Hundred Block War three years ago. Hirplakker's confidence that they would win the Hundred Block War boosted their self-esteem up to new heights. Unfortunately, the comprehensive defeat they suffered at the hands of Arclight brought them crashing back down again.

organisation

The general affairs of the corporation are overseen by the Combinat, a diverse group of interests representing the various divisions, subsidiaries and interest groups within the massive company. At any one time, the Combinat has had up to eighty-seven members, all competing to have their voices heard. All decisions are made by a simple majority vote, subject to the advice of a group without whom no decisions can be made about the company: the Intellects. Hirplakker places massive store in the power of their Intellects to maintain their position. All matters of top-line strategy are handled by the seven Intellects, artificial intellgences created hundreds of years ago. Intelligent beyond the power of humankind, these beings are as near to gods as you are likely to find in The City. Their powers of perception and deduction are second to none. They can out think and out manoeuvre any other brain in The City. Which leads people to wonder why Hirplakker lost the Hundred Block War. Even a master strategist like Arclight's General van den Haas could not hope to compete with the sheer power of an Intellect. Yet, Arclight consistently out manoeuvred and out fought Hirplakker. Murmuring can be heard from deep within Hirplakker. murmurings of dissent, murmurings of that most heretical of thoughts: doubting the Intellects.

security forces

Hirplakker maintains a huge standing army. Called the Cadre, this massive force was thought to be able to crush any opposition in The City. That is, until the Hundred Block War. Mired by a seeming lack of coherent strategy, The Cadre floundered about the battlefields, wasting precious resources and destroying any strategic or tactical advantage it had ever possessed. Most disgraced of all were the much-vaunted GenePool Troopers (GPTs). The GPTs were meant to be the ultimate infantryman, stronger, faster, more skilful. In battle they were a disaster. Sent up against Brigade of Light Tentenel forces, they were decimated. Survivors mutinied, causing panic in the ranks. Courts martial were arranged and many troopers were executed, spreading dissent amongst the ranks. The current Cadre is yet to recover from the humiliation of the Hundred Block War. The GPTs are less than fifteen percent of the strength they had prior to the war. Infantry units are still depleted and the armoured units are virtually useless. Still drained by the wound that is the Contested Grounds, some fear that the Cadre will never recover.

highlighted personality

giovanni rohm

Age: 28
Height/Build: 5' 6"/Very slight
Eye/Hair Colour: Brown/Black
Occupation: AI Technician
Affiliations: Hirplakker

One of the few trusted individuals who maintain the systems supporting the Hirplakker Intellects, Rohm is a nervous, twittering little man, always flapping his hands and mopping his brow. The Intellect techs are well respected in the Combine, even a fidgeting flutterer like Giovanni. He knows he is in a position of trust and also knows that through his education, skill and intelligence, he more than deserves the position. Despite this, he has nagging doubts. He has become sceptical of the implicit trust which the leaders of the company put

in the Intellects. In the back of his mind there is a worm of doubt, gradually wriggling it's way to the surface. He suspects that what he is thinking may be heretical to the corporation, grounds for dismissal, disgrace or possibly even death. Despite this, he continues to think, to observe the Intellects and wonder what is going on.

i-lok

Status: Macrocorp (disputed)
Headquarters: N/A
Product(s)/Service(s): Everything from foodstuffs and clothing, to weapons and dingins. The business comprising I-LOK cover the full spectrum of interests.

overview

i-lok are an enigma even to the other macrocorps. An amorphous mass of dissimilar business. A web of mercantile relationships. I-LOK has seemingly no central control, no governing board, no centralised security service and no corporate goals. Yet, it has the same immense buying power as the other macrocorps, employs vast numbers of citizens, and purchases all kinds of resources in huge quantities. Even The Council seems baffled by I-LOK and its mannerisms. At Council meetings, members are never sure who will be representing I-LOK. One meeting it may be a shopkeeper from Sleeping Vale, at another meeting it may be the foreman of a toolworks in Folly Hills, at another it may be the slick president of a software company. This random attitude extends through almost all business dealings

organisation

The myriad businesses which make up I-LOK are not organised an any meaningful fashion, merely a web of amorphous interrelationships and business dealings. A tool factory affiliated to I-LOK might buy its steel from another I-LOK business while sending out its products on barges owned by another separate business. Most of the other macrocorps argue that I-LOK should not even be afford the status of a macrocorp, that it is just a glorified co-operative, a bunch of small businessmen laughing up their sleeves at the other seven. However, whatever they want to call I-LOK it does have one thing that they have: access to resources from The Outlands. No other small business have this, none come even close. Only a macrocorp has this kind of power.

highlighted personality

No one person can be said to represent a single aspect of I-LOK or its interests, hence the lack of a highlighted personality.

nakamura-yebisu group

Status: Territory owning macrocorp
Headquarters: The Forbidden City
Product(s)/Service(s): Power production, power production systems, aircraft, ground vehicles.

overview

Aside from the strange business dealings of I-LOK, Nakamura-Yebisu is probably the most enigmatic and least understood of all the macrocorps. Their origins are hazy at best, darkly mysterious at worst. Folklore surrounds the company and its imposing, fortress-like headquarters on the edge of The Trench, the Forbidden City. Unlike the other macrocorporations, the average man in the street has little, if any, knowledge of Nakamura-Yebisu and its activities. They are not as brash and militant as Trilhoeven, as arrogant and obstinate as Hirplakker or as omnipresent and obsessive as Sideband. They go about their business quietly and without fuss, maintaining their position through keen intelligence, low cunning and an utterly ruthless business strategy developed over many centuries of existence.

organisation

A highly laterally diversified company, kept under strict vertical control, Nakamura-Yebisu likes to keep itself very much to itself. Its vehicles are common on the canals and streets and it markets some of the best known prestige boat, automobile and powerbike brands in The City, making it very highly regarded in nomenklatura and upper level macrocorp circles. They are in fierce competition with GRID for the provision of power systems to smaller companies, although as yet they have exhibited no interest in challenging GRIDs monopoly on general power supply.

The company itself is run on an almost feudal basis, with the officers of the company having ranks and titles such as Lord and Lady. Where this archaic and unusual practice stems from, outside observers are unsure. It does, however, serve to give ranking members of the Nakamura-Yebisu hierarchy a somewhat smug and self-righteous attitude when dealing with the representatives of other macrocorps.

security forces

Nakamura-Yebisu maintains a small, strictly regimented military force to protect its interests. The force, known simply as the Weapons Division, comprises infantry, armour units, marines (who patrol the numerous sub-surface waterways which lead from The Trench and wind under the Forbidden City) and aerial forces. Most of these forces are concentrated in and around the Forbidden City, rarely becoming involved in wider conflicts. Popular opinion asserts that the Weapons Division has the best mikefighter pilots in The City as well as some of the best actual mikefighter aircraft. This opinion is mostly based on cunning Nakamura-Yebisu propaganda and the occasional, rare dogfight between Weapons Division mikefighters and those of other macrocorps.

highlighted personality

lady karen nakamura

Age: 47
Height/Build: 5' 6"/Stocky
Eye/Hair Colour: Blue/Brown
Occupation: Business leader
Affiliations: Nakamura-Yebisu Group

Elder scion of the Nakamura family, Karen is being primed to inherit the position of Chief Executive from her uncle, Lord Joseph Nakamura. A women of singular determination, she is known to have advocated the involvement of Nakamura-Yebisu in the Hundred Block War, desiring to intervene on the side of Hirplakker. The motivation for this was, publicly, the quasi-friendly relationship that has always existed between the two macrocorps, if such an improbable thing can be said to truly exist. Privately, the real reason was rumoured to be an irrational hatred of Katerina van den Haas, commander of Arclight's military wing, the Brigade of Light, and one of the senior figures in the macrocorp. Where this (alleged and unsubstantiated) hatred springs from, confidantes are unwilling to say.

Unimposing and plain at first sight, Lady Karen is not a women to whom suitors are constantly flocking. Her iron-hard demeanour and ruthless attitude put many potential swains off. The closest she can be said to have to a friend is her shadowy intelligence adviser Ernst Ruse. When he is not engaged in his nefarious activities out in The City, Ruse is almost constantly by Lady Karen's side, leading to a whole raft of rumour, innuendo and suspicion about their relationship.

Sideband Media

Status: Territory owning macrocorp

Headquarters: The Cathedral,

Product(s)/Service(s): Films, television, tri-D, newspapers, Dataflow access services, media analysis, intelligence gathering.

Overview

Working out of the massive, gargoyle encrusted edifice that is the Cathedral, Sideband dominate the media landscape of The City. No other corporation can claim to have such an influence over the daily lives of so many citizens of the urban sprawl. They wire themselves into the consciousness of The City, feeding dreams and playing off nightmares. Sideband holds a vital position in keeping the citizens sedated. Without the entertainments they produce, the entire city would simply descend into chaos. The controllers of the corporation are well aware of this, using their perceived power to influence other organisations. Cutting off TV services to a burgh can have drastic effects as the population are isolated from their electronic sedative. More than once have Sideband used this tactic and more than once they have got their way.

Organisation

Each of the eight departments has an equal controlling interest in the corporation. In many ways, each of the departments can be seen as a separate corporation, competing for market share and scarce resources. SBMT (Sideband Media Technologies, providers of TV, Tri-D and pay-per view cable) compete in the same marketplace as Cinematographics (who produce feature films). Laydown (newspapers and Dataflow newswire services) compete against HiGloss (magazines and Dataflow information services for the well-off). This often results in bitter infighting between the departments as they scrabble to attract the attention of the jaded consuming public. In the many vaulted cafeterias and restrooms of the Cathedral, fights are commonplace between employees of varying departments and Media Break (the security arm of Sideband) are often called out to intervene.

Perhaps the most lucrative part of the Sideband operation is its intelligence gathering operations. With the vast flow of data which pours into the Cathedral, everything is useful to someone and the corporation are willing to sell information to anyone. SideScan are the department responsible for intelligence gathering and information sales. Everything has a price and no request (apart from the monumentally unreasonable) will be refused.

Security Forces

As mentioned before, the corporation maintains a reasonable security force in the form of Media Break. Their purpose is mainly to provide internal security services, as most of the other corporations see Sideband operations as too vastly labyrinthine to even contemplate a violent take-over. Employees of the corporation view Media Break as a harsh, authoritarian part of the company, and, indeed, they are. They have no bias towards any part of the company, despite the influencing tactics that other departments employ. In addition to their more obvious security function, they also provide an arbitration service between squabbling sections and departments. Their smooth, urbane negotiators are the last word in diplomacy, exercising their skills for the good of the corporation.

Highlighted Personality

Brandon Shape

Age: 43

Height/Build: 6' 7"/Very well muscled

Eye/Hair Colour: Green/Light Brown

Occupation: Head of Security, Sideband Media

Affiliations: Employed by Sideband Media, alleged connections to the 3rd Syndicate.

Respected by his superiors, peers and staff, Brandon Shape is a man of great cunning, wit and immense physical presence. Standing a fraction over six and a half feet tall, he is an impressive figure, always clad in immaculately pressed black suits.

After a stint in the armed forces of an unspecified company, he joined Sideband at the lowest level of their security operation but, after many years of hard work, perseverance and success in his field, he has now gravitated to the very highest echelons of his profession. He oversees all aspects of security operations for the Cathedral with a precision and dedication which almost defies belief.

It is said that he knows the name and career record of every single one of his security personnel. A career corporate, it is rumoured that he has close ties with the 3rd Syndicate, although he remains characteristically tight lipped and the 3rd's are certainly saying nothing.

trilhoeven

Status: Territory owning macrocorp
Headquarters: Konkret
Product(s)/Service(s): Armaments, battlefield electronics, vehicles, security services and consultation.

overview

Most militant of the macrocorps, Trilhoeven also presents the most outwardly secretive face to the world. All company facilities are built in a style which one commentator wryly referred to as 'bunker chic'. Trilhoeven is one of the main suppliers to many security and militant organisations and its weapons, armour and security systems can be found city-wide.

Serious analysts rank Trilhoeven as the most powerful of the eight macrocorps, making it the most powerful organisation in The City. The corporation is not unaware of its position and more often than not uses its financial and military muscle to get its way. Many communities have found Trilhoeven facilities springing up in their neighbourhood without so much as a by-your-leave. The other macrocorps seem happy to let Trilhoeven carry on in this manner, biding their time, watching.

Aside from its militancy, Trilhoeven is a massive employer, bringing succour and shelter to tens of thousands. This does not come without a price: conditions in the smokey, ill-lit factories are amongst the worst in any macrocorporate facilities, earning them a reputation for insanitary conditions and colossal injury rates. However, with a teeming population begging for employment, Trilhoeven cares little for the welfare of its workers. They are packed into reeking towerblocks and flats, often with two or three families crammed into each tiny apartment. When virulent diseases break out in the workers housing (which they do with alarming frequency), Trilhoeven simply blocks off the entrances and exits with cordons of troops and waits for the disease to run its course. When the last of the infected are so raddled with disease they are unable to move, flamethrower equipped units are sent in to 'cleanse' the affected buildings before scores of new workers desperate for housing are brought in.

organisation

The affairs of Trilhoeven are overseen by an eleven person corporate board, chosen from the highest-ranking executives within the company structure. These officials vote for one of their number to be Chief Executive Officer, a post which is held for 3 years at a time. The current incumbent of this office is Tyron Weller, androgynous scion of the powerful Weller family.

security forces

Trilhoeven maintains vast numbers of corporate militant forces, stationing them about its facilities in massive and obvious numbers. Despite this, it is not the regular troopers who are feared by the workers and the population at large, but the secretive and ruthless Grauschjager. The Grauschjager can be likened to a combination of secret police, internal affairs and special forces unit. They are Trilhoevens most elite security/paramilitary unit and they have a fearsome reputation for ruthlessness, cunning and efficiency. When seen by the public, they are always dressed in heavy, ankle length, dark grey coats and unadorned military style caps. No badges of name, unit or rank are ever visible on their forbidding uniform. Very little is really known about the unit, except that they have recognisance to operate as both an internal and external security force and have seeming carte blanche to use any methods they wish.

highlighted personality

beezer holmes

Age: 32
Height/Build: 6' 4"/Skinny
Eye/Hair Colour: Dark blue/Black
Occupation: Combat engineer
Affiliations: Trilhoeven

Pre-eminent in Trilhoeven for his architectural and engineering skills, Holmes is a man in demand. Specialising in the design of military buildings and equipment, he has helped the macrcorp turn out some of the best and most durable combat systems in The City over the last decade. Despite his occupation, he is a quiet, modest man, slightly unworldly, seemingly unaware of the violent uses which his creations are put to.

Highly regarded by the top echelons of the company, some people discount him a slightly effete, naïve individual of little or no worth. Then they learn of his reputation. This bookish young man has the ear of some very powerful figures, to insult or demean him would be an astonishingly bad move, and a swift visit from the Grauschjager would most likely follow: a hard lesson in respect.

Minor companies

firefinger

Status: Independent corporation
Headquarters: 208-217 Rue Pascal, Calculus Tor
Product(s)/Service(s): Dingin software

overview

A fiercely independent small corporation, Firefinger have positioned themselves at the leading edge of dingin software development. Disliked by some for their seemingly close ties to Arclight, the company is seen as a prime target for a hostile takeover. Firefinger supplied much of the offensive software used by Arclight forces against Hirplakker during the Hundred Block War, software which has now found its way on to the open market, much to the dismay of the larger corporations.

The company has concentrated much of it's activity into producing cutting edge combat programmes for micro and nano-scale dingins. Their sophisticated pattern recognition programmes helped to improve the targeting sensor capabilities of Arclight Tentenel troops and their high speed code generating software has also proved extremely popular amongst a wide spectrum of users.

In the wider marketplace, the company is mainly known for its codebreaking/generating programmes, much beloved of flowghosts across The City. Their 'HyperCypher' series of microtapes have been bought, hacked, copied and modified by flowghosts far and wide. Indeed, what was originally Firefinger software forms the basis of much of the basic arsenal of cryptologists across The City.

organisation

Firefinger are, much to the dismay of many of their customers, a pretty chaotic and disorganised company. No one is entirely sure who is in charge. When asked, some point at Trishe Maden, the senior software developer, whilst others will casually wave in the direction of Kent Uls, sometime sales director and marketing executive at large.

Despite the chaos, everyone in the company seems to know what they are doing and when they are meant to do it.

Their rambling, slightly shabby office and labs in Calculus Tor are not the kind of premises that immediately inspire confidence. Developed from an old three story tenement block, they have something of an organic style about them, with bubbletents, dormer rooms and greenhouses tacked on to walls and roofs. Fibrelines and gel-feed lines run everywhere, the air is alive with the clicking and clattering of various dingins, from massive old macroscales to the latest in experimental nanoscale models kindly provided by some of their more generous macrocorporate clients.

security forces

Firefinger does not maintain a standing security force but has an extended contract with the up and coming Eisenblitz militant corporation to provide security for its buildings and personnel.

highlighted personality

trishe maden, senior software developer
Age: 29
Height/Build: 5' 10"/slim
Eye/Hair Colour: Blue/Blond
Occupation: Software designer
Affiliations: Firefinger

One of the driving forces behind Firefinger's current success, Maden has been the subject of more job offers, attempted kidnappings, bungled assassinations and botched bribes than almost any other individual in The City. Arclight have made no secret of the fact that they would dearly love to have her working for them, leading to the other macrocorps being pretty certain that they want her too, even if they're not sure why. Constantly shadowed by some of the best operatives Eisenblitz has to offer, she's come through all relatively unscathed.

Developer of the original 'Rumbled!' pattern recognition software and one of the main continuing developers on 'HyperCypher' (currently on v178.8), she is relatively self-effacing about her abilities. However, when she gets drunk, she is less than modest about her abilities and will brag at length about how she helped Arclight win the Hundred Block War. A very noticeable scar on her left cheek is the result of making just such a boast in the presence of an ex-Hirplakker trooper who happened to be in her Eisenblitz entourage at the time.

iron hand security

Status: Militant organisation
Headquarters: Furstein House, 23-27 Hoffman Strasse, Sleeping Vale
Product(s)/Service(s): Protection, extraction, contract combat forces

organisation

One of the oldest of the currently extant militant organisations, Iron Hand Security have established a reputation for ruthless efficiency and brutal adherence to the wishes of their employers. Organised along strictly military lines, the company prospers by never refusing to take on a contract, no matter how inimical the situation involved may prove to be. This has, at times, led to the decimation of large numbers of Iron Hand Security (IHS) troops (the destruction caused by the Border Canal Rights Dispute twenty three years ago has not yet been forgotten) and the loss of valuable material. However, because of their reputation, IHS can charge fees which are well above the normal rates for militant organisations.

Most Iron Hand troopers are culled from various prisons, mental asylums and deep slums and are trained to the peak of physical fitness. Nothing is done to remove any edge of criminal behaviour or psychosis; these are seen as positive attributes in their line of work. Indeed, Iron Hand is one of the few active militant organisations to offer suicide troops on its roster of services.

The level of equipment supplied to the troops varies according to the wishes of the client and the needs of the mission. While they do have access to limited numbers of hitech weapons, troopers are, in the main, equipped with basic cartridge rifles and pistols. Certain special troops such as snipers are routinely equipped with the latest hitech weapons, purchased at ruinous cost from macrocorps such as Trilhoeven.

Current commander of field operations for Iron Hand is Major Scott Nicholas, a veteran of twenty-five years service and one of the few troopers to survive the disastrous Border Canal Rights Dispute. An extreme paranoid sociopath, Major Nicholas takes an obsessive, and some would say intrusive, interest in all field affairs. His sudden visits to Iron Hand units stationed around The City are well known. His other obsession is the maintenance of the organisations aging and decrepit air fleet. Currently, the fleet consists of three cargo aerostats, the oldest of which is over two hundred years old, and two mikefighters. When things go wrong with the air fleet, he has been know to summarily execute the maintenance personnel. This does not make him a popular figure amongst the technical troops.

security forces

The manpower of Iron Hand is in a constant state of flux, depending on the contracts currently engaged in and the success of recent recruiting campaigns. Even when large numbers of recruits have been brought on board, this is no guarantee that losses will be made up. Due to the nature of the people that the company employs, a large proportion of potential troopers do not survive basic training or a deemed just too unstable or dangerous for employment. This usually results in the individual being sent back to the institution or slum that they came from or, on occasion, dumped out on the streets.

highlighted personality

major scott nicholas

Age: 40
Height/Build: 6' 2"/Well-muscled
Eye/Hair Colour: No one ever looks him in the eyes/Brown
Occupation: Militant officer
Affiliations: Iron Hand Militant Group

Obsessed with military hardware and more than a little paranoid, Major Nicholas runs field operations for Iron hand with, well, an iron hand. Board members of the company would be more than happy to see the Major removed from his post but are extremely wary about incurring the wrath of this highly unstable individual. His instability can be traced to a lifetime of constant danger and exposure to stressful combat situations.

As a survivor of the Border Canal Rights Dispute, that disastrous campaign is still cast up to him as an example of Iron Hand's 'victory at all costs' policy. Even though he was only a very young trooper at the time, he remains very sensitive about the subject and mentioning it in his presence can result in something similar to controlled demolition.

Pan-urban organisations

the ancient & honourable guild of fulgurators

Status: Pan-urban guild
Headquarters: CrossBar Terminus, Fogwarren
Product(s)/Service(s): Power production and rail transport

overview

Claiming to be the oldest organisation of any kind in The City, the Ancient & Honourable Guild of Fulgurators certainly has a long and interesting history, even if their claim to have pre-Shift origins is derided as somewhat spurious. The Guild's main business is generating and supplying power to various parts of The City, in direct competition with the might of GRID. However, compared with the macrocorporations, the Guild is a ramshackle, archaic organisation stumbling along, ever threatening to fall apart at the seams.

The power production facilities of the Guild are as timeworn and ramshackle as the order itself. Ranging from failing, frequently broken, centuries old fusion reactors to clusters of wind turbines, the Guild sells power to industries and burghs who cannot afford the charges laid down by GRID. The Guild also has wide-ranging interests in other areas, controlling the railways which twine through The City, providing transport services and hiring out Guild members as 'consultants'. As previously discussed, the railways are just as ramshackle as any other element of the Guild, a crumbling, overlapping network of overhead and underground lines, all coming together at the Guild headquarters of CrossBar Terminus in the seething, mist shrouded depths of Fogwarren burgh.

Guild members themselves are a disparate bunch: some members come from families who have been in the service of the Guild for generations, others join because of a desire for supposedly arcane knowledge, or for the simpler reason of a place to sleep and something to belong to. Often portrayed in The City as a misogynistic, quasi-monastical institution, the Guild actually accepts both male and female members, making distinction only in terms of technical ability and length of service. Whilst it is true that members refer to each other as 'Brother', there is no 'glass ceiling' preventing female members rising to the upper echelons of the organisation. Indeed, there have been many female Masters of the Guild in the past. Uniformly clad in their heavy, rubberised, insulated black coats, dark goggles and thick gloves, Guild members can present a somewhat intimidating sight. Most brothers are scarred or burned in some way, a relic of having to deal with miles of corroded cabling and dangerously unpredictable generating mechanisms.

Revered amongst the ordinary members are those brothers chosen to act as train crews on the vast railway network. It is seen as a position of great responsibility and singular honour. Out of all those who work on the railways, only the train crews are themselves members of the Guild. Conductors, ticket collectors and Transit Militia, while employed by the Guild, are not permitted to become members, unless it is under very special circumstances.

organisation

Such is the complex nature of the Guild, no one person can be said to control the entire teetering edifice. In nominal (very nominal, in fact) charge of the Guild is the Master of the Order, a position endowed with considerable power, respect and responsibility. The Master is supposed to represent the Guild at all official functions, such as meetings of the Council, and be spokesman for the Guild on all matters of City-wide importance. Below the Master are the many layers of Guild bureaucracy, down through Commissioners, High Electricians, Sub-masters of the Forge, Fusioneers Depute, Senior Brothers and right on down through to ordinary brothers.

The only non-Guild members to have a say in important matters are the senior officers of the Transit Militia. As the de facto security arm and paramilitary wing of the Guild, they wield a substantial amount of power, being able to influence key decisions and even, at times, dictate Guild policy.

security forces

The Guild maintains order through the Transit Militia. Aside from the Militia, many other brothers are trained in the use of weapons, rather unsurprising given the somewhat militant and distrusting outlook of the Guild. It is also rumoured that the Guild maintains a substantial cache of ancient, possibly non-functional, but allegedly deadly weapons at a secret location somewhere in The City. Known only as 'The Keep', this secret arsenal seems never to be officially discussed within the Guild and is the subject of rampant rumour and debate within the lower orders. Even the macrocorps have become interested in the stories of The Keep, but their centuries long investigations have so far yielded little, if any, concrete information on this mysterious phantom.

highlighted personality

senior brother almayer grudd
Age: 42
Height/Build: 6' 1"/Wiry
Eye/Hair Colour: Blue/Bald
Occupation: Guild enforcer
Affiliations: Ancient & Honourable Guild of Fulgurators, Transit Militia

Enforcer, troubleshooter and all-round hardcase, Grudd is the Guild's man-on-the-spot in situations where things are getting a bit heated. Adept at sorting things out via negotiation, coercion or even outright violence, he is a man feared by even the most hardened officers of the Transit Militia. When Grudd appears on the scene, you can be sure that things are going to get resolved very quickly and possibly not to your advantage.

Clad in the same black uniform as other Guild Brothers, Grudd packs a surprisingly diverse array of weaponry beneath his insulated coat. From sparklocks to magnetic repeater SMGs, he has armament for every conceivable occasion. Aside from his martial prowess, he is also a skilled orator, negotiator and debater, adept at spinning a web of argument, counter-argument and deceit. Most who have a verbal encounter with him come away feeling that, no matter how strongly they have argued their position, they have somehow been backed into a corner and forced to change their views.

None within the Guild feel safe in the presence of Almayer Grudd, although none can doubt that he has saved the reputation of this fractious, perfidious and terminally unstable organisation on many occasions.

the crypt
Status: ?
Headquarters: ?
Product(s)/Service(s): None

overview

A shadowy organisation, only rumoured to exist. Legend has it that The Crypt controls everything in the city, from the gangs right up to the macrocorps. Other rumours indicate that The Crypt is somehow connected with The Shifted. Whatever the story, nobody actually knows anybody who even met someone who could confirm the existence of The Crypt. It is largely discounted by the more 'rational' inhabitants of The City and is often used as a threat by parents to their children, "Behave, or The Crypt will come for you".

organisation

Unknown. Many rumours and folklore abound about the organisation of The Crypt, from it being a cabal of macro-corporate executives in league with The Shifted to and unholy alliance of religious and criminal figures bent on enslaving the population of The City. Suffice to say, The Crypt remains to this day nothing more than an intangible phantom.

security forces
Unknown.

highlighted personality
None.

the transit militia

Status: Pan-urban organisation
Headquarters: CrossBar Terminus, Fogwarren
Product(s)/Service(s): Railway network security

overview

The brutal, thuggish, quasi-military arm of the Ancient and Honourable Guild of Fulgurators, the Transit Militia are charged with keeping law and order on the railways. Approaching their task with scarcely concealed relish, they are a harsh, authoritarian group whose activities sometimes bring embarrassment to the entire guild. First appearing as a coherent force over three hundred years ago, they have evolved over time into the sprawling police organisation that they are now recognised as.

Whilst some individuals within the militia are dedicated, hard working law enforcers, many officers are vicious ruffians, attracted by the thought of being able to openly carry weapons and subject weaker citizens to violence and humiliation. Indeed, the vast majority of militiamen (and women) are little more than bullys. Clad in their rough grey greatcoats and stern peaked caps, the militia present a stern, forbidding face to the world. Their bulky garments are padded in order to increase the intimidation factor and their hats cast concealing shadows over their eyes. The copper badge of the militia sits on the left breast of the coat, displaying the seal of the Transit Militia and the officers number.

While being a sadistic, cruel organisation, the militia are, in fact, underfunded, undermanned and poorly paid. Most officers carry sparklocks which they have purchased themselves, and it is very rare to meet a militiaman with anything more hitech. Their uniforms are ancient and threadbare, handed down through the generations, repeatedly darned, patched and repaired.

structure

Nominally controlled from the sprawling structure that is CrossBar Terminus, local militia operations at each of the stations along the railway line is pretty much left up to the decision of the commander on the spot. Most of the militia forces at the stations are commanded by an Inspector or a Sergeant if the station is particularly small or insignificant. Manpower can range from one or two constables, right up to forces numbering twenty or more for particularly busy stations. Overall operations on a single railway line are overseen by a Chief Inspector, whose powers are both considerable and variable. Militiamen are often to be seen riding the railways, travelling on carriages with the passengers, keeping an eye on things, checking tickets, watching out for vandals. Then again, some commanders choose to keep their men solely within the confines of the station, ignoring crimes against passengers on the trains. At the top of the Transit Militia are the Superintendents, a group of men and women of variable number who report directly to the High and Exalted Council of the Guild.

enforcement policy

There is one crime which ranks above all others in the eyes of the Transit Militia. A crime so heinous that it turns the stomachs of ordinary militiamen. A crime which, if left unchecked, could devastate the railway system; dodging the fare. The militia have an almost pathological hatred of fare dodgers. If someone fails to produce a ticket, they are arrested and given a brutal beating as well as being fined. If they run, the militia open fire. It's the law of the railway that runners get shot. Other serious crimes are damaging the railway mechanisms, interfering with an officer in the execution of his duty and causing the trains to run late. With so much discretion in the hands of individual station commanders, application of the laws of the railway is variable in the extreme.

highlighted personality

inspector irina hasek

Age: 37
Height/Build: 5' 4"/stocky
Eye/Hair Colour: Grey/Grey
Occupation: Transit Militia officer
Affiliations: Transit Militia, The Ancient and Honourable Guild of Fulgurators, The Mortal God Church

Officer in charge of the Folly Hills Central station, Inspector Hasek has fifteen militiamen under her command. A rigorous, by-the-book officer, she runs her little force with the greatest precision and remarkable efficiency. Regarded as something of a nitpicker and pedant by the officers under her command, she demands the best from her platoon, insisting on smart turnout at all times. In truth, Inspector Hasek has strong views about the dignity of the militia as a organisation and is not quite the typical senior officer. Despite being in one of the rougher areas of Folly Hills, Folly Hills Central is kept immaculately clean and tidy, the ordinary Guild staff being coerced by Hasek into working by her rules. Despite her stern demeanour, she is a warm, thoughtful woman, given much to speculation and deep thought. She also writes awful poetry, regaling passers by with badly composed verses in bastardised iambic pentameter.

Despite their back-room grumblings, the militiamen have a certain fondness of Inspector Hasek. Her methods have gained the Transit Militia slightly more goodwill and respect in the area, a massive change from the atmosphere of fear and resentment that usually surrounds militia activities.

religious groups

religion and cultism

The City is a fertile seedbed for all manner of religious and quasi-religious organisations. Millenarian cults, animist klatches and apocalyptic suicide sects all play their part in the decaying tapestry of life. Religion is a vital part of life for many people, providing them with a bulwark against the horrors of everyday life. It provides the column which gives them strength in a horrible, dark place.

millenarian groups

By the common reckoning, The Bombardment and The Shift occurred 997 City-years ago. This means that it is nearly one thousand years since the terrible events which so shaped life in The City. In recent decades, there has been an explosive rise in the number of sects whose beliefs are centred on the upcoming millennium. Groups such as this have always existed, most of them believing that there is a thousand-year cycle of destruction, chaos and re-building. However, as the thousand-year mark draws closer, many more extreme groups have sprung into being, with views and practices that challenge even the hardened sensibilities of The City. Most common are groups which believe another Shift is on the way and that they alone hold the key to living through the event. Sacrifice, torture and self-mutilation are hallmarks of these sects. Believers generally have tenets that revolve around extreme practices, practices which guarantee their survival during the next Shift.

One of the most radical of the millenarian groups are the Soldiers of Change. They are almost exclusively made up of veterans of the ongoing conflict in the Contested Grounds, most of them driven to the edge of insanity (and beyond) by their experiences. Having a strict code of martial discipline and religious observance, their rigorously regimented hierarchy demands that any transgressions are punishable by death and all orders from the senior officers must be followed to the absolute letter, even if it means death or injury for the soldiers concerned. Their central belief is that only through martial virtue and discipline will man be prepared for the trials of the next Shift. Unsurprisingly, the Contested Grounds have become the spiritual home of the Soldiers of Change, a place where they learn to master themselves and indulge their compulsion to kill. Driven by their nightmares and personal demons, they see most people as traitors, infiltrators, spies, an enemy to be rooted out, tortured and executed. The

Soldiers of Change are a dangerous, violent and unstable group of people (probably amounting to no more than a few hundred individuals) who could, if they desired, wreak major havoc in The City.

macrotists

Some citizens choose strange idols to worship. To many people, those who belong to the macrocorps are beautiful figures who come down from on high, dressed in wonderful finery, skin unblemished by soot or pollution, beautiful in every aspect. Macrocorporate worship assumes many forms, from idolisation of a particular figure or product, to a building or even the organisation itself. Within all of this, there a two distinct types of worship: spontaneous and conceived.

Spontaneous worship (as the name would suggest) arises naturally, as individuals or small groups start to hold certain aspects of macrocorporate life as the acme of existence or examples of the divine. In recent years, one of the most notable aspects of spontaneous worship is that associated with Luminosity Tower, the headquarters of Arclight. So impressive is the building, shining with an almost heavenly glow, that many have come to believe that it has indeed been divinely inspired. Some choose to believe that the structure itself was created by a deity figure, others choose to believe that, although built by men, the tower is a symbol of holiness and divine wisdom.

Conceived worship is an altogether different matter. Some elements within the macrocorps noted the existence of corporate worship and decided that such beliefs could be valuable to their interests. Through various means, certain macrocorp interests manipulate people into macrotism. Some choose to 'plant' individuals who preach belief in certain divine aspects of the company, whilst others choose subtle manipulation via television and the media. Others choose even more insidious methods, such as drug manipulation of entire workforces to make them susceptible to religious suggestion. Whatever the means, worshipping macrocorps has become a part of life in The City. Although fractured and disparate, the number of believers steadily grows, becoming ever stronger as the years roll by.

animism

Some within The City hold the belief that natural objects, places and even The City itself have a 'spirit', a binding force which unifies all things. Most animists or groups of animists have differing views on what exactly constitutes a 'spirit' and how it is manifested, yet all adhere to the same basic beliefs. Animists quite often recive revelations from the spirits in the form of dreams and visions, often connected with the presence of a particular things or place. Some areas in The City have attracted large numbers of animists to live in and around them. The Forest and Central Park are both popular locations, due to their bountiful natural resources. Much of the time, the authorities in these areas tolerate people building tiny shrines under trees or next to flowering shrubs. They realise that the believers are highly unlike to damage the objects which they venerate and are, in most cases, more likely to tend the item in question. There are some cases where animists stray dangerously close to Shift worshippers and there is some cross-fertilisation of belief between the two. Some of the more extreme animist sects see The Shifted as spirits of The City, to be worshipped and communed with. This, from any reasonable standpoint, is a fairly bad idea which can only end in trouble.

One of the more notable and widespread animist religions are the Greenkeepers. Each Greenkeeper worships their own personal plant, which they must tend and respect. Each plant is grown from a cutting taken from a gigantic, ancient tree which grows at a secret location somewhere in The City. Only the inner circle of believers know where the tree is located and they guard it with a fierce determination. Members of the religion believe that by tending for the plant, there is a two-way process which benefits both the plant and the tender. There may be a certain amount of truth in this, as Greenkeepers tend to be marginally happier and better balanced than your average citizen.

apocalyptic cults

Often confused with some of the millenarian groups, most apocalyptic cults believe that The Shift and The Bombardment were a literal apocalypse and that the world, as it existed prior to these events, no longer exists. In many senses, this is true. Life in The City is radically changed from what it once was; it is now a cauldron of social problems gone hopelessly insane. These cults believe that the inhabitants of The City are literally living in a hell. Some of their beliefs are not so far removed from the tenets of the Third Church of God The Architect. Indeed, some apocalyptic cults are splinter factions of the Third Church. These cults vary in the extreme in their beliefs. Some believe that as the populace has been condemned to hell, then it must be because mankind is essentially evil and deserves as much punishment as possible. In a contrary view, some believe that the only way to release mankind from this apocalyptic state is by doing good, by exhibiting kindness and compassion. This view is exemplified by the Children of Beneficent Compassion and Blessed Relief. Although not very widespread, they run a number of poorhouses, orphanages, hospitals and schools in an attempt to bring succour and assistance to as many poor souls as possible. Taking a opposite line to the Children are the Despondent Brothers, a quasi-monastic group which believe that extreme penitence through starvation, flagellation and self-mutilation are they key to achieving external rest. Needless to say, the Brothers attract the more unusual citizens of The City into their fold, sadists, masochists, the insane and the hopelessly weak-willed.

Shift worship

Disturbed, deranged and quite possibly demented. This is the common perception of those who worship and adore Shifted beings, venerating them as deities. However, the truth is, if anything, even more disturbing. Not all Shifted worshippers are the deranged lunatics of popular folklore, sacrificing themselves in bloody services and ending their miserable lives in a frenzy of destruction. Many see the power of The Shifted as a key to greater power for themselves. Respected citizens, powerful executives and admired sportsmen and women have been know to be followers of The Shifted, worshipping them for their own ends. In truth, worshipping The Shifted is dangerous; at best, a path to insanity, at worst, a road to death. The incomprehensible nature of The Shifted makes dealing with them a shaky proposition, one founded on misunderstanding, confusion and hatred. If The Shifted do, in their own way, decide to 'assist' worshippers, it is usually for their own mysterious ends rather than for the ends of the worshippers. Yet, many still flock to the underground churches, the darkened back rooms, the secluded courtyards to pray and beseech in the hope of attracting those whom they fear and venerate.

the mortal god church

Status: Citywide religious organisation
Headquarters: The Empty Shrine
Membership: Estimated to be 3 - 5% of the population of The City

overview

The second largest organised religion in the city, The Mortal God Church is deeply factionalised and ridden with schisms. Whilst all sharing the same main tenets, the four main factions all furiously stick to their own interpretation of the Churches beliefs. The core of these beliefs is that God has died and that man is now alone. It was Gods death which caused The Shift and imprisoned mankind in this city. However, the four main factions all have different theories on why exactly God died.

the mans folly faction

Most powerful of the four factions, the Mans Folly faction believe it was the evil of man and a lack of spirituality in humanity as whole which caused God to die. Sect members believe that man must atone for his mistakes if a New God is to be born into the universe and allow man to leave his imprisonment in The City.

the unfair universe faction

Ridiculed by the other factions and derided for being simplistic and trite, the Unfair Universe faction preaches that God died and The Shift occurred because that's just life, and life can be really unfair to man at times. They believe that there is no going back, that man will just have to learn to cope on his own and get on with things as best they can.

the godless incursors faction

The Godless Incursors faction present the most controversial (in the eyes of the other factions) theory on why God died. They believe that a race other than humanity managed, through twisted science and evil machinations, to kill the Supreme Being. Man can therefore rest easy in the knowledge that there was little that could be done to prevent this. However, sect members must always be on the lookout for Incursor activity, ready to defend humanity if they return to carry on their evil work.

the triumph of evil faction

The Shifted are to blame. The Shift was not the result of Gods death, but what caused His death. The Shifted beings, by creating The Shift, killed God and therefore allowed evil to triumph. Sect members violently hate The Shifted, blaming them for the current plight of mankind, actively attempting to destroy The Shifted, in an attempt to cleanse The City and allow a new God to come to the fore.

organisation

Technically, all the factions of the Church come under the control of the Arch Propagator of The Faith. However, in reality, this is most certainly not the case. While the adherents of the Mans Folly faction have for a long time been the most powerful of the factions and have therefore elected the Arch Propagator, this august personage really only has authority over those within his own faction. The schismatic factions all elect their own Arch Propagator, each one of them claiming to be the true spiritual leader of the entire Church.

If truth be known, many followers of the Church are desperate to see an end to this factional infighting and divisive bickering. They wish to see a unified, strong Mortal God Church, with the ability to challenge the dominance of the Third Church of God The Architect. These followers have organised themselves into the 'All Together Now' group, a cross factional talking-shop and force for change (or so they believe). Many of the more zealous factional members believe the 'All Together Now' group to be a bunch of dangerous radicals who wish to drag the Church into dark age of ignorance.

Overall, each faction follows similar organisational lines, with the Arch Propagator at the top and the lesser members of the Church following a sliding scale of influence and respect. Just below the Arch Propagator are the handful of Demi-Propagators, below them are Learned Propagators, Revered Propagators and at the bottom, the lowly Propagators, the rank and file priests of the Church.

security forces

Unlike the Third Church of God The Architect, the Mortal God Church has little in the way of an armed force. However, many members of the laity and even some members of the priesthood go armed, mainly to protect themselves from attacks by other factions.

highlighted personality

learned propagator myron linebarger

Age: 43
Height/Build: 6' 4"/muscular
Eye/Hair Colour: Blue/Bald
Occupation: Propagator of The Mortal God Church
Affiliations: The Mortal God Church (Triumph of Evil faction), The Hohler Gang

Former streetfighter, mugger, petty criminal, sometime pit-fighter and all round ne'erdowell, religion caught up with Myron Linebarger late in life. His moment of epiphany came whilst languishing in a dank cell in Fogwarren, having been arrested for some minor infraction of local law. While he remains silent as to what caused his conversion, he emerged from captivity with a new found zeal and desire to carry out good works. Since then, he has been an ardent member of the Triumph of Evil faction of the Church, rising to the rank of Learned Propagator, with a roving portfolio covering anywhere he chooses to go within The City.

A rock-like bruiser of a man, Linebarger preaches with a confidence and piety that proves the old maxim that there's none so righteous as the converted. In his fifteen years of service to the Church, he has scarcely put a foot wrong, even going so far as to bring some of his erstwhile criminal colleagues into the fold. Such is the power of his oratory, other factions are beginning to see him as a threat, such is his ability to sway the mob and gain conversions.

the Shining Sky

Status: City-wide religious organisation
Headquarters: The Observatory, Shore Ditch Warrens
Membership: Estimated to be between 1 and 5% of the population of The City

overview

One of the more recent manifestations of the desire for an explanation of the situation which The City finds itself in, the Shining Sky religion has gathered a remarkable number of devotees in a relatively short space of time. Originating as just another small sect, meeting in the shambles of Shore Ditch Warrens, it has grown over the last few decades into a belief system adhered to by a substantial number of people of a wide variety of social classes.

The basic belief of the religion is that The City is encapsulated in a bubble (hence the reason no one can leave), wrenched from it's position in the base earth and placed in a crystal sphere for the edification of the unseen but omnipotent Observers. On the rare occasions when the night sky can be seen, the twinkling lights are the eyes of the ever present Observers, watching with amusements the comings and goings of the citizens of The City. The daytime sun is a powerful light shone by the Observers to illuminate their subjects.

Some have pointed out that the basic notion of the religion is on somewhat shaky foundations, as the barren wastes of The Outlands prove. Believers decry this as foolishness, pointing out that as no one can leave The City, The Outlands must be an illusion placed there by the Observers to test the reactions of their subjects. Most outsiders sigh at this point and walk away, feeling that there is no point in arguing with deep-seated faith.

Derided by both the Third Church of God The Architect and the Mortal God Church (both much larger and, as they see it, more worthy religions) for being naïve, simplistic and downright unbelievable (which is exactly what large numbers of people say about the Third Church and the Mortal God Church), the Shining Sky rides out the frequent pot-shots taken at it with a smugness and sense of self-worth which borders on the intolerable. In fact, it is the sheer smugness and self-regard which the Shining Sky breeds within its believers that irritates most people. Members often pontificate at length about the arcane knowledge which has been passed down to them through the ages. This is considered a bit rich coming from a sect which has only been in existence for about six decades (give or take a few years here and there).

organisation

The Shining Sky is non-hierarchical to the point of manic obsession. Believers in a given area organise themselves into 'watch groups', each group carefully maintaining their own Holy Telescope through which they can watch the heavens and hopefully gain some insight into the activities of the Observers. They gather together to watch, pray and offer mutual support or relate any recent revelations they may have regarding the purpose of the Observers. Each member carries a notebook and pen with them everywhere they go, ready to note any insights they may have or to record any observations made through the Holy Telescope.

security forces

Pacifistic in the extreme, Shining Sky members are forbidden by the Holy Tenets from carrying weapons of any kind. This frequently leads to watch groups being the target for robbery, muggings and assorted petty theft.

highlighted personality

July Middenthatch

Age: 37
Height/Build: 5' 5"/Slight
Eye/Hair Colour: Blue/Brown
Occupation: Priest
Affiliations: The Shining Sky

A long time devotee of the Shining Sky, July balances her life as a dingin software developer with her religious beliefs in a highly precarious fashion. Continually teased by her colleagues, she spends most of her off duty hours at the eyepiece of her watch groups Holy Telescope, watching the night sky and meticulously taking notes on what she sees through the scratched and fogged lens. Recently, however, she has been spending more and more time looking through the telescope and less and less time at work, a fact which has not gone unnoticed by her employers, Firefinger. They are less than pleased at the religious devotion that July exhibits, especially when it interferes with the good running of their business. This is also causing tension in her local watch group, as she has been accused of "hogging the Holy Telescope" and spending far too much time watching and not letting her fellow believers have their fair share of eyepiece time.

All in all, July's life is on a downhill slope leading to a crevasse marked 'disaster'.

the third church of god the architect

Status: Citywide religious organisation
Headquarters: Colsetter Parish
Membership: Estimated to be between 15 and 25% of the population of The City

overview

Austerity. Penitence. Toil. These are the hallmarks of the Third Church of God The Architect. Born out of the schismatic fires of the Second Church, the Third Church has grown to be even more powerful and popular than its more lenient predecessor. Hundreds of thousands worship God in His aspect as the Great Architect, creator of this penitential domain and judge over all. The core belief of the Church is simple: God created The City as a testing ground for the faithful, to see who was fit to enter His Eternal Heavenly City or be forever cast into the Many-Cursed Slums of the Great Demolisher. Only those who show true devotion to the Church, who live an appropriately humble and austere life, who regularly sing the Seventeen Virtues and Devotions and who work to further the glory of God can even have a hope of entering His Eternal Heavenly City. Everyone else is just in the shit.

organisation

The Church is ruled over by the High Cardinal, supreme leader of all the faithful. The High Cardinal is chosen from the ranks of ordinary cardinals upon the death or abdication of the previous incumbent. This is by no means a position for life and more than one High Cardinal has been persuaded to abdicate his office in light of certain matters.

Under the cardinals are the numerous bishops who take care of the day to day running of the Church. It is they who hold the true power within the Church, as it is the bishops who carry out the vast amounts of clerical and organisational work required to keep the Church running. The lowest rung on the ladder of ordained members of the Church are the ordinary priests. Their duties can range from presiding over a given parish, assisting in clerical (in the administrative sense)

matters, carrying out diplomatic work or any number of duties which the bishops and cardinals might find for them. The ordained hierarchy is exclusively male, the Church forbidding women from taking holy orders.

While not hugely vocal, there have always been factions in the Church who seek to change the status quo and allow female adherents to become priests. However, these movements are never very large and rarely manage to obtain the support of higher officials within the hierarchy.

Working alongside the priests, bishops and cardinals, there are numerous members of the laity who have chosen to dedicate their life to the Church. These are the deacons and sub-deacons. While many deacons act as assistants and advisers to members of the clergy, a large proportion of their number serves in the Lay Reserves Martial, the military arm of the Church. Ordinary priests are forbidden from taking up arms except for ceremonial purposes. It is the sub-deacons and deacons who act as non-commissioned and junior officers within the Reserves. The higher ranks are held by bishops and some of the more senior and well-regarded deacons.

security forces

As has been mentioned, the Church maintains a large armed force in the form of the Lay Reserves Martial. Each member of the Church, male or female, is expected to serve at least two years in the armed forces.

An almost monastic organisation, the Reserves indoctrinate its members with a fanatical devotion to the Church and to God. Combining the functions of police force, army and intelligence agency, they are a stern and forbidding group, clad in their tight fitting black uniforms and proudly displaying the elaborate tonsures which are their marks of rank. As rank increases, the tonsure become even more elaborate, the highest ranking officers must maintain their hair on an almost daily basis if they do not wish to be reprimanded and suffer loss of face in front of their fellow believers.

The vast majority of the reserves are formed into infantry companies, they have no air force as air travel is considered a sin against God and His Creation. Armaments vary widely, with the most lowly units simply being armed with sparklocks, while expensively purchased hitech weapons are reserved for the members of the Chosen Path: the personal guard of the High Cardinal.

highlighted Personality

the reverend Jaimes Mickitrik

Age: 37
Height/Build: 5' 5"/Slight
Eye/Hair Colour: Blue/Brown
Occupation: Priest
Affiliations: The Third Church of God The Architect

A lowly parish priest, Mickitrik tends to the needs of his parishioners in the densely populated slums of Fogwarren with a care and attention to duty which surprises even his superiors. He seems to be one of those rare individuals who actually care for the wellbeing and safety of others above all else. Many laugh and deride his efforts to help the poor, the sick, the starving and the mad. However, despite his seeming naivete, the people of Fogwarren have taken him to their hearts. His trust is rarely abused, his Chapel left relatively untouched and he can even walk in safety through the roughest neighbourhoods. His chapel has expanded from a single, small stone building in to a structure large enough to house a sanatorium, hospital, dormitory, soup kitchens and meeting hall. Physically, Mickitrik is a small, unassuming, prematurely balding man of quiet demeanour. He evangelises to a certain extent, but most take this as small penance for the good works that he carries out.

"It's not right, you're not right, he's not right, nothing's RIGHT! Concrete, blood, iron, tracks, canals, houses, trees, towers, knives, axes, fire, fury, wealth, poverty, shit, death. None of this matters, you don't matter, he don't matter, I don't fucking MATTER! Nobody cares. That's the point. Nobody cares. At all. Any time. We are all dead men. We're born into the shit and just don't realise until a bullet tears our spine out. You just don't get it, neither does he. Because I know. I KNOW! I FUCKING KNOW!"

Prisoner 74019, Wing 32, 'Inferno' Mental Institution.

the procedure

In a/state, all primary attributes and skills are defined by a number from one to one hundred. If a player wishes to have their character try their hand at a particular test of a skill or attribute, the player must roll a 100-sided die (hereafter referred to as a D100) on or under the appropriate attribute or skill in order to succeed. Under normal circumstances, rolling on or under the attribute means that the character is successful and passes the test. If a number greater than the attribute or skill level is rolled, then the character fails the test.

modifying the roll

Sometimes, circumstances will conspire to make it easier or harder for the character to pass an attribute or skill test. When a skill or attribute is modified (either positively or negatively) the modified number is known as the 'Effective Total'. This is the number which must be rolled on or under in order that the character is successful in the test.

The difficulties and the level by which they modify the appropriate skill or attribute are shown below.

Difficulty	Modifier
Absurdly Easy	+80
Very Easy	+60
Easy	+50
Simple	+40
Routine	+30
Complicated	+10
Challenging	0
Difficult	-10
Very Difficult	-30
Extremely Difficult	-50
Formidable	-70
Impossible	-90

example

John is playing the character of Janus Kripitsch, a type of character known as a Lostfinder. Kripitsch is attempting to follow a suspected thief silently and without being observed. Unfortunately, the thief heads down a silent alley strewn with discarded rubbish, making it rather difficult to move quickly. The GM informs John that he must make a successful Shadowing roll in order that the thief remains unaware of Kripitsch's presence. Kripitsch is rather good at this and has a Shadowing skill of 70%. However, due to the circumstances, the GM states that this is a Difficult roll, meaning that John must subtract 10 from Kripitsch's skill

level in Shadowing. This gives an Effective Total of 60%. John makes his roll. The dice come up 25, Kripitsch has passed the test and the thief remains blissfully unaware that he is being followed.

However, a roll of 01 will always pass and a roll of 00 will always fail. This serves to at least give characters a small chance of succeeding, even in a hopeless situation, and makes characters with very high skills nervous, as there is always the chance of failing.

skill and attribute challenges

On certain occasions, a character will be called upon to pit a particular skill, or attribute, against that of another character, creature or even an inanimate object. This is known as a Skill (or Attribute) Challenge. Resolving such a challenge is very simple. Both sides roll against their base skill or attribute. Whoever passes by the most or fails by the least has won the challenge. Simple as that.

example

Local Mire End loudmouth and all round bully Valentin Brady is in a local pub one night. Out of sheer braggadoccio, he challenges another man to an arm wrestle. Brady has a Strength of 70 (the appropriate attribute for such a challenge) and his opponent has a Strength of only 40. Should be easy to beat. The player playing Brady rolls first and the dice turn up a score of 75, Brady fails his roll by five. The GM rolls for his opponent and gets a 35, passing by five. Much to his surprise, Brady is defeated by the weaker man.

skills and skill modifiers

Skills are organised into groups of related skills know as 'Skill Areas'. These Skill Areas serve to indicate what attribute or attributes should be used to modify a particular skill. Each Skill Area (see 'Skill Descriptions' in 'The Players' for a full list of skill areas and skills) has an attribute, or attributes, associated with it. The associated attribute(s) serve to modify the skill.

In order to work out what the modifier is, take one tenth of the attribute (or one tenth of the average of the attributes) associated with the skills in the area and use this as a positive modifier in any skill roll. Note: Skill areas cannot be bought, you have to buy the individuals skills separately in that area.

This is explained further in 'The Players'.

combat

In a/state, the best way to avoid being killed or injured is to avoid a fight in the first place. Even if a stab wound or a gunshot doesn't kill you straight off, there's a good chance you'll succumb to infection, medical care being what it is in The City. Unless you're rich, affiliated with a macrocorp or have managed to scavenge some decent medical gear, medical care will be primitive and not particularly effective. Take the hint: don't get into a fight, and if you do, keep behind cover and out of the line of fire.

basics

Combat can be divided into two types: melee combat and ranged combat. The end result is essentially the same in that the object is to kill or injure your opponent. However, there are specifics for each which must be covered in detail. Before we get into that, though, there are some basics which apply to both types of combat.

rounds

Combat is arbitrarily divided into one second segments called 'Rounds'. Within this timescale, an individual can perform a single action, such as run a given distance, fire a gun a certain number of times, throw a knife and so on. How quickly a character can react in combat is determined by the Reaction (REA) rating. The higher Reaction is, the faster your character can react in a high pressure combat environment. Base Reaction is found by taking the average of Awareness, Intelligence and Agility, and rounding down to the nearest whole number if the fraction is below .5 and rounding up if the fraction is .5 or above and adding or subtracting certain modifiers. The combat round runs from the highest Reaction to the lowest, thus allowing faster, more aware characters to get the drop on slower opponents.

A character can also choose to hold their action, waiting until their opponent has moved before taking action. This allows a quick character to instantly react to manoeuvres. When a character has chosen to hold action and reacts to an opponent's move, both the actions of the opponent and the character are considered to have happened simultaneously.

example

Jane Card, a ghostfighter has an AWR of 70, INT of 50 and AGL of 80. Her Reaction is therefore the average of these three numbers, giving an REA of 67 (66.67, rounded up). She's just been challenged by Flash Valentine, a well known local gang leader. Valentine has an AWR of 65, and INT of 40 and an AGL of 60. His Reaction is therefore 55. Card can therefore either strike at Valentine before he has a chance to move or can hold action until he moves and choose an appropriate response.

melee combat

Melee combat, whether using weapons such as knives and clubs, or using fists and feet can be a messy, brutal business. Generally, no one gets out of a fight completely unscathed. Melee weapons (from table legs to laminate combat blades) are all defined by the following stats:

Damage Value (DAM)

The basic level of damage which the weapon will do to a target. The damage level of a hand held weapon is added to a character's Punch Damage.

Penetration (PEN)

How good the weapon is at penetrating armour.

Reach (RCH)

How much the weapon extends your effective reach, generally based on the length of the weapon.

Reaction Modifier (REM)

How the size and mass of the weapon affects the reaction time of the user.

Mass (MSS)

How heavy the weapon is.

Cost (CST)

The basic retail cost, in pounds, shillings and pence, of the weapon.

For weapons such as knives and swords, PEN will usually have two ratings separated by a slash. The number before the slash represents the PEN when stabbing with the weapon, the number after the slash represents the PEN when cutting with the weapon.

example

The profile for a Llive looks like this:

DAM	PEN	RCH	REM	MSS
6	10/20	+0	+5	2

Characters who are within two meters of each other may make melee attacks, using any appropriate close combat skill.

hitting the target

Taking into account any appropriate modifiers (see next page) a character may attempt to strike an opponent with fists, feet, knives or their melee weapon of choice.

The attacker must specify where they are striking, taking the appropriate modifier shown in the table below

Area	Penalty
Head	-20
Chest	-10
Abdomen	-10
Arm	-15
Upper Leg	-10
Lower Leg	-15

A Challenge roll must be made between the attacker and the defender. Whoever makes the roll by the most or fails by the least makes a successful attack or defence. Defending does not count as an action on the part of the defender, allowing them to strike back when their turn comes.

fire combat

Fire combat is a deadly and dangerous business, usually over and done with in a few seconds, with one or both sets of combatants either injured or dead. Firearms (and this covers gauss weapons, lasers and all ranged weapons) are defined by the following attributes:

Damage Value (DAM)

The basic level of damage which a standard round from the weapon will do to a target.

Penetration (PEN)

How good a standard round from the weapon is at penetrating armour.

Range (RNG)

The close range (in metres) of the weapon.

Rate Of Fire (ROF)

How many times in a one second combat round the weapon can be discharged.

Reaction Modifier (REM)

How the size and mass of the weapon affects the reaction time of the user.

Clip (CLP)

How many shots a single clip for the weapon contains.

Mass (MSS)

How heavy the weapon is.

example

The profile for a medium sparklock looks like this:

DAM	PEN	RNG	ROF	REM	CLP	MSS
7	5	10	1	+10	1	2.5

hitting the target

Actually hitting the target in fire combat is a combination of many factors including, but not limited to, the skill of the user, the range to the target, the quality of the weapon, the ambient light, movement, etc. In order to hit the target, the firer must make a skill roll against the appropriate skill for the weapon they are using (i.e.: firing a sparklock pistol requires the use of the Pistol skill, firing a shotgun requires the use of the Longarms skill). In ideal conditions (which never, ever exist) the skill of the firer is merely modified by the range to the target and the modified skill is rolled against to see if the round hits. This is always the first step in determining if you can hit the target. The Range (RNG) stat for a given weapon shows the Close Range in Metres of the weapon. Medium range is between the figure for close range and twice that number. The figure for Long Range is between twice and four times Close Range and the figure for Extreme Range is between four and eight times this number.

example

The profile for the Medium Sparklock given above shows a RNG figure of 10. Therefore, the range bands are:

Close	10
Medium	20
Long	40
Extreme	80

As the range to a target increases, it becomes increasingly difficult to hit the target. Each range band has a different modifier, as shown below:

Close	00%
Medium	-20%
Long	-50%
Extreme	-80%

Range is not the only modifier. Movement, lighting, rain, tiredness and a vast range of situational modifiers can all conspire to turn the best marksman into a hopeless shot. The list given below is not exhaustive and GMs should feel free to change the modifiers and make up new ones as the situation demands it.

Situation	Modifier
Walking	-10
Jogging	-20
Running	-30
Sprinting	-40
Poor Light	-10
Bad Light	-30
Near Dark	-70
Mist	-20
Fog/Smog	-40
Light Rain	-10
Heavy Rain	-30
Poor Footing	-10
Restricted Movement	-10
Aiming (1 second)	+10
Aiming (2 seconds)	+20
Aiming (4 seconds)	+30
Aiming (8 seconds)	+40
Laser Targeting	+20

example

A character running through mist and attempting to hit a target fifteen metres away with the aforementioned medium sparklock, would suffer a whopping -70% penalty to hit.

Called Shots

Sometimes, it may be better to try and hit a specific part of a target rather than just randomly blazing away, hoping that something vital will be hit. In this instance, the firer can declare a called shot and take a penalty to hit based on the area of the body they are attempting to shoot.

Area	Penalty
Head	-40
Chest	-20
Abdomen	-20
Arm	-30
Upper Leg	-20
Lower Leg	-30

Rate Of Fire

The Rate Of Fire (ROF) of any weapon determines how many single shots or bursts it can fire in any combat round. For example, a semi-automatic cartridge pistol has a ROF of 4, meaning that it can fire up to four shots per combat round. Automatic weapons (i.e.: those that can fire continuous streams of bullets) will have their ROF show like this : 4(5). This means that the weapon can fire up to four single shots or four bursts of five rounds each. Burst fire can either be Aimed or Suppressive.

Aimed burst fire is treated exactly like firing a single shot at a target, only multiple rounds are being fired at once. A single hit roll is made for each burst, all rounds either hit or miss. When a target is hit by a burst, all rounds strike the same area. Needless to say, a well aimed burst can have a devastating effect on a target.

Suppressive burst fire is mainly designed to cover an area or keep opponents heads down. A single burst can be used to cover an area one meter wide and the chance to hit a target within that area equals:

(number of bursts fired x number of rounds in each burst) x2, modified by various range modifiers.

The chance to hit is doubled at close range and halved at extreme range. As an example, an automatic rifle with a ROF of 4(5) could spray bullets across an area four meters wide in one combat round, giving a chance to hit targets within the area of 10% (modified for range, if appropriate). Or, the firer could concentrate all four bursts on an area one meter wide, giving a chance to hit of 40% (modified for range, if appropriate). Targets caught by a suppressive burst will be struck by 1D10/2 rounds, up to a maximum of the number of rounds in a single burst.

recoil

All firearms produce recoil and this can quite easily throw off the aim of the firer. To represent this, each shot or burst fired AFTER the first shot or burst in a round takes an additional, cumulative - 10% to hit (so the second shot is at -10%. third shot is at -20% and so on). Of course, this rule does not apply to lasers. That would be silly.

cover

In some situations, a target may have benefit of cover: walls, barrels, tables and so on. Cover is defined as either full or partial. Full cover, as the name would suggest, provides protection to the character's entire body whilst partial cover provides protection to either the upper or lower half of the body.

Cover effectively provides extra armour for the character, depending on the construction of the cover. So, a brick wall provides more protection than a wooden table, for example. Sample AVs for some common types of cover are given below.

Cover Type	AV
Brick Wall	10
Plasterboard Wall	03
Reinforced Concrete	40
Table	02
Wooden Door	03

If a character is in full cover, then the AV of the cover applies to any hit location. If the character is in partial cover, the AV only applies to those areas of the body which are behind cover.

hit location

Once it has been determined that the target has actually been hit, then the attacker must roll to see where he or she hits the target (with a called shot, this part of the process is unnecessary, as the attacker will either hit the chosen area or

miss completely). Rolling on the table below will determine where the bullet or blow hits.

D10 Role	Location
1	Head
2,3	Chest
4	Abdomen
5	Right Arm
6	Left Arm
7	Upper Right Leg
8	Upper Left Leg
9	Lower Right Leg
10	Lower Left Leg

The hit location will come into effect later on when determining armour effects and damage results.

penetrating armour

Each weapon has a Penetration (PEN) rating and each item of armour has an Armour Value (AV). The basic rule of thumb is that if PEN is greater than or equal to AV, then the round hits the target with no reduction in the damage. If, however, the PEN is less than the AV, one point is subtracted from damage for each point PEN is less than AV. Armour is only effective if the area which it covers has been hit. A character wearing an armour vest would be protected if hit in the chest or abdomen, but not if hit in the head, legs or arms.

Soft armour (chainmail, armoured clothing, etc) have no effect against blunt melee attacks (club, fists, etc). Hard armour (such as a flak vest) has half effect against blunt attacks. Melee weapons such as knives, swords and axes use the full armour value.

damage

trauma damage

All characters and NPCs will have a resistance to damage known as Resilience (hereafter referred to as RES). When a target is struck by a projectile, melee weapon, fist, foot or whatever, compare the damage (taking any armour effects into account) with the RES of the target. If the DAM is less than RES, then the character takes a light wound. If the DAM is equal to or more than RES, then the character takes a moderate wound. If the DAM is equal to or more than twice RES, then the character takes a serious wound.

The effects of wounds are decided in terms of Shock Points, which combine blood loss, trauma, broken bones and the effects of shock into one number. The table below will show the number of shock points a specific wound on a specific area will cause.

However, for each five points that DAM exceeds the serious wound level for the character (twice RES), an additional Shock Point is added.

	Light	Moderate	Serious
Head	1S	4S	Dead
Chest	2S	4S	Dead
Abdomen	1S	2S	4S
Upper Leg	1S	2S	3S
Lower Leg	Bleeding	1S	2S
Arm	Bleeding	1S	2S

example

A character with a RES of 5 is wearing an armour vest with an AV of 10. He is shot by an attacker with a rifle which has a PEN of 7 and a DAM of 20. Comparing the PEN with the AV, we see that AV exceeds PEN, therefore reducing the DAM by 3 points (AV of 10, minus PEN of 7 = 3). The damage is now reduced to 17. The target has been hit in the upper right leg with the adjusted DV of 17. This is more than twice the target's RES, inflicting a serious wound. Normally, this would give 3 Shock Points. However, the DV of 17 exceeds the serious wound level for the character by seven points, inflicting another Shock Point, bringing the total to 4, a very serious wound.

blunt trauma damage

Attacks with feet, fists, clubs (or indeed any non-penetrating melee attack) and non-penetrating projectile attacks (such as stones or bricks) do what is known as blunt trauma damage. Blunt trauma damage is worked out in the same manner as trauma damage, only there is no blood loss effect.

Projectiles which fail to penetrate armour are still capable of doing severe damage. Take the damage level which was stopped by the armour and divide by five. The number which is arrived at is taken as blunt trauma damage, measured against RES to determine actual damage in the normal way.

unconsciousness & death

When a characters total number of shock point becomes greater than his or her RES, then they must make a Willpower check with a modifier of -(10x number of Shock Points). If they fail, they lapse into unconsciousness. This check must be taken each time another Shock Point is gained.

When a characters total of Shock Points equals RES x1.5, they are about to die and only immediate first aid can save them. At this point, characters will die in a number of minutes equal to their basic RES unless a successful first aid roll is made (see below).

damage effects on skills

When characters receive Shock Points, they automatically receive a penalty to all skill use equal to the total number of Shock Points x10.

medical aid and healing

After being shot, stabbed, cut, kicked, punched or generally injured in some way, the first thing a character will probably want to do is get some form of medical aid. For the purposes of the game, there are essentially two forms of medical aid: First Aid and Long-term Aid.

First aid refers to any treatment which is administered shortly after an injury being received. It is, in the main, designed to stop bleeding, set bones and hopefully ameliorate the damaging effects of shock.

Long-term aid refers to any medical care which is received after first aid. This can range from something simple, like taking pills, to something more complex, like an extended stay in an intensive care unit.

When a character has been injured, first aid may be attempted in order to prevent further damage from a particular injury. The individual giving aid must make a basic roll against their First Aid skill, modified according to the conditions and the severity of the wound, as laid out below.

Light Wound	+0%
Moderate Wound	-20%
Serious Wound	-40%
Using Extemporised Materials	-20%
Working Under Poor Conditions (e.g.: in a rain-soaked alley)	-20%
Working Under Terrible Conditions (e.g.: in a combat zone with mortar shells falling all around)	-40%

If the character giving the aid make the roll successfully, then the character being treated will have had the bleeding stopped and had basic treatment of his or her injuries.

However, if the first aid roll is unsuccessful, the character will continue to accumulate Shock Points at the following rate:

Most Severe Wound Is	Additional Shock Points
Light	+1 per hour
Moderate	+1 per 30 mins
Serious	+1 per 10 mins

However, first aid does not necessarily mean that the character will recover successfully from his or her injuries. Injuries take a long time to heal, the more serious the injury, the longer the healing time.

recovery from injuries

A character will naturally recover from one shock point per week. This can be increased through the use of drugs and medical care. Rolling for any of the tasks below will allow shock points to be regained over the period specified in the task. The skill used is the General Medicine skill of whoever is carrying out the treatment.

Intensive hospital care	+20%	1 shock point regained per day
Hospital care	+0%	1 shock point regained per 2 days
In-home care	-20%	1 shock point regained per 4 days

other forms of damage

explosive damage

Explosives inflict damage in exactly the same way as other weapons, dealing out damage through a combination of concussion, blast and fragmentation. Like other weapons, explosive devices have a PEN and DAM rating. However, they also have an additional stat: Blast Radius (BR). The BR gives an indication of how powerful the explosive is and what damage it will do at a given distance. BR is given in metres from the centre of the explosion and within the BR, the explosion does full damage and deals out full penetration as shown in the stats for the device.

At distances up to twice the BR, DAM and PEN are both quartered.

At distances up to four times the BR, DAM and PEN are one eighth of their initial level.

At distances up to eight times the BR, DAM and PEN are one sixteenth of their initial level.

So, for example, an explosive device with a PEN of 16, a DAM of 32 and a BR of 2 metres will do the following damages at the following ranges:

0 - 2 metres	PEN 16, DAM 32
2 - 4 metres	PEN 4, DAM 8
4 - 8 metres	PEN 2, DAM 4
8 - 16 metres	PEN 1, DAM 2

Explosions do damage to the whole body, using the Chest hit section of the damage table to determine the effects of the wound.

electric shocks

Electric shocks are a constant hazard in The City, with ancient generators, corroded cables and hanging wires an omnipresent danger. Shocks can range in severity from the merely irritating to the instantly deadly. A mild shock (such as that received from a large battery) should be considered equal to a light chest wound, a more powerful shock equal to a moderate chest wound (such as that from a household mains circuit) and a really powerful shock (such as touching the outputs of a large generator) equal to a serious chest wound.

falling

Gravity is your friend. Most of the time. Unless you happen to fall from a tall building, then it's most certainly your enemy. Hitting the ground from great heights (or even not so great heights) can have a fairly serious effect on the human body.

Falls are treated as chest hits for the purposes of damage, with DAM worked out according to the height fallen from, as shown on the table below:

Height	Damage
0 - 2m	06
3 - 4m	10
5 - 7m	14
8 - 10m	18
10m+	20

poisoning

Toxins, poisons and drugs can all have serious effects on the body, effects ranging from mild twitches and hot flushes to agonizing death. All toxins are rated according to their Potency (POT), the higher the Potency, the more dangerous the toxin. When a target is attacked with poison, the table below should be consulted to find out the results. Like physical combat damage, RES is used to determine the seriousness of the damage. If the POT is less than RES, then the target barely notices the effects. If the POT is greater than or equal to RES but less than twice RES, then the target has a mild version of the full effect of the poison. If POT is greater than or equal to twice RES, the target takes the full effect of the poison.

generic poisons

Paralytic

Paralytic poisons cause the target (or a particular part of the target) to become immobilised. They can be administered through injection, contact, gas or a variety of other forms. They are generally not lethal unless administered in abnormally large quantities.

POT: 15
Effects: Causes temporary paralysis in the target.
Time: Takes RES x 5 secs to have full effect.

Neurotoxin

Acting against the central nervous system of the target, neurotoxins are invariably fatal in their effects. Many of the really effective neurotoxins are natural in origin, extracted from plants or animals and concentrated to improve their effects.

POT: 20
Effects: Death.
Time: Takes RES x 1 sec to have full effect

Knockout

Ranging from stun gases used by macrocorporate security forces to simple liquids administered to a cloth and held over the victims face, knockout toxins come in a staggering variety of forms. As with paralysis toxins, most knockout toxins are not lethal unless administered in abnormally large doses.

POT: 12
Effects: Causes unconsciousness in the target.
Time: Takes RES x 5 secs to have full effect

Vehicle Combat

Vehicle combat is not handled that much differently from man-to-man combat, with the exception that vehicles are bigger, faster and more often than not, more heavily armed and armoured.

Vehicle Stats

Vehicles are rated according to several stats, some of which will be familiar from the man-to-man combat section.

The stats are explained below.

Resilience (RES)

Like the personal stat, this represents how resistant to damage the vehicle is.

Armour Value (AV)

Almost self-explanatory, the higher the AV rating, the more powerful weapons the vehicle can take hits from without being damaged.

Manoeuvrability (MAN)

Some vehicles can turn tighter than others. MAN represents the handling of a vehicle.

Speed (SPD)

This is the top speed of the vehicle, expressed in metres per one second combat round. To find the top speed in miles per hour, multiply the SPD by 2.24.

Acceleration (ACC)

Each turn, a vehicle with a given acceleration can increase its speed by that amount.

Deceleration (DEC)

Each turn, a vehicle with a given deceleration can decrease its speed by that amount.

Crew (CRW)

How many individuals it takes to operate the vehicle at optimum efficiency.

Passengers (PSS)

How many passengers the vehicle is designed to carry.

Cargo (CRG)

How much weight the vehicle is designed to carry.

Example

A small electrically driven skiff may have a profile like this:

RES:	10
AV:	0
MAN:	5
SPD:	8
ACC:	1
DEC:	3
CRW:	1
PSS:	4
CRG:	200kg

Combat Manoeuvring

In a hectic combat scene, sticking rigidly to the rules is not the best plan. Handling things in a more 'cinematic' fashion often works well, engendering the scene with greater excitement and generally giving better game play. The rules given below are not intended to accurately model how vehicles behave in the real world, merely to give a basic framework on which to hang vehicle combat in a/state. GMs and players are actively encouraged to discard or ignore rules and make things up as they go along, anything, in fact, which contributes to a more enjoyable game.

Manoeuvring is carried out by testing the skill associated with the particular vehicle being driven/piloted and so on. Each particular manoeuvre has a difficulty modifier and the task is further modified by the MAN stat of the vehicle. MAN runs from 1 (a particularly poorly handling vehicle) to 10 (a vehicle which has supreme handling). The MAN stat gives a modifier to all manoeuvres carried out with that vehicle, a modifier that can be either negative or positive, as shown below.

MAN	Modifier
1	-40
2	-30
3	-20
4	-10
5	+0
6	+10
7	+20
8	+30
9	+40
10	+50

The different manoeuvring tasks have difficulty modifiers as shown below.

Task	Modifier
Drive/pilot in a straight line	0
Shallow turn	-10
Medium turn	-20
Sharp turn	-40
Gentle weaving	-20
Violent dodging	-50
Sharp braking	-30
Bootlegger turn (ground vehicles only)	-60
Power dive (aircraft only)	-40

All modifiers are cumulative. So, if the pilot of a small skiff were attempting to execute a sharp turn and brake violently at the same time, the modifier would be -70% And this is without taking into account the MAN stat. If someone fails a manoeuvre roll, the GM should exercise his or her judgement in what the results are, taking into account the speed at which the manoeuvre was carried out, the surrounding area and any other random factors which might come in to play. As vehicle RES and AV are rated on the same scale as that used by man-sized targets, it's easy to gauge how effective fire from a person will be against a vehicle and vice versa. The following rules allow for vehicle to vehicle and man to vehicle combat.

hitting the target

Some vehicles can move very fast and move very violently, presenting quite a difficult target to hit. A mikefighter moving at 300mph and dodging violently between tenement blocks is quite obviously a more difficult target to hit than a man standing still ten metres away from you. However, the mikefighter is considerably larger than a man, thus negating a certain amount of the disadvantage. When a person fires at a vehicle or when a vehicle fires at a vehicle, the following modifiers can be used to simulate the effects of speed, size and manoeuvring. Range modifiers are the same in vehicle combat as in man to man combat.

Close	-10%
Medium	-20%
Long	-50%
Extreme	-80%

Like people, vehicles have a variety of hit locations. When a hit has been achieved, a roll is made on the table below in order to determine which components of the vehicle have been hit.

D10	Location
1	Superstructure
2	Superstructure
3	Powerplant
4	Powerplant
5	Drivetrain
6	Controls
7	Sensors
8	Weapons
9	Passengers
10	Crew

Like individuals, vehicles can take three levels of damage: Light Damage, Moderate Damage and Serious Damage. The seriousness of the damage inflicted upon a vehicle is worked out in exactly the same way as that for people. The PEN of the weapon being fired at the vehicle is compared with the AV for the vehicle. If PEN is greater than AV, then the shot goes straight through the armour and uses its full damage. For each point that PEN is less than AV, DAM is reduced by one point. Should this reduce DAM to zero, then the shot simply bounces off the vehicle's armour. Penetrating damage is then compared with the Resilience (RES) of the vehicle. If the DAM is less than RES, then Light Damage is taken. If the DAM is greater than or equal to RES but less than twice RES, then Moderate Damage is taken. If DAM is greater than or equal to twice the RES of the vehicle, then Serious Damage is taken. The damage received should be cross-referenced to the hit location as determined above in order to work out exactly what damage has been done to the vehicle.

	Light	Medium	Heavy
Controls	MAN reduced by 2 levels.	MAN reduced by 5 levels.	Vehicle is uncontrollable.
Crew	1 crew member takes hit at 50% of penetrating damage.	All crew take hit at 50% of penetrating damage.	Crew killed.
Passengers	1 passenger takes hit at 50% of penetrating damage.	All passengers take hits at 50% of penetrating damage.	Passengers killed.
Weapons	1 weapon out of action. Repairable.	1 weapon destroyed.	All weapons destroyed.
Superstructure	Holes in superstructure, minor damage, RES reduced by 10% (round up)	Noticeable damage to superstructure, RES reduced by 30%.	Catastrophic damage.
Powerplant	ACC and SPD reduced by 25%	ACC and SPD reduced by 50%.	Catastrophic damage.
Drivetrain	ACC, DEC and SPD reduced by 25%	ACC, DEC and SPD reduced by 50%.	Destroyed.
Sensors	1 sensor put out of action. Repairable.	1 sensor destroyed.	All sensors destroyed.

Catastrophic damage: The vehicle is totally destroyed. All passengers and crew take damage equivalent 50% of that which penetrated the vehicle.
Destroyed: The component in question is rendered useless and unrepairable.

"Why am I happy? Because I've managed to make peace with myself. There are too many people in this city who are bent on causing misery for others. I choose a different path. Make a difference. Bring some light into peoples lives. Give them hope. That's the key. Hope is important."

Florentina Venkatseramany, Streethealer, Hangside.

the players

The a/state character creation system is designed to allow players to create rounded, realistic characters. Although this involves a large number of individual choices, the process is laid out in as simple and straightforward a manner as possible, making it easier for both player and GM.

Character creation follows seven stages:

1) In discussion with the GM, the player should come up with a character concept that both are happy with.

2) Choose Advantages and Disadvantages.

3) Choose an Origin for the character.

4) Choose an Upbringing for the character.

5) Purchase the character's attributes, using the attribute point pool.

6) Purchase the character's skills, using the skill point pool.

7) Round out the character and purchase any appropriate personal possessions.

attributes

Before going any further into the character creation system, we should have a look at the main attributes which define characters in a/state. These are:

Strength (STR)
This represents the raw physical power of the character. A character with Strength 10 is very weak, while a character with Strength 90 is exceptionally strong.

Agility (AGL)
Sense of balance, physical flexibility and control of large-scale bodily movements.

Dexterity (DEX)
Fine manipulation with the hands (or occasionally, feet) and control of small-scale bodily movements.

Health (HLT)
The general state of health and resistance to disease and injury.

Awareness (AWR)
The spatial awareness and generalised sensory acuity of the character. Awareness covers all five senses and the more nebulous category of 'intuition'.

Intelligence (INT)
The 'brainpower' of the character, the ability to learn and use knowledge.

Willpower (WIL)
How mentally strong the character is. A character with Willpower 10 is remarkably gullible and phenomenally easily lead. Whereas a character with Willpower 90 would be a leader of men and able to bend others to his or her will.

Personality (PER)
How likeable, friendly and charismatic the character is. Personality 10 would be someone remarkably unapproachable, dull and not in the least likeable. Whereas, someone with personality 90 would be the life and soul of any party going.

buying attributes and skills

Attributes and skills are bought using Attribute Points (APs) and Skill Points (SPs). Starting APs and SPs for all characters are 360AP and 500SP. These amounts can be modified by taking advantages and disadvantages. Buying attributes and skills is a simple 'one for one' process until you reach 70%, when both attributes and skills become more expensive, as shown on the table below:

Skill/Attributes	Cost
70 - 79%	X2
80 - 89%	X3
90 - 100%	X4

Some skills on the Skill Table have the letter 'd' in brackets after them. This means they are difficult to learn, either because of their complexity or rarity. Learning these skills costs 50% more than normal. For example, learning to pilot an ekranoplan is quite a difficult business, so to get a level of 40% in this skill would require the expenditure of 60 skill points.

Certain skills have sub-skills which form part of the whole. On the skill table, these are indicated by being indented under the main skill. If a character wishes to be more specialised in particular areas of a skill, he or she can choose to purchase sub-skills if appropriate. Sub-skills add their level to the main skill when rolling for success in the particular skill area. Sub-skills are purchased at half the cost of normal skills, but can only be taken to half of the level of the main skill. For example, a character has the skill of Unarmed Combat, which means she can punch, kick, grapple, etc. However, the player wants their character to be good at kicking, so decides to spend some SPs buying the Kick sub-skill. With an Unarmed Combat skill of 60%, the character can take Kick up to +30%. So, when in close combat and using a kick, the character (if the maximum level of skill was purchased) could kick with a skill of 90%. All other melee attacks would be at 60%, unless sub-skills in other areas were purchased.

Each skill area has a 'controlling attribute'. This gives an additional bonus when using the skill. This bonus is equal to 10% of the attribute in question. For example, a character with a DEX of 50 and a Pistol skill of 60 would make rolls against a total skill of 65%.

All characters can speak Common at their INT x1.5. Characters from the Lower Middle Class, Upper Middle Class, Nomenklatura, Low Corporate, Median Corporate and High Corporate origins also gain Common (read and write) at a level equal to their INT. Characters from the Dispossessed, Redundant and Drudge origins also gain a base level in the Folklore skill equal to 20% of their INT stat.

character concept

The first and most important stage of character creation is the basic concept. Where is the character from? What do they look like? What is their outlook on life? By answering a series of questions about the character (given below), the player will create a broad picture of what this person is like, making the more number based sections of character creation far easier.

questions to be asked

1) The name, age and sex of the character.

2) What part of The City was the character born in?

3) What social class were the character's parents?

4) What were the character's parents' occupations?

5) What was family life like?

6) Did the character have siblings?

7) Why did your character eventually leave the family home (if at all)?

8) What kind of things did your character learn as a child?

9) What does your character look like?

10) Does your character have any notable physical strengths or weaknesses?

11) Does your character have any notable mental strengths or weaknesses?

12) What does your character do for a living?

13) What kind of training (if any) has your character received?

14) What are your character's main goals in life?

15) What motivates the character?

16) Are there any particular traits which the character respects/dislikes in people?

17) Does the character have any close friends, dependants etc?

advantages and disadvantages

In order to make a character more rounded and realistic, a player can choose to have a number of advantages and disadvantages for their character. These can be physical, mental, monetary, social etc. All will have an effect on the character's life and the course of the game at some point.

Advantages are purchased using either attribute or skill points, depending on what particular advantage is chosen. Disadvantages give points back into the attribute or skill point pools, either balancing out advantages or giving increased points to spend on attributes or skills. The GM has the final say on how many advantages and disadvantages characters may have. As each character starts with 360 attribute points and 500 skill points, players can choose to have characters with many advantages and few disadvantages, but who are slightly lacking in skills or attributes. Conversely, a player could take many disadvantages and few advantages, thus giving the character bonuses in skills and attributes.

age

Age has a definite effect on the skills and abilities of a character. Older characters may have great knowledge and skills, but may be slightly less able physically. Characters who are very young will have lesser skills, knowledge and attributes, but their ages gives many advantages.

Age	AP/SP
5-12	-150/-200
13-17	-50/-80
18-25	+40/-50
26-35	+0/+0
36-45	-40/+50
46-60	-80/+100
60+	-100/+150

contact

A contact can range from a casual acquaintance, right up to a lifelong friend who would gladly give their life for the character. There are three grades of contact: Minor, Moderate and Major. Minor contacts will pass over titbits of information, find out the 'word on the street' etc. Moderate contacts will carry out tasks which involve some small risk to themselves. Major contacts would do almost anything for the character. This is not to be taken as carte blanche to use major contacts as cannon fodder. These are friends, who have built up trust or a strong professional relationship over many years. Their friendship is not to be taken lightly. Very few people would have more than two or three major contacts.

Minor:	-05 AP or SP
Moderate:	-10 AP or SP
Major:	-20 AP or SP

enemy

Someone or something out there doesn't like you. As with contacts, there are three grades of enemy: Minor, Moderate and Major. Minor enemies merely dislike you and may, on occasion, take action to disrupt what you are doing or cause you minor harm. Moderate enemies would actively like to see you harmed, put out of business, jailed or otherwise inconvenienced in a serious way. Major enemies want to see you dead, crippled or incarcerated for life. Major enemies should not be taken lightly.

Minor:	+05 AP or SP
Moderate:	+10 AP or SP
Major:	+20 AP or SP

fame

Hey, you're famous! At least, to a greater or lesser extent. You might be a Lostfinder who is well known and respected in her local area. Or, you could be a Class A ekranoplan pilot, known across The City and admired by millions. Fame runs from Minor (a single burgh or parish), through Moderate (several burghs or parishes) to Major (city-wide). Fame can also act only within a certain culture, society or group of people. Fame which is specific to a single group comes at half cost.

Minor:	-05 AP or SP
Moderate:	-10 AP or SP
Major:	-15 AP or SP

infamy

Hey, you're infamous! This can be just as widespread and talked about as fame, but a lot more sinister. Infamy comes about because you've done (or are rumoured to have done) something bad, or possibly downright evil. Whether this is true or false is up to the player and GM, but mud sticks and an infamous reputation is hard to get rid of. Like fame, infamy runs from Minor (a single burgh or parish), through Moderate (several burghs or parishes) to Major (city-wide). Infamy can also act only within a certain culture, society or group of people. Infamy which is specific to a single group gives only half of the normal additional points (rounded down).

Minor:	+05 AP or SP
Moderate:	+10 AP or SP
Major:	+15 AP or SP

mental advantage

As the name would suggest, mental advantages are mental traits which allow the character to function that little bit better in a certain area. Examples include better memory than most, the ability to concentrate harder and for longer periods of time or a natural talent with languages and dialects. The examples given below are by no means exhaustive and GMs should feel free to add their own as and when necessary. Unlike mental disadvantages, mental advantages are not rated. You have the advantage or you don't. When appropriate, a mental advantage gives a +10% skill or attribute bonus in an applicable situation.

Examples:

Charming	Concentration
Eidetic Memory	Empathy
Extreme Patience	Mental Calculator
Pain Tolerance	Perceptive

Cost:	-10AP

mental disadvantage

Mental disadvantages come in many shapes and forms, from being mildly impatient to outright psychosis. All mental disadvantages are rated as Minor, Moderate or Major. The actual points a character gains for taking specific types of advantage are given below. Major mental disadvantages should not be taken lightly, as they can represent extreme mental illness and psychosis.

Examples:

Arrogance	Big Mouth
Combat Fatigue	Flashbacks
Impatient	Low Pain Tolerance
Nightmares	Phobia
Psychosis	Shy

Minor:	+05 AP
Moderate:	+10AP
Major:	+15AP

physical advantage

A Physical Advantage represents some 'edge' that the character has over your average human being. Physical advantages are things which are not represented wholly by attributes. For example, just being 'strong' would not be a physical attribute, as this could be represented simply by the Strength attribute. However, 'strong grip' could be a physical advantage, representing strength in a particular area. A physical advantage can be either Minor, Moderate or Major. A Minor advantage confers a bonus of +5% to the appropriate attribute when in use, a Moderate advantage confers a +10% bonus and a Major advantage confers a +20% bonus.

Sample advantages are shown below.

Examples:

Ambidextrous (-10AP)	Balance
Good Hearing	Good Sight
Good Speaking Voice	Handsome
Sound Sleeper	Strong Grip

Minor:	-03AP
Moderate:	-08AP
Major:	-15AP

physical disadvantage

A physical disadvantage is some form of limitation which will affect the character's actions at some point in their daily life. Some are barely noticeable (such as wearing spectacles) while others may be very obvious (such as having no legs). Physical disadvantages are rated as Minor, Moderate or Major. Minor disadvantages are almost unnoticeable and will not affect the character too much. However, a major disadvantage is extremely noticeable and/or limiting. For example, a Minor Disadvantage of Bad Sight may result in the character wearing spectacles. However, a Major Disadvantage in Bad Sight would result in the character being near blind or totally blind.

Examples:

Addict	Allergy
Bad Hearing	Bad Sight
Bad Sleeper	Bad Speech
Disfigured	Illness
Injury	Ugly

Minor:	+05 AP or SP
Moderate:	+10AP or SP
Major:	+15AP or SP

poverty

Many people in The City live in conditions of extreme poverty, earning way below the average wage of £5 per week. Players can choose to have their characters live in penurious circumstances in order to increase the number of APs or SPs they have to spend. Minor poverty reduces the characters starting Wealth Level by 1, Moderate poverty

reduces the characters starting Wealth Level by 3 and Major poverty reduces the characters starting wealth level by 5. However, the lowest the Wealth Level can go is 1, characters cannot take a Poverty disadvantage which would reduce their Wealth Level below 1.

Minor:	+05 AP or SP
Moderate:	+10AP or SP
Major:	+20AP or SP

wealth

In direct opposition to the Poverty disadvantage, the Wealth advantage assumes that the character has been particularly successful in their career, business dealings, inheritance or whatever. Minor wealth increases the characters starting Wealth Level by 1, Moderate wealth increases the characters starting wealth level by 2 and Major wealth increases the characters starting Wealth Level by 3. No characters can start with a Wealth Level greater than 10.

Minor:	-05AP or SP
Moderate:	-15AP or SP
Major:	-30AP or SP

origin

Origin tells you what kind of family your character comes from. This should be firmly based in the Character Concept and reflect the answers given by the player. Each different origin offers the character a choice of certain skills. The player can choose to purchase two, all, or any number in between of these skills for their character. However, no starting skill may be greater than 20%. The player has 40 skill points (not part of the starting total of skill points) to spend on Origin skills.

Each origin also confers a bonus in one or more attributes. For example, someone with the Drudge origin would receive a bonus of +10% to STR.

dispossessed

The lowest of the low. Dispossessed is an origin where characters are born into the serried ranks of the homeless that inhabit The City. It is a rough upbringing that teaches you to look after yourself, sure as hell no one else will.

Skill Picks: Armed Combat, Unarmed Combat, Sneak, Folklore, Foraging, Fast-talk.

Bonus: +10 AWR

redundant

Lucky enough to have a place to live but not lucky enough to have a job, the redundant are a step above the dispossessed, but only just.

Skill Picks: Unarmed Combat, Mechanics, Folklore, Foraging, Economics.

Bonus: +10 AWR

drudge

Born into a family which slaves through a life of hard, manual work. Most of the drudge class work for the lowest echelons of monolithic corporate organisations.

Skill Picks: Unarmed Combat, Mechanics, Machinist, Electrician, Folklore, any Trades skill.

Bonus: +10 STR

middle class, lower

Mildly affluent, the lower middle classes are made up of shop owners, small businessmen and the lower ranking professionals. Their life is not extravagant but they are comfortable in their situation.

Skill Picks: Mechanical Computing, Economics, Writing, Ground Vehicles, Bureaucracy.

Bonus: +10 WIL

middle class, upper

Professionals, skilled tradesmen and the owners of mini or microcorps go towards making up the majority of the upper middle classes in The City.

Skill Picks: Negotiation, Economics, Diplomacy, Bureaucracy, Writing.

Bonus: +10 WIL

nomenklatura

The nomenklatura are respected professionals of high rank or those who have been born into inherited wealth. They are the cream of non-corporate society in The City.

Skill Picks: Act, Diplomacy, History, Politics, Economics.

Bonus: +10 PER

low corporate

Perhaps skilled tradesmen or lower echelon managerial staff, low corporates have security and a regular wage, which is more than many can boast.

Skill Picks: Mechanical Computing, One Trades or Scientific skill, Ground Vehicles, Persuasion.

Bonus: +10 WIL

median corporate

The people who truly run the corporate monsters, they live comfortable lives, mostly secluded from the rough and tumble of the city streets.

Skill Picks: 2 Scientific, Trades or Administrative skills, Mechanical Computing, Negotiation, Persuasion.

Bonus: +10 HLT

high corporate

The very top echelons of corporate society, an individual born into this stratum of society can expect a life of luxury and privilege unparalleled anywhere else in the City.

Skill Picks: 3 Scientific or 3 Academic skills, Act, Diplomacy.

Bonus: +10 HLT and +10 PER

upbringing

Again, this is a choice which the player must make based on answers given during the creation of the character concept. The player may only choose one upbringing, and this choice is influenced by the origin of the character. The 'Available To:' line under the title of the upbringing shows which origins can have this type of upbringing. For example, someone with a dispossessed origin, could not choose the Academic upbringing, as this is only available to the Upper Middle Class, Nomenklatura, Low Corporate, Median Corporate and High Corporate. However, the player, in consultation with the GM, can choose an upbringing which is not normally allowed by the origin, if the character concept warrants it.

As for the origin, upbringing bestows certain extra skills on the character. The player can choose to purchase two, all, or any number in between of these skills for their character. However, no starting skill may be greater than 20%. The player has 40 skill points (not part of the starting total of skills points) to spend on upbringing skills.

academic

Available To: Upper Middle Class, Nomenklatura, Low Corporate, Median Corporate, High Corporate.

Skill Picks: Any 4 Scientific and Academic skills, Writing.

apprenticed

Available To: Dispossessed, Redundant, Drudge, Lower Middle Class, Low Corporate.

Skill Picks: Any Trades skill, Economics, Mechanical Computing, Ground Vehicles or Water Vehicles.

Corporate (MacroCorp or Smaller Business)

Available To: Low Corporate, Median Corporate, High Corporate.
Skill Picks: Economics, Writing, Law, Diplomacy, Act.

Criminal

Available To: All.
Skill Picks: Pistol, Unarmed Combat, Sneak, Fast-talk, Criminal Culture.

Dangerous

Available To: Dispossessed, Redundant, Drudge, Lower Middle Class, Low Corporate.
Skill Picks: Pistol, Armed Combat, Unarmed Combat, Tracking, Tactics.

Independently Minded

Available To: All.
Skill Picks: Unarmed Combat, Negotiation, Psychology, Economics, any Trades skill.

Militaristic

Available To: All.
Skill Picks: Longarm, Armed Combat, Ground Vehicles, Unarmed Combat, Tactics.

Minority Group

Available To: All.
Skill Picks: Unarmed Combat, Act, Diplomacy, Negotiation, Running, Hide.

Political

Available To: Upper Middle Class, Nomenklatura, Median Corporate, High Corporate.
Skill Picks: Writing, Economics, Politics, Psychology, Act.

Poor

Available To: Dispossessed, Redundant, Drudge.
Skill Picks: Foraging, Economics, Unarmed Combat, First Aid, Negotiation.

Religious

Available To: All.
Skill Picks: Theology, Psychology, Oration, Writing, History (Own Religion)

Sheltered Life

Available To: All.
Skill Picks: Any 2 Scientific or Academic skills, First Aid, Writing, Musical Instrument.

Transient or Nomad

Available To: Dispossessed, Redundant, Drudge.
Skill Picks: Ground or Water Vehicles, Foraging, Fishing, First Aid, Negotiation, Persuasion.

Wealthy

Available To: Upper Middle Class, Nomenklatura, Median Corporate, High Corporate.
Skill Picks: Economics, History, Musical Instrument, Bureaucracy, Diplomacy.

Types of Character in the City

This particular section outlines different types of character which can be found in The City. Each character type gives a brief description of the essentials of the character, as well as listing some recommended skills for that particular type. However, everyone is an individual, and these are merely guidelines. A player may think that the ghostfighter is a great character type, but wants something a little different. So, they may decide that instead of using knives, their ghostfighter only uses blunt weapons such as clubs, nightsticks or coshes. This is only a small change to the character type, but serves to make it unique. Character type also has an influence on the starting wealth for the character. This is explained further in the section entitled 'Starting Wealth'.

Activist

The scent of power lures many into the shady, shadowy world of local politics. The many and varied burgh and parish councils, local committees and advisory boards are always stocked with the ambitious, the cunning, the concerned and the glory seeking. People come into politics for different reasons. Some would seek to make things better for their fellow citizens, some merely do it in order to exercise some feeble and meaningless power over others, whilst others use it as a means of making a living via graft and corruption. Whatever their reasons, Activists are all strongly motivated, forceful individuals.

Recommended Skills: Bureaucracy, Diplomacy, Oration, Negotiation, Persuasion, Act, Fast-talk.
Resource: A small office (either owned or rented), typewriter and printing press.
Wealth Level: 6

antiquities hunter

Layers of history lie beneath The City. In dusty libraries and dank archives, stores of information wait to be uncovered. In musty lofts and attics, venerable artworks hang unappreciated and unwanted. Yet, there are always those willing to pay for an item, no matter how hard it may be to track down. To pay someone to discover whether or not a folktale or legend is true. This is where antiquities hunters come in. Specialists in tracking down that which has been lost for years, decades or even centuries. Antiquities hunters must have the investigative skills of a lostfinder, the tenacity of a stringer and the hardiness of a flowghost. Tracking leads and myths in half-forgotten libraries. Clambering through disused tunnels and vaults. Wresting items from the hands of those who would rather not let go. The life of a hunter is hard, but the rewards can be huge.

Recommended Skills: Armed Combat, Archaeology, Climbing, Criminal Culture, Folklore, History, Investigation, Negotiation, Pistol
Resource: Collection of notes on folklore and history, archaeological equipment and a strong will!
Wealth Level: 3 to 9

artist

Some are drawn to art as an escape from the drab and depressing environment of The City. Others feel the need to create well up from inside them, as an expression of man's creativity. Others just do it to make money. Regardless of their reasons, there are many artists in The City, poets, musicians, painters, sculptors, composers and so on. The majority scratch away in dim garret rooms, dreaming of patronage and fame, whilst the lucky few live in opulent surroundings, reaping the benefits of obtaining a wealthy patron. All look forward to the day that their work is recognised and revered by the populace of The City.

Specialisations: Composer, Musician, Painter, Poet, Sculptor, Writer
Recommended Skills: Artistic skill depending of specialisation, Economics, Diplomacy, Negotiation
Resource: Varies widely according to what the artist does, their level of fame etc. The GM should make a decision based upon the rest of the character creation process.
Wealth Level: 1 to 9

clergy

For the millions who seek solace in religion, the clergy are their spiritual and moral leaders, passing on the word of God (or Gods) to the masses of the laity. From the rigid, dour priests of the Third Church of God the Architect to the voluble, demonstrative orators of The Shining Sky, many tend to the welfare of their flock and to the survival of their religion with great devotion. However, some slip from the true path and become more self serving, more interested in worldly possessions and physical pleasures than inner piety. Members of the clergy can vary between these extremes, often exhibiting a pragmatic view of life, counselling where necessary and holding their tongues as the occasion demands.

Recommended Skills: Psychology, Theology, Music, Writing, Oration, Persuasion, Folklore.
Resource: Holy items and garb.
Wealth Level: 1 to 5

criminal

If there is one thing that The City has more than enough of, it's criminals. From the common cutpurse working the canalsides and back alleys to the heads of the massive organised crime syndicates, they all contribute to the criminal culture of The City. In many ways, the vast majority of The City's population are criminals in one way or the other. However, to actually make a living through a life of crime requires a special mindset and a particular kind of person.

Specialisations: Ganger, Scrounger/Scavenger, Fence, Crook, Cutpurse.
Recommended Skills: Unarmed Combat, Armed Combat, Running, Persuasion, Act, Hide, Sneak, Criminal Culture.
Resource: Varies, from a bludgeon to an entire gang.
Wealth Level: 1 to 9

driver

Transport is vital in The City, whether it be via the stinking, teeming canals or through the winding, narrow streets. Many of The City's residents earn a living transporting people and produce from one place to another. Such characters tend to have a good knowledge of the areas they work in, where and where not to go, who to speak to for 'specialist' goods and a never ending supply of local gossip. Some travel all over The City and can profess knowledge of large chunks of the crushing urban sprawl. However, most are content to ply their trade within one or two burghs.

Specialisations: Rickshaw Driver, Taxi Driver, Aerostat Pilot.
Recommended Skills: Appropriate Vehicle skill, Mechanics, Electrician, Folklore, Machinist.
Resource: Generally a lot of fellow feeling exists amongst drivers of a particular type and a character may be able to call upon the aid of his fellow drivers at some point.
Wealth Level: 2 to 5

entrepreneur

Small businessmen and women, shopowners and traders: they represent the most basic level in the economic life of The City. The entrepreneur can vary from the settled stallholder, who inherited his pitch from parents or grandparents, to a thrusting young go-getter who firmly believes her schemes and dealings will one day challenge the might of the macro-corps. Whatever goods they deal in and whatever methods they choose to make a living, entrepreneurs must be loquacious salesmen and steely-eyed negotiators.

Recommended Skills: Mechanical Computing, Economics, Bureaucracy, Negotiation, Persuasion, Bribery, Fast-talk.
Resource: Depending on the kind of business and the success it has achieved, the entrepreneur may have anything from a small tray around his neck to substantial business premises.
Wealth Level: 2 to 7

flowghost

Prowling the pathways of the Dataflow, the calling of the Flowghost is a dangerous one. Nobody likes their information being stolen and some groups will pay Flowghosts back with the proverbial six inches of steel. Incompetent Flowghosts, therefore, are few and far between. Skilled in cryptology, mathematics and the science of The Dataflow, they are adept at using both dingin and electronic computer systems to trawl the vast pool of information, cutting into secure systems and extracting the juiciest morsels. Unlike netrunners, matrix jockeys and hackers in other game settings, Flowghosts are more closely related to cryptographers and codebreakers than to the prototypical cyberspace cowboy. Such is the nature of the Dataflow and so widespread the use of mechanical dingins, that having a bank of programs ready to assault a datacore is just not enough. Careful perception, skilled manipulation and intelligent application of mathematics will see the successful 'ghost through. There is no 'jacking in' and perceiving the Dataflow as a 360 degree simulation. Flowghosts must observe what happens on screens, tanks or mechanical displays, listening to sounds through headphones, handsets or speakers. The skill of Dataflow Perception is not easily picked up and takes a lot of trial and error. Simple visual cues are not enough, the successful Flowghost must listen, observe and often act on instinct and intuition.

Recommended Skills: Dataflow Perception, Mathematics, Cryptography, Electrician, Mechanics, Dinginsmith, Mechanical Computing, Investigation.
Resource: Microscale dingin and peripherals.
Wealth Level: 7

ghostfighter

The ghostfighters of The City are a breed apart from the common guffer or militant trooper, having honed their skills in knife fighting and stealthy attack to a remarkable degree. The most talented of ghostfighters are prosperous and in demand. Untalented ghostfighters are dead.

A ghostfighter is quite simply an individual who has trained themselves to a high degree of expertise in stealth, infiltration and armed combat. Do not make the mistake of thinking that they are assassins. They are stand up fighters, preferring to look their enemy straight in the face before delivering the killer strike. Many notable figures employ a ghostfighter or two as unobtrusive bodyguards at exorbitant prices.

Recommended Skills: Unarmed Combat, Armed Combat, Thrown Weapon, Tactics, Running, Climbing, Hide, Sneak, Shadow, Tracking.
Resource: 2 melee weapons
Wealth Level: 6

jake

Bundles of rags huddled in a shop doorway, soaking figures slumped by the side of a canal, crouching shapes sheltering in wrecked barges. The jakes are the street dwellers of The City, tramps and beggars ignored by the vast majority of the population. The overwhelming majority beg for a living, while some turn to petty crime in order to have enough money to buy food, booze or drugs. Living in squalor, jakes are often riddled with disease and parasitic infections, wracked by the side effects of cheap drugs or bad drink. It's a hard life on the streets: no one turns to help his fellow man and the only rule is that the one person you can trust is you.

Recommended Skills: Sneak, Hide, Persuasion, Fast-talk, Criminal Culture, Folklore, Foraging, Fishing.
Resource: Very little other than a few shabby personal possessions and some ragged clothes.
Wealth Level: 1

labour

The toiling masses of The City. Labourers struggle in the factories, mills, and works. They scrabble in mines, unload cargo and construct new buildings. Being a labourer is a harsh, rough, unyielding lifestyle which offers little reward for hours of toil. Many members of the labouring classes supplement their meagre income through petty crime or some kind of shady second job. Labourers in the employ of the macrocorps fare slightly (only slightly, mind you) better than their fellows working for smaller companies or local councils.

Specialisations: Factory Worker, Labourer, Construction Worker.
Recommended Skills: Unarmed Combat, Machinist, Drinking, Folklore, Bureaucracy, Criminal Culture, Mechanics.
Resource: The resources available to the common labourer are understandably limited. They may have a few tools, specialised working clothes, etc.
Wealth Level: 2 to 4

law enforcer

The streets and canals of The City are riddled with crime and corruption. Someone must protect the citizenry from the predations of the criminal classes. Unfortunately, the very people charged with upholding laws are often guilty of lawbreaking themselves. Law enforcers range from the Provosts of the Three Canals Metropolitan Area, down to scops employed by the private security companies. Most feared of all law enforcers in The City are the Transit Militia, who guard the tracks, trains and stations of the ageing, crumbling railway network.

Specialisations: Provost, Scop, Transit Militia.
Recommended Skills: Pistol, Armed Combat, Unarmed Combat, Investigation, Negotiation, Forensics, Shadow, Criminal Culture.
Resource: A gun, a badge and a cynical attitude.
Wealth Level: 5

lostfinder

Seekers, searchers, investigators. Lostfinders take a quasi-mystical approach to their work, seeking to be in harmony with The City and its people in order to better carry out their chosen tasks. As a result of this, Lostfinders will never accept payment in cash, only in kind or in the form of simple goodwill. An investigation of weeks into the disappearance of a child may result in no more payment than a hot meal and the long-lasting thanks of a poor family. In the parish or burgh where they work, Lostfinders are often figures of respect, trusted by the community for their altruistic efforts to help others. It is a foolish person, however, who betrays the trust of a Lostfinder. For not only will they incur they anger of an individual, they will incur the wrath of the entire community. Such is the place of the Lostfinder, a semi-religious force for good in a dark place.

Recommended Skills: Investigation, Law, Diplomacy, Negotiation, Shadow, Forensics, Criminal Culture.
Resource: The goodwill of community is a resource not to be underestimated.
Wealth Level: 2

mapmaker

Deals must be done and bargains must be struck. But what if two parties are unwilling or unable to make contact, to be seen speaking with a mortal enemy. This is where the mapmakers come in. An in dispensable part of the criminal culture of The City, mapmakers organise deals, act as intermediaries and arbitrators between the factionalised and fractious criminal elements. Always careful to rigorously maintain their independence, they take a reasonable percentage of any deal they help to broker or ask a simple flat fee for arranging meetings or transferring messages. They walk a quaking tightrope between violently aggressive organisations, maintaining a careful balancing act, to ever avoid dropping into the abyss.

Recommended Skills: Bribery, Criminal Culture, Economics, Fast Talk,

Negotiation, Persuasion, Politics, Psychology.
Resource: 3 Minor (Criminal) contacts.
Wealth Level: Depending on reputation and success, between 3 and 8.

Medical

Medicine in The City is truly a fractured thing. The majority of the population go without organised medical facilities, either looking after themselves or paying exorbitant amounts to private medical centres. In the domains of the macrocorps, medical science is at its most advanced. Treatments regarded with a reverential awe by the general populace are handed out with dull regularity. Longevity, bodily enhancement and perfect health are all within the scope of the services provided by the macrocorps. Those who toil in the factories receive somewhat lesser medical care, which amounts to not much more than first aid. Some have chosen to wander the streets, dispensing aid to the needy, in return for food or a bed for the night. These are the streethealers, wandering doctors who tramp the lanes of The City or travel along its canals practising their craft.

Specialisations: Doctor, Medic, Streethealer.
Recommended Skills: First Aid, General Medicine, Pharmacology, Surgery, Diplomacy, Persuasion, Biology, Chemistry.
Resource: Medical equipment appropriate to the sophistication and status of the character.
Wealth Level: 1 to 7

Military

From the sparklock wielding militia of the Third Church to the armoured fist of Arclight's Tentenel troopers, military forces across The City vary widely in their training, skill and level of equipment. However, all share a broad ethos and similar battlefield techniques. Many people in The City have had experience with weapons at some point in their lives, but the military or former military character has been extensively trained in weapons, tactics and military procedure. In hitech forces, there are also vehicular forces, such as the armoured divisions of the Red Canal Collectivist Republic.

Specialisations: Third Church Lay Reserves Martial, Arclight Brigade of Light, Gorunna Internal Order Cadre, Trilhoeven Militia, RCCR Peoples Guards.
Recommended Skills (infantry): Longarm, Armed Combat, Tactics, Thrown Weapon, Demolition, Running, First Aid, Hide, Orienteering.
Recommended Skills (armoured): Pistol, Tactics, Mechanical Computing, Mechanics, Ground Vehicles, Vehicular Weapons.

Resource: Serving military personal will have access to a range of equipment appropriate to the technological level and wealth of the organisation which they serve. Ex-military characters will have a few bits and pieces left over from their service, maybe a sidearm, a few bits of armour, a helmet or other non-combat items of kit.
Wealth Level: 1 to 8, depending on rank and organisation.

Mikefighter Pilot (ex)

"One centimetre too tall, one kilo too heavy". So runs the credo of the former Mikefighter pilots. Most have finished their careers by the time they are sixteen, if they are lucky. Once they are too tall or too heavy for maximum combat efficiency, they get thrown out by their corporate masters, out onto the streets where they must use their skills as best they can. Even aged sixteen, most ex-mikefighter pilots are combat hardened veterans, carrying a casual contempt for life and limb. Despite being skilled pilots, they often find it difficult to find work. Getting a job as an aerostat pilot is prized, but rare. Most live out their lives in criminal activities, never to take to the air again.

Recommended Skills: Pistol, Unarmed Combat, Tactics, Air Vehicles, Vehicular Weapons, Navigation.
Resource: Flight suit, small handgun.
Wealth Level: 3

Mudlark

Also known as Bankers, Canal Rakers and Dockers, Mudlarks are specialists at loading and unloading barges, rigging lines and dredging the canals. Many are transient, moving from place to place as work varies. Unlike nomads, they may stay in one place for long periods of time, becoming established in a burgh before moving on. Others live by the same canal their entire lives, with entire families working in the same business. Often, they can be found in small boats, dredging the canals for saleable items, for silt and trash to sell as fertiliser or simply to keep the waterways open. Many use primitive, home made diving suits and hand cranked air pumps to scour the canal bottoms for anything of value. The life of the mudlark is a hard one, full of dangerous work, hard drinking and brutal fighting.

Recommended Skills: Armed Combat, Drinking, First Aid, Fishing, Folklore, Mechanics, Navigation, Negotiation, Unarmed Combat, Water Vehicles.
Resource: Sometimes a small boat and accoutrements, most often a knife, boathook or pike and some rough, hard wearing clothes.
Wealth Level: 2 to 4

nomad

Nomads wander the canals and streets, having chosen a life without a permanent home, rather than having the existence thrust upon them like a jake. All their worldly possession are carried in a pack, a carpetbag or some other easily carried piece of luggage. Due to their wide-ranging travels, nomads are experienced in the many diverse cultures of The City and often have an excellent grasp of idiosyncratic local laws and customs which could catch the unwary by surprise.

Recommended Skills: Longarm, Unarmed Combat, Mechanics, Fish Farming, Folklore, Negotiation, Water Vehicles, Orienteering, Navigation.
Resource: Small boat (if waterbourne), bundle of possessions (bedroll, cooking pan, oil stove, etc.)
Wealth Level: 3

scientist

Whether they be experimenting in pristine white clean rooms or dissecting a mutated fish in a dingy garret room, scientists throughout The City all share a passion for research and the advancement of knowledge. Sometimes, this is perverted for their, or their employer's, ends, resulting in horrific experiments or dubious technological 'advances'. The life of a scientist can range from one of great wealth and prestige to an existence little better than that of a jake. Great discoveries tend to go unnoticed when the discoverer dies of alcohol poisoning, slumped in a urine soaked alley.

Recommended Skills: Electronic Computing, Mechanical Computing, Investigation, Writing, Biology, Chemistry, Physics, Bureaucracy, Pharmacology.
Resource: Lab (standard of which depends on the reputation, status and wealth of the character).
Wealth Level: 2 to 8

sportsman

Famous sportsmen are the true heroes of The City. Top ekranoplan pilots, elite cripplecut players and the best cardsharps are all lauded and admired by the serried ranks of the population. However, very few ever reach this level of fame, wealth and adulation. The majority of sportsmen and women live a hand to mouth existence, often labouring to supplement their meagre sporting incomes. Few live to see middle age, piloting infeasably dangerous ramshackle ekranoplans or fighting in disorganised and bloody cripplecut pits.

Specialisations: Ekranoplan racer, cripplecut fighter.
Recommended Skills: Armed Combat, First Aid, Negotiation, Running, Swimming, Unarmed Combat.
Resource: Depends entirely on which sport the character competes in. For a cripplecut fighter, it might be some knives and body armour.
Wealth Level: 3 to 9

stringer

Digging in the dirt for juicy stories, stringers are the lowest level of the media system which encompasses The City. Some are crusading journalists, out to expose the cruelties of the macrocorps or the schemings of the crime syndicates. others are simply greasy hacks looking of a titillating bit of gossip that they can sell to a newswire for a few shillings. All Stringers are skilled at wheedling information out of people, putting two and two together (often arriving at a figure of five), watching, waiting and following.

The average citizen has an intense dislike of stringers, viewing them as parasites trying to burrow under their skin. The only hope for many stringers is that one day they will be taken on by the vast empire of Sideband Media, where a comfortable office, regular pay and the admiration of one's peers awaits.

Recommended Skills: Investigation, Politics, Writing, Bureaucracy, Negotiation, Persuasion, Act, Disguise, Shadow, Fast-talk, Folklore.
Resource: Notepads and pencils, recording device of some kind.
Wealth Level: 3

technical

Vital to the continuing existence of The City, technically skilled (and often not so skilled) personnel maintain the lights, trains, water supplies, cablecars, canal locks, trams, televisions and all the other parts of the infrastructure which make life possible. The range of skills, expertise and motivation are understandably highly varied, ranging from ill-paid, under-supported technician maintaining a shoddy, leaking local gas supply to inspired architects dreaming up bold new designs for wealthy citizens.

Specialisations: Fulgurator, Mechanic, Technician, Inventor, Architect, Engineer, Artisan.
Recommended Skills: Scientific, Trades and Technical skills as appropriate, Writing, Mechanical Computing, Draw, Bureaucracy.
Resource: Very varied. A lowly maintenance worker may get by with a bag of tools, an engineer may have a studio filled with drafting boards, modelling tables and suchlike.
Wealth Level: 3 to 9

starting wealth

Each character has certain amount of money to begin with, representing cash on hand, savings, property etc. There can be wide variations in this, according to social status, occupation etc. Each character profession has a Wealth Level. This level is cross referenced with a D10 roll on the table below to find out how much wealth the character starts with. Some professions have a range of Wealth Levels. It is up to the GM to decide which level within the range to use, according to the fame, skill or otherwise of the character in question. Wealth Level can also be modified by the Wealth advantage from the 'Advantages and Disadvantages' section.

rounding out the character

Rounding out the character is simply a matter of defining various secondary attributes and deciding on such things as height, weight, hair colour, etc (taking into account the answers given when deciding the basic character concept). The secondary attributes are as follows:

Reaction (REA)

Reaction is found by taking the average of Awareness, Intelligence and Agility, rounding down if the number has a fraction below 0.5 and rounding up if the number has a fraction of 0.5 or above.

Resilience (RES)

This is the character's resistance to injury and disease. Resilience is found by dividing Health by 10 , rounding down if the number has a fraction below 0.5, rounding up if the number has a fraction of 0.5 or above.

Encumbrance (ENC)

The maximum weight (in kilos) a character can carry before he or she starts to feel weighed down and have his or her actions slowed. Encumbrance is found by dividing Strength by two.

Kick Damage

The damage a character can do with a kick equals STR/15.

Punch Damage

The damage a character can do with a punch equals STR/20.

example of character generation

The following example leads you through the character creation process in order to illustrate how a typical character is created.

Firstly, in conjunction with the GM , the player should go through the list of questions given under 'Character Concept' in order to come up with a basic idea for the character.

Roll	1	2	3	4	5	6	7	8	9	10
Wealth										
1	£0	£0.05s	£0.10s	£1	£1.10s	£2	£2.10s	£3	£3.10s	£4
2	£1	£2	£3	£4	£5	£6	£7	£8	£9	£10
3	£5	£8	£11	£14	£17	£20	£23	£26	£29	£32
4	£8	£12	£16	£20	£24	£28	£32	£36	£40	£44
5	£10	£15	£20	£25	£30	£35	£40	£45	£50	£55
6	£20	£30	£40	£50	£60	£70	£80	£90	£100	£110
7	£40	£60	£80	£100	£120	£140	£160	£180	£200	£220
8	£60	£100	£140	£180	£220	£260	£300	£340	£380	£420
9	£100	£200	£300	£400	£500	£600	£700	£800	£900	£1000
10	£1000	£2000	£4000	£6000	£8000	£10,000	£15,000	£20,000	£25,000	£30,000

Character Concept

Name, age and sex
Andy, the player, decides that his character will be called Camden Derr, be 36 years of age and male.

What part of The City was the character born in?
Looking through 'The Place', Andy decides that he wants Derr to come from a fairly rough background and so chooses Bankside, one of the roughest spots in The City!

What social class were the characters parents?
What were their occupations?: Given that he was born in Bankside, Derr is unlikely to come from a wealthy nomenklatura family. So, Andy decides that his parents both were self-employed, running a small blacksmithing workshop in the depths of Bankside. While they work with their hands, they are skilled tradesmen and respected by others in the community.

What was family life like?
Thinking on this, Andy decides that Derr's family life was hard but fair. The family were poor but his parents were not unduly harsh or uncaring.

Did the character have any siblings?
Yes, Derr had a younger brother and a younger sister.

Why did your character eventually leave the family home (if at all)?
Derr chose to leave home because of his desire to be an ekranoplan pilot! Andy has decided at this early stage that this is the driving force in Derr's life. He saw illegal ekranoplan races as a child and was enthralled by the speed and glamour. Age fifteen, he ran away from his parents to seek his fortune as a racer!

What kind of things did your character learn as a child?
Given his parents jobs, Derr obviously learnt a bit about metalworking, machining and other basic mechanical tasks.

What does the character look like?
Andy has a think about what Camden Derr might look like and settles on the following description: He is of average height (5' 10") and fairly wiry build. He has rough, callused hands, dark blue eyes, straggly black hair and some old, but fairly severe, burn scars on his upper torso and face.

Does the character have any notable physical strengths or weaknesses?
Andy chooses not to highlight any particular part of Derr for attention here.

Does the character have any notable metal strengths or weaknesses?
Derr doesn't suffer fools gladly and can be fairly obstinate when he wants to be. However, he is pretty strong willed and not easily intimidated by threats of force or violence.

What does the character do for a living?
As mentioned above, Derr ran away from home to become an ekranoplan racer. But Andy wants to make him a bit more interesting than this, so plumps for a fairly tortuous career path. After blagging his way into a small Limited Class team as general dogsbody and tool-carrier, he learns a bit about repairing and maintaining ekranoplans. Eventually he is allowed a race and shows a certain aptitude for piloting. After a few successful races and a couple of wins, he is spotted by the Hirplakker Speed Division and snatched away from his old team with offers of money, women and glory. His career is disastrously short. After a couple of successful trial runs and low-level races for HSD, he is entered in the Grand Canal 2000 as the 3rd pilot in the team. He crashes. Badly, taking out another HSD ship and a couple of other ekranoplans, handing victory to Darrat-Emvax. Finding himself fired and out on the street, he attempts to scratch a living doing odd jobs. After a while, he ends up back in his old home of Bankside, working out of a canalside workshop, gradually improving his skills.

Now, age 36, he has a thriving business in Bankside, fixing failing mechanical item and fabricating bits and pieces. His main project is building an illegal racing ekranoplan for a local gang who think they can make big money by entering it in races.

What kind of training (if any) has your character received?
The only formal training was some tuition and training whilst a pilot for HSD.

What are the characters main goals in life?
Andy decides that Derrs main goal is to run a successful racing team. While this may not seem likely when working from a run down workshop in one of the worst slums in The City, he's a man with a great amount of hope and optimism.

What motivates the character?
The desire to win and be successful.

Are there any particular traits which the character respects in people?
Thinking on this, Andy decides that Derr respects people who are strong-minded, loyal and honest.

Are there any particular traits which the character dislikes in people?

From the information given above, it's easy to see that Derr dislikes people who are sneaky, liars and the weak-willed.

Does the character have any close friends, dependants, etc?

Andy thinks about all the information on Derr that he's come up with so far and decides that he's not on great terms with his family (who still live in Bankside). The closest Derr has to a dependant is his apprentice at the workshop, a ragged youth whom he took on more out of sympathy than any particular need for an assistant.

So, the basis of the character is already coming together. Andy has come up with a character concept for a man who has seen a bit of life. He's experienced dizzying highs and crushing lows. He's seen the opulent side of The City and the less salubrious side of life. A man with varied skills and a strong sense of purpose, he nonetheless has suffered a few defeats in his time but still harbours a desire to win.

Now that this stage is sorted, Andy can go on to working out Derrs advantages, disadvantages, attributes and skills.

advantages & disadvantages

Looking at the life of Camden Derr so far, Andy decides on the following advantages and disadvantages:

Advantages

Contact, former racing team buddy	(Moderate)	-10SP
Contact, local Bankside gang	(Moderate)	-10SP
Fame	(Minor)	-5SP

Disadvantages

Age:36		-40AP/+50SP
Enemy, former member of HSD team	(Moderate)	+10AP
Enemy, bookmaker	(Minor)	+5AP
Enemy, gang leader	(Minor)	+5AP
Mental Disadvantage, impatient	(Moderate)	+10AP
Mental Disadvantage, obstinate	(Moderate)	+10AP
Physical Disadvantage, bad scarring	(Minor)	+5AP
Poverty	(Minor)	+5AP

Doing a bit of adding up, this gives Derr a total of 370 Attribute Points and 525 Skill Points to play with.

attributes

Andy spends the Attribute Points as follows:

Strength: 55	Cost: 45 (+10 to STR for Origin)
Agility: 35	Cost: 35
Dexterity: 60	Cost: 60
Health: 30	Cost: 30
Awareness: 55	Cost: 55
Intelligence: 50	Cost: 50
Personality: 40	Cost: 40
Willpower: 55	Cost: 55

Now we move on to skills. Firstly, Andy must decide on the Origin and Upbringing of Camden Derr. However, this has pretty much been decided by the answers to the character concept questions.

origin

Given that he grew up in Bankside and his parents were relatively skilled artisans, Derr's origin is Drudge (which, as noted above, gives +10% to STR). From the skill list for Drudge, Andy selected the following skills for Derr:

Electrician	10
Mechanics	10
Machinist	15
Unarmed Combat	5

As he comes from the Drudge origin, Derr also gains Folklore at 10% (20% of his INT).

upbringing

Derr's upbringing was not harsh or brutal, but his parents were firm. Andy therefore selects the Apprenticed upbringing and buys the following skills from the list:

Blacksmith	10
Mechanics	30 (20, plus 10 already gained from Origin)
Water Vehicles	10

So, at the end of the Origin and Upbringing stages of character creation, Camden Derr has the following skills:

Blacksmith	10
Electrician	10
Machinist	15
Mechanics	30
Unarmed Combat	5
Water Vehicles	10

skills

Now Andy gets on to spending the Skill Points that he's accumulated for Camden Derr. Given his upbringing, background, life experience and all the information that came out during the character concept, Andy spends the 525 skill points as follows, taking in to account the skills gained as part of the origin and upbringing stages:

Blacksmithing	25
Common (spoken)	75 (free skill)
Common (written)	50
Commerce (spoken)	50
Criminal Culture	60
Ekranoplan	40
Racing	+20
Electrician	50
Fast Talk	50
First Aid	20
Folklore	10
Machinist	50
Mechanics	60
Negotiation	30
Pistol	20
Swimming	35
Unarmed Combat	30
Water Vehicle	30

rounding out the character

Now that attributes and skills have been purchased, all that remains is to finalise the character and buy some equipment. Derr's secondary attributes work out as follows:

Reaction: 4
(Average of Agility, Awareness and Intelligence, rounded down)

Resilience: 3
(Health divided by ten, rounded down)

Encumbrance: 23kg
(Strength divided by two, rounded down)

Kick Damage: 3
(Strength divided by 15)

Punch Damage: 2
(Strength divided by 20, rounded down)

Consulting with the GM and taking into account the fact that Derr has the Poverty (Minor) disadvantage, Andy rolls for starting wealth. The GM assigns Derr a starting wealth of 5 (which includes the fact that he has a workshop and some tools) but this is reduced to 4 by the Poverty disadvantage. Andy rolls an 8 on a D10 and cross-references this with a wealth level of 4 on the wealth table. He ends up with £36 starting wealth. Spending some money, Derr ends up with the following equipment:

Small workshop	Tools
Medium sparklock pistol	Small skiff

skill descriptions

combat (aimed) - dex

Heavy Weapon: Semi-portable, fixed and support weapons. (Specialisations: Medium Machinegun, Heavy Machinegun, Man Portable Cannon.)

Launcher: Covers the use of all rocket, missile and grenade launchers. (Specialisations: Grenade Launcher, Missile Launcher, Mortar, Rocket Launcher.)

Longarm: The use of all rifles, shotguns and man-portable machineguns. (Specialisations: Crossbow, Light Machinegun, Rifle, Shotgun.)

Pistol: Skill required to use all types of handgun and one handed automatic weapons. (Specialisations: Single-shot, Revolver, Semi-auto, Submachinegun.)

Thrown Weapons: The ability to accurately throw an object is a skill in itself and covers knives, grenades, bolas, axes and any other form of thrown weapon. (Specialisations: Axe, Grenade, Improvised, Knife, Spear/Javelin.)

Vehicular Weapons: Covers the use of any weapons mounted on a vehicle. (Specialisations: Light Weapons, Heavy Weapons, Launchers.)

combat (melee) - agl

Armed Combat: Hand to hand combat using knives, swords, axes, polearms, clubs or any other form of melee weapon. (Specialisations: Axe, Club, Improvised, Knife, Polearm, Sword.)

Unarmed Combat: Utilisation of fists, feet, elbows and other body parts to inflict damage on an opponent. (Specialisations: Block, Grapple, Hold, Kick, Punch, Throw.)

combat (miscellaneous) - int

Command: The ability to command others is a skill harnessed by few but can prove valuable when attempting to control subordinates. Command can be used to control and influence others in a combat situation. How effective this is and how far it can be taken is up to the GM.

Logistics: The supply of combat related materials and associated formations in the field.

Strategy: The use and deployment of large scale military formations in combat.

Tactics: The use and deployment of small units in combat.

combat (aimed) - dex

Heavy Weapons
- HeavyMG
- Man-portable Cannon
- Medium MG

Launcher
- Grenade Launcher
- Missile Launcher
- Mortar
- Rocket Launcher

Longarm
- Crossbow
- Light MG
- Rifle
- Shotgun

Pistol
- Semi-auto
- Single Shot
- SMG
- Revolver

Thrown Weapons
- Axe
- Grenade
- Improvised
- Knife
- Spear/Javelin

Vehicular Weapons
- Heavy Weapon
- Launchers
- Light Weapons

combat (melee) - agl

Armed Combat
- Axe
- Club
- Improvised
- Knife
- Polearm
- Sword

Unarmed Combat
- Block
- Grapple
- Hold
- Kick
- Punch
- Throw

combat (misc.) - int

Command
Logistics
Strategy
Tactics

computing - int

Dataflow Perception
Electronic Computing (d)
Mechanical Computing

academic - int

Anthropology
Archaeology
Economics
Folklore
History
Law
- Specific Burgh/Organisation
Investigation
Philosophy
Politics
Psychology
Sociology
Theology
Writing

language - int

Commerce (spoken)
- Electrospeak
- Fighting Talk
Commerce (read & write)
- Electrospeak
Common (spoken)
- Broken
- Menace
Common (read & write)
Culture (spoken)
- Cant
Culture (read & write)
- Cant

scientific - int

Architecture
Biology
Chemistry
Cryptology
- Cryptanalysis
- Cryptography
Engineering
Genetics
Mathematics
Physics
Shift Studies (d)

technical - int/dex

Demolition
Dinginsmith
- Macroscale
- Microscale
- Nanoscale
Electrical Systems
Electrician
Electronics (d)
Gas Systems
Locksmith
Machinist
Mechanical Systems
Mechanics

trades - int/dex

Agriculture
- Aquaculture
- Hydroponics
Animal Husbandry
Blacksmith
Cooking
Fish Farming
Jeweller
Watchmaker

administrative - per

Bureaucracy
Diplomacy
Man-management

athletic - hlt

Climbing
- Abseiling
- Free Climbing
- Rappelling
Drinking
Running
- Distance Running
- Sprinting
Swimming

communications - per

Fast Talk
Negotiation
Oration
Persuasion
- Intimidation
- Seduction

artistic - awr/int

Act
Creative Writing
Dance
Draw
Moviemaking
Music
Musical Instrument
- Accordion
- Barrel Organ
- Drums
- Harp
- Guitar
- Mouth-organ
- Penny whistle
- Piano/Organ
- Squeezebox
- Violin
Paint
Photography
Poetry
Sculpture
Sing
Songwriting

medical - int

First Aid
Forensics (d)
General Medicine (d)
Pharmacology
Surgery (d)

vehicles - awr/dex

Air Vehicles
- Aerostat
- Dirigible
- Mikefighter
Ekranoplan (d)
- Military
- Racing
Ground Vehicles
- Automobile
- Haulage Wagon
- Powerbike
Trains
- Cablecar
- Funicular/Tram
- Train
Tracked Vehicles
Water Vehicles
- Large Barge
- Large Skiff
- Small Barge
- Small Skiff

subterfuge - awr/dex

Bribery
Criminal Culture
- Specific Area/Group
Disguise
Forgery
Hide
Lockpick
Pickpocket
Shadow
Sneak

survival - awr/int

Fishing
- Line
- Net
- Rod
- Spear
Foraging
Gardening
- Flowers
- Trees & Shrubs
- Vegetable
Navigation
Orienteering
Tracking

computing - int

Dataflow Perception: The ability to make sense out of the sensory chaos of the dataflow, pulling out relevant information and retrieving desired data.

Electronic Computing (d): The programming and operation of electronic computers, a rare and little used skill in The City.

Mechanical Computing: The programming and operation of dingins.

academic - int

Anthropology: The social science which studies the origins and social relationships of human beings.

Archaeology: The interpretation and study of places, cultures and people from the past through the examination of items dug from the ground.

Economics: The ability to understand the arcane and often confusing workings of economic systems and trends.

Folklore: Not quite an academic field of study, but presented here for convenience. Folklore is the knowledge of the many tales, myths and legends, both ancient and modern, which have sprung up in The City.

History: The study and theory of events and people in the past.

Investigation: Use of investigative techniques (searching records, interviewing people, looking for evidence, etc) to ascertain facts or come to conclusions.

Law: The study of legal and judicial systems, their practice and application. (Specialisations: Specific burgh/organisation.)

Philosophy: The study of various schools of thought.

Politics: Understanding of the purpose and processes of governments and institutions, ranging from tenement councils to macrocorporate structures.

Psychology: Can be used to gain understanding of the subconscious feelings affecting an individual's actions and emotions.

Sociology: The study of social groups, individuals and their interactions.

Theology: The study of religion.

Writing: The ability to write reports, theses, essays and dissertations in a coherent and understandable way.

language - int

Commerce (spoken) and Commerce (read and write): The language of business and trade in The City. (Specialisations: Electrospeak, Fighting Talk.)

Common (spoken) and Common (read and write): Most widely spoken of all languages and used by the vast majority of citizens. (Specialisations: Broken, Menace.)

Culture (spoken) and Culture (read and write): The language of the arts and the upper classes. (Specialisations: Cant.)

scientific - int

Architecture: The application of architectural principles to the design of buildings.

Biology: Knowledge of organic life and how it functions.

Chemistry: Understanding of the workings, composition and interaction of chemicals and chemical processes.

Cryptology: The study and application of codes and code-breaking. (Specialisations: Cryptanalysis, Cryptography.)

Engineering: The design and application of engineering principles to a wide variety of manufactured items, from bridges to powerbikes.

Genetics: Understanding of the genetic makeup of organisms.

Mathematics: The ability to understand and utilise mathematical systems such as algebra, trigonometry and geometry.

Physics: The science of matter and energy.

Shift Studies (d): The study of the phenomenon known as The Shift, the entities known as The Shifted and the effects of both on The City and its inhabitants. Note: It is extremely unlikely that any character would have a very high skill in this, if at all. It is a little known, poorly understood area, mostly the preserve of a select group of scientists and academics.

technical - int/dex

Demolition: Knowledge of how to use explosives effectively to demolish buildings or vehicles.

Dinginsmith: The construction of dingins. (Specialisations: Macroscale, Microscale, Nanoscale.)

Electrical Systems: Design, usage, building and repair of large scale power systems such as cable networks.

Electrician: Design, usage, building and repair of small scale power systems.

Electronics (d): The ability to operate, repair and design electronic equipment. A rare skill in The City

Gas Systems: Design, usage and repair of large scale gas transfer systems such as those which supply gas for heating and lighting to many houses in The City.

Locksmith: The construction and operation of mechanical locks.

Machinist: Skilled at using lathes, drills, presses and other machinery to fabricate items.

Mechanical Systems: Design, usage, building and repair of large scale mechanical systems.

Mechanics: The ability to operate, repair and design mechanical equipment.

trades - dex/int

Agriculture: The skills required to effectively farm fruits and vegetables on a medium to large scale.
(Specialisations: Aquaculture, Hydroponics)

Animal Husbandry: Knowledge of how to breed and care for animals for the purposes of food production. In The City, this mostly applies to dogs.

Blacksmith: The ability to use furnaces and tools to manufacture items from iron, usually less intricate, more functional items than someone would produce using Machinist skill.

Cooking: The skills and abilities required to make tasty, appealing and nutrious meals or foodstuffs.

Fish Farming: Knowledge of how to breed, care for and harvest fish for sale or consumption.

Jeweller: The ability to produce items of jewellery from a variety of materials.

Watchmaker: The construction and operation of intricate clockwork mechanisms for use in timepieces.

administrative - per

Bureaucracy: Knowledge of the ins and outs of any bureaucratic system and how to manipulate and utilise them to best effect.

Diplomacy: The subtle art of representing the interests of one group to another group or to an individual.

Man Management: The effective use, deployment and treatment of individuals within an organisation.

athletic - hlt

Climbing: The ability to climb using a variety of equipment or simply using hands and feet. (Specialisations: Free Climbing, Rappelling, Abseiling.)

Drinking: The ability to consume large quantities of alcohol over a short period of time or in some form of 'sporting' competition.

Running: The ability to run particularly fast or for extended periods. (Specialisations: Distance Running, Sprinting.)

Swimming: The basic ability to swim.

communications - per

Fast-talk: Bamboozling, confusing and confounding another individual by rapid-fire discussion.

Negotiation: Mainly used in mercantile transactions, negotiation allows the manipulation and alteration of the flow of communication to give the successful user advantage.

Oration: The ability to influence people's attitudes and behaviour patterns through powerful and effective public speaking.

Persuasion: The ability, through reason and psychological manipulation, to influence individuals to change their opinions or actions. (Specialisations: Intimidation, Seduction)

artistic - awr/int

Act: The ability to use dramatic techniques to portray character or emotion.

Creative Writing: Skill in crafting words to induce emotions in the reader.

Dance: Allows the skilled performance of many forms of dance.

Draw: Skill at rendering images with pen, pencil or charcoal.

Moviemaking: Usage of various equipment and techniques to make moving pictures.

Music: The ability to compose musical scores.

Musical Instrument: Ability to play a chosen instrument (this skill must be taken once for each instrument the character can play). (Specialisations: Accordion, Barrel Organ, Drums, Guitar, Harp, Mouth Organ, Penny Whistle, Piano/Organ, Squeeze Box, Violin.)

Paint: Skill at rendering images using various types of paint.

Photography: Skill at using photographic equipment to take pleasing, accurate or otherwise effective images.

Poetry: The ability to craft words into a variety of poetical forms.

Sculpture: The ability to carve or construct sculptures from a variety of materials.

Singing: The innate or learned ability to tunefully vocalise in a pleasing or effective manner.

Songwriting: The ability to write pleasing or effective lyrics.

Medical - int

First Aid: Emergency medical treatment given shortly after an injury.

Forensics (d): A branch of medicine concerned with identifying causes of death and any criminal circumstances surrounding it.

General Medicine (d): An education in medical care and treatment, such as that a doctor would receive.

Pharmacology: The ability to make, use and identify a variety of drugs and medicinal compounds.

Surgery (d): Use of instruments to alter, repair or remove parts of the human body.

Vehicles awr/dex

Air Vehicles: Covers the ability to take off, land and perform manoeuvres in a variety of aircraft. (Specialisations: Aerostat, Dirigible, Mikefighter.)

Ekranoplan (d): A fairly rare skill, this is the ability to pilot the dangerous, unstable and fast ground effect planes used for racing in The City. (Specialisations: Military, Racing.)

Ground Vehicles: Any wheeled vehicles. (Specialisations: Automobile, Haulage Wagon, Powerbike.)

Tracked Vehicles: Any ground vehicles which run on caterpillar tracks, such as warcrawls and APCs.

Trains: The ability required to control the mechanisms of the train systems which run throughout The City. (Specialisations: Cablecar, Funicular/Tram, Train.)

Water Vehicles: Covers the piloting of boats and barges of all sizes. (Specialisations: Small Skiff, Large Skiff, Small Barge, Large Barge.)

Subterfuge - awr/dex

Bribery: A knowledge of who, where, how and when to bribe officials, functionaries, policemen and others in authority.

Criminal Culture: Knowledge and awareness of the structure and operation of criminal organisations in The City. (Specialisations: Specific area of The City or a specific criminal group/organisation)

Disguise: Use of various means (makeup, false hair, costume and suchlike) to resemble someone else or to alter one's own appearance.

Forgery: In conjunction with various artistic skills, forgery can replicate (to a greater or lesser extent) money, coins, documents, paintings and so forth.

Hide: The ability to make maximum use of cover and concealment to remain unseen in a static position.

Lockpick: The use of specialist tools to open purely mechanical locks.

Pickpocket: The theft of items from pockets and bags, either by directly lifting them or by cutpursing.

Shadow: Unobtrusively tailing another individual.

Sneak: Using concealment, shadow, cover and stealth to move quietly and unobtrusively around.

Survival - awr/int

Fishing: Use of rod, line, net or spear to catch fish to eat. (Specialisations: Line, net, rod, spear.)

Foraging: The ability to find edible plants and animals.

Gardening: The small-scale equivalent of the Agriculture skill, gardening relates to the tending of small plots of land in order to produce foodstuffs for personal use or to provide an attractive display of plant life. (Specialisations: Vegetable, Flowers, Trees & Shrubs)

Orienteering: The determination of location using known or easily identifiable landmarks.

Navigation: The determination of location, distance travelled and course taken using a variety of maps and instruments.

Tracking: The ability to follow the signs left on the environment by a person or animal, thereby allowing it to be followed.

Character advancement

Characters in a/state can improve attributes, skill and so on through the acquisition and use of Improvement Points (IPs). IPs are awarded by the GM based on quality of role-playing, achievement of goals and the more nebulous category of 'hope'.

Guidelines for awarding ips

Before an adventure, the GM should have some idea of how many IPs it should be worth if the players complete the adventure successfully. This should not be a large amount, as the majority of IPs should come from quality role-playing and through engendering hope in the populace. A short adventure, perhaps lasting one session, may be worth 5 IPs if completed successfully. A longer adventure, perhaps spread over several sessions, might be worth 20 IPs. GMs should feel free to reduce or increase the adventure IP award, particularly for players who have either contributed very little or contributed a lot to the enjoyment of the game.

role-playing

Did the player portray their character successfully? This should be the most important guiding question when deciding awards for role-playing. For example, a player whose character was written as a kindly, curiously inquisitive Lostfinder but played him as a gung-ho weapons nut, would

not receive much in the way of role-playing awards. However, this is all up to the judgement of the GM. Someone who plays their character to an average level and contributes an average amount to the game should probably receive about 10 IPs per session. A player who played their character convincingly, utilising various traits, skills, background, advantages and disadvantages might warrant an award of 20 or more IPs.

The GM can also hold a secret ballot amongst the players to rate the other players in the group on their role-playing. Getting players to rate each other on a scale of 1 to 10 will allow you to judge how they think each other have performed. Emphasise to them that a rating of 5 is average and anything above 7 constitutes particularly good, amusing or convincing role-playing. The average of all ratings can be doubled to find out the individual players IP award for role-playing.

example:

After a session, the GM hands out blank slips of paper and asks each of his four players to rate each other on the quality of their role-playing.

The players rate each other as follows:

	Player 1	Player 2	Player 3	Player 4
Player 1	X	5	5	5
Player 2	3	X	4	3
Player 3	5	6	X	5
Player 4	8	8	8	X

So, it can be seen that Player 4 was considered to have role-played rather well, whilst Player 2 role-played fairly badly. Taking the average rating for each player and doubling it, the players gain the following IPs:

Player 1:	10 IPs
Player 2:	6 IPs
Player 3:	10 IPs
Player 4:	16 IPs

'hope'

The City is a grim place, full of hopelessness, despair and evil. Sometimes characters may contribute to this hopelessness and despair in some way, but there are many ways in which they can improve people's lives, even if only by a small amount.

The GM can make substantial IP awards to individual characters or groups for doing good, giving people a bright spark in their lives, helping others and suchlike. This does not mean that groups of players should constantly behave like a bunch of do-gooders on a mission. However, players who, even inadvertently, do something to assist others should be rewarded for this.

example:

We've already been through the creation of Camden Derr: former ekranoplan racer turned mechanic, down on his luck, working out of a small, dilapidated workshop in his native Bankside. Desperate for money, he has agreed to help some friends investigate a disappearance in Folly Hills. He's not convinced about the entire thing and constantly questions why he is here. During their investigations, a small boy runs up to Derr clutching and faded old sepiatone daguerreotype showing Derr back in the old days, leaning against an ekranoplan, proudly holding his sponsor's product.

Does Derr brush the boy off? No.

His player decides to talk to the boy, indulge in a bit of friendly banter and offer to sign the crumbling picture. The boy, needless to say, delighted and this alone would be enough to gain some IPs. However, Derr goes one step further and enquires of the boy (who has already stated that he comes from an extremely impoverished family) if he would like to become his apprentice. The boy is delighted, as are his family when he tells them. This raises the family's standing in the tenement where they live and everyone is proud of the boy for gaining an apprenticeship.

This small encounter serves to give the boy a future, his family a little money and immense pride and causes no small amount of good cheer in many local residents.

This simple act of kindness would be worth up to 20 IPs for the player of Camden Derr.

Some sample Hope awards are as follows:

A small act of kindness to an individual

(e.g.: giving some small change to a beggar): 1IP

A substantial act of kindness to an individual

(arranging a room in a hostel for a beggar and getting him or her a new set of clothes): 5IP

Minor self-sacrifice

(eg: giving up a moderate amount of money to help others): 5IP

Major self-sacrifice

(e.g.: taking a scrape addict into your home and trying to get him/her off the drug): 10IP

Altruistic act towards a group of people

(e.g.: ridding a burgh of a gang leader who has been terrorising the inhabitants): 15IP

Potential life threatening situation to help others

(e.g.: running into a burning tenement to rescue trapped children): 10IP

Spending IPs

IPs can be used to improve skills and attributes. To improve any skill or attribute, a certain amount of points must be spent. In the case of skills, this is equal to half the level the skill is being raised to. In the case of attributes, this is equal to twice the level the attribute is being raised to. All fractions are rounded up.

example

The above mentioned character Camden Derr has ended an adventure with a grand total of 50 IPs. The player checks out Derr's skills an decides to improve a few of them. His Shadowing skill is currently 20 and the player thinks this could do with being a bit better. To improve the skill from 20 to 21 costs 11 IPs, from 21 to 22 costs another 11 and from 22 to 23 costs another 12. The player stops there, having managed a three point increase in Shadowing for a cost of 34 IPs. With 16 IPs left, the player notices that Derr's current Pistol skill stands at 33. To increase this to 34, would cost 17 IPs, one more than the amount left over. The player therefore holds these points back to spend at another time.

NPCS

There follows a selection of stock NPCs for use in a/state games. Basic statistics, four key skills and some typical gear are given for each, as well as a short rundown on what the character is like.

vociferous activist

Whether it be haranguing the crowd from the hustings or doing shady deals in smoke filled rooms, the vociferous activist always has his own best interests at heart. Occasionally there are deals done which benefit the people whom the activist represents but this is a rare and surprising event.

AWR:	50	AGL:	40
INT:	50	DEX:	40
PER:	70	HLT:	60
WIL:	60	STR:	40

Skills

Oration	70
Diplomacy	50
Fast Talk	60
Persuasion	60

Gear

Sheaf of leaflets.
Hectoring tone of voice.
Selection of banners.
A small office and maybe a couple of loyal supporters.

penniless artist

Locked away in a stuffy garret or dingy basement, the artist works in poverty for the love of her art. Creating something of beauty in a decaying world is her goal, selling simple sketches and portraits in order to get by.

AWR:	60	AGL:	40
INT:	60	DEX:	65
PER:	50	HLT:	30
WIL:	50	STR:	40

Skills

Artistic Skill of Choice	70
Economics	50
Persuasion	50
Foraging	50

Gear

Art materials.
Dusty garret room somewhere.

entrepreneurial businessman

In any situation, there's money to be made. From selling electricity or gas illicitly tapped from cables and pipes to fattening dogs for the kill, there are a million money making schemes to be tried. Every opportunity must be analysed and assessed, every penny counted and re-counted, every deal squeezed dry.

AWR:	70	AGL:	40
INT:	60	DEX:	40
PER:	50	HLT:	50
WIL:	70	STR:	50

Skills

Negotiation	70
Economics	60
Fast Talk	60
Bribery	50

Gear

Varies widely, from a skiff full of stock to a notebook of contacts and a brain full of ideas. Depends very much on the business he/she is involved in.

hard-bitten law enforcer

Years spent on the beat, standing guard or taking statements behind a worm-eaten desk have removed every last vestige of doubt about the realities of life from this hard-nosed lawman. Every crime that can be committed has been witnessed by those dull eyes, every form of human degradation has passed by. Nothing surprises this bearer of the burden of justice, cynicism is his stock in trade.

AWR:	60	AGL:	50
INT:	55	DEX:	50
PER:	40	HLT:	50
WIL:	60	STR:	60

Skills

Investigation	60
Pistol	60
Armed Combat	60
Criminal Culture	50

Gear

Depends very much on who he or she works for. A Three Canals Provost might carry a heavy sparklock pistol, a truncheon and key to access bunkers, rest sheds or telephone boxes. On the other hand, a security operative working in an upper class area such as Lucent Heights might have access to a magnetic repeater sidearm, body armour and a personal aerostat.

disgruntled labourer

A twelve hour stretch in a hot, foetid, roaring factory would be enough to embitter most folk. Putting up with all this whilst being harassed by petty management and bullying foremen makes it even worse. Still, it's better than no job at all. Only the prospect of a lonely life on the streets, slowly dying by inches, keeps this one of the thousands of labourers in The City toiling away.

AWR:	40	**AGL:**	50
INT:	40	**DEX:**	50
PER:	50	**HLT:**	50
WIL:	40	**STR:**	65

Skills

Machinist	60
Drinking	60
Unarmed Combat	50
Bureaucracy	40

Gear

Heavy work clothes.
Old boots.
Battered lunchbox.

thrusting macrocorp exec

It's tough at the top. It's hard at the bottom. In the middle, the pressure is at its worst. Seen as a target by subordinates and a threat by superiors, life in the cut-throat world of the macrocorps is a battle for survival. Fail, and it's all over: the comfortable dwelling, the pay, the access to consumer goods. Slip and it's finished. The only way to avoid it is to keep pushing ever upwards.

AWR:	50	**AGL:**	50
INT:	60	**DEX:**	50
PER:	60	**HLT:**	70
WIL:	80	**STR:**	40

Skills

Negotiation	70
Act	60
Diplomacy	60
Man Management	60

Gear

Office equipped with dingin and the use of a secretary or PA.
Range of stylish clothing.
Expensive, hand-crafted pocket watch.
Smart apartment or house in a reasonably nice area.
Membership of a select club or two.

knowledgeable nomad

Spending a lifetime slowly wending your way around the canals teaches you a thing or two. The nomad is wise in the ways of many areas of The City, cultures, customs, laws and folklore. They are useful sources of information and gossip, but seldom stay in any one place long. They stop for a while to buy and sell, exchange news and then move on to somewhere new.

AWR:	70	**AGL:**	60
INT:	55	**DEX:**	50
PER:	50	**HLT:**	40
WIL:	50	**STR:**	50

Skills

Folklore	50
Foraging	70
Fishing	60
Navigation	60

Gear

Sparklock carbine.
Small skiff or hand drawn cart.
Bedding.
Foodstuffs.
Portable stove.
Fishing gear.

invasive stringer

Some people think that having a private life means just that. Well, they're wrong. Nobody's life is private, everything is in the public domain. At least, that's what this avid news-hound thinks. Twisting truth and inventing lies, she delves into misery, corruption, crime and death in an attempt to get the stories that will catapult her to fame and fortune.

AWR:	60	**AGL:**	50
INT:	50	**DEX:**	60
PER:	60	**HLT:**	40
WIL:	70	**STR:**	40

Skills

Folklore	40
Shadow	60
Investigation	60
Writing	50

Gear

Notepad and writing instruments.
Lotech camera.
List of contacts.

cocky street ganger

Young, independent, loud-mouth: the archetypal street gang member is all of these and more, Practically living their lives on the streets, most of these youngsters either end their days bleeding to death in a deserted alley or graduating on to the higher echelons of the criminal world. On their own territory, they have they edge, confident of the back-up of their brothers and sisters in the gang.

AWR:	50	AGL:	55
INT:	45	DEX:	55
PER:	55	HLT:	35
WIL:	60	STR:	40

Skills

Pistol	40
Armed Combat	40
Unarmed Combat	50
Criminal Culture	30

Gear

Knife or weighted cosh.

Extensive gang tattoos.

Poor quality, rough clothes, perhaps with a few gang symbols stitched into them.

Maybe access two one or two rather old and unreliable sparklocks owned by the gang.

cynical jake

A bundle of rags slumped in an alley, hands tightly gripping a half empty bottle. The cynical jake has seen all the life of The City pass before his eyes, nothing surprises him any more. Perhaps no one is more inured to the violence and degradation of life in The City, or more exposed to its many variations.

AWR:	60	AGL:	30
INT:	50	DEX:	40
PER:	50	HLT:	20
WIL:	30	STR:	30

Skills

Foraging	70
Persuasion	60
Hide	50
Sneak	50

Gear

The clothes on his or her back.

Begging bowl, hat or tin.

tough soldier

Fight or die. Adapt to survive. Kill or be killed. There are many who bear arms in The City but few can truly call themselves soldiers. Those who do have been hardened by conflict, toughened by combat. Few occurrences can disturb such a veteran, for he's seen it all before.

AWR:	55	AGL:	60
INT:	50	DEX:	60
PER:	50	HLT:	40
WIL:	60	STR:	60

Skills

Longarm 65

Armed Combat 65

Unarmed Combat 60

Hide 60

Gear

A rifle of some sort, ranging from a sparklock to a magnetic repeater.

Sidearm, same situation as above.

Body armour of some kind and probably a helmet.

Knife or bayonet.

Mess kit.

Various scavenged or looted personal effects.

boatman

Those who remain forever on the land lose out on the true pulse of The City, the lifelines which allow it to survive. The boatman has seen it all in his time, whether it be lugging crates of parts up and down the Grand Canal, ferrying anxious travellers through darkened cappilaries or carefully picking his way through the labyrinth of Long Pond. Boatmen and women see and hear many things, see the passage of life and know the rumours which float along the canals.

AWR:	50	AGL:	50
INT:	50	DEX:	40
PER:	55	HLT:	50
WIL:	40	STR:	55

Skills

Navigation	60
Negotiation	50
Swimming	60
Water Vehicle	70

Gear

A small skiff, ranging from an oar powered variant, to something a little more powerful.

Knife.

Ropes.

mudlark

Lift. Fetch. Carry. Hoist. Rig. Dredge. Mudlarks have a hard, demanding, physical life. Years spent unloading barges, yanking on ropes, scouring the bottoms of the canals breeds a class of tough, self-sufficient people, unafraid of the harshness of extreme physical labour. Docks, wharves, warehouses and jetties are magnets for rumour, gossip, superstition and folklore. Thye mudlarks pick up on all of this and weave it into the ongoing tapestry of their lives. Tales are bandied about in low pubs, boats are made and vast quantities of drink consumed.

AWR:	45	AGL:	55
INT:	45	DEX:	55
PER:	50	HLT:	40
WIL:	60	STR:	65

Skills

Armed Combat	60
Drinking	70
Folklore	50
Unarmed Combat	60

Gear

Boathook or pike.
Knife.
Rope splicing tools.

mapmaker

In the cracks between the various shadowy organisations, the mapmakers live. Brokering deals, organising meetings, arbitrating in bitter gang disputes. They go where others fear to tread, walking the fine line between intrinsically violent groups, forever making sure of their absolute impartiality. Mapmakers know many things, much of whish must remain forever hidden. To betray secrets is the mark of death for a mapmaker. Once trust is lost, then life finishes; either dying by slow inches as work dries up, or ending up as a cooling corpse slumped in an alley.

AWR:	65	AGL:	35
INT:	60	DEX:	45
PER:	55	HLT:	40
WIL:	60	STR:	40

Skills

Criminal Culture	70
Economics	60
Negotiation	70
Persuasion	60

Gear

Notebooks.
Small sidearm.
Plenty of criminal contacts.

P re-generated characters

Over the next ten pages, you'll find a selection of pre-gener-
ated characters, ready for use in any a/state game. From a
wily macrocorp executive to a cocky ganger, from a hard-bit-
ten Transit Militia officer to an inquisitve scientist, you'll find a
range of characters to use or to provide a basis for your own
creations.

wealthy dilettante

History and Desription

Born and brought up in the glittering seclusion of Lucent Heights, you've never known the drudgery and poverty that the vast majority of citizen face. Educated by private tutors and boarded in exclusive dorms at Longshore University, life has never been hard. Now finished university and with precious little to do, you lounge about with similarly rich young friends, living off the inherited wealth of your parents, scoffing at the tribulations of the lower orders. Occasionally, you venture out into the wider world, visiting poorer areas of The City to sample what you imagine to be the 'wild' side of life. Well-educated and wealthy, you are nonetheless devoid of any real understanding of how things work in the real world.

Origin:	Nomenklatura
Upbringing:	Wealthy
Age:	23

Attributes

Physical	Level	Cost
Agility	60	60
Dexterity	45	45
Health	60	60
Strength	27	27

Mental		
Awareness	30	30
Intelligence	50	50
Personality (bonus)	70	60
Willpower	60	60

Skills

Skill	Level	Cost
Act	60	60
Bribery	30	30
Common (Read & Write)	70	20
Common (Spoken)	85	20
Culture (Read & Write)	60	60
Culture (Spoken)	70	70
Diplomacy	50	50
Economics	40	40
Fast Talk	40	40
Musical Instrument (Violin)	40	40
Persuasion	65	65
Politics	30	30

Advantages & Disadvantages

Advantages	Level	+/-
Mental Adv (Confidence)	/	-10AP
Physical Adv (Poise)	Mod	-8AP

Disadvantages	Level	+/-
Enemy (Ex-boyfriend)	Min	+5SP
Enemy (Other socialite)	Mod	+10SP
Mental Disad (Superior)	Mod	+10AP

Possessions

Pretty much anything she fancies. A nice apartment in Lucent Heights for starters.

Money: £600

penniless ex-mikefighter pilot

History and Desription

Born into abject poverty in the infested subterranean lanes of Shore Ditch Warrens, your parents barely earned the pennies required to pay the slum landlord who owned the dripping, foetid room you called home. Shortly after your seventh birthday, your parents took you on a train journey, a journey to see some of the fabulous sights of the City. After the journey, they returned. You did not. Sold into virtual slavery, you were trained to fly tiny aircraft for one of the macrocorps, flitting through the spaces between towerblocks and tenements. Of your class of thirty, only you survived to reach age sixteen and an unceremonious end to your career. Now you live on the streets, attempting to survive as best you can.

Origin:	Dispossessed
Upbringing:	Militaristic
Age:	18

Attributes

Physical	Level	Cost
Agility	65	65
Dexterity	65	65
Health	40	40
Strength	40	40

Mental		
Awareness (bonus)	70	60
Intelligence	47	47
Personality	40	40
Willpower	50	50

Advantages & Disadvantages

Advantages	Level	+/-
Phys Ad (good balance)	Moderate	-8AP
Contact (macrocorp military)	Minor	-5AP
Contact (fence/dealer)	Minor	-5SP

Disadvantages	Level	+/-
Ment. Disad (flashbacks)	Moderate	+10AP
Ment. Disad (acrophobia)	Moderate	+10AP
Poverty	Major	+20SP
Phys Disad (addict)	Minor	+5SP

Skills

Skill	Level	Cost
Air Vehicles	50	50
Mikefighter	+20	10
Armed Combat	30	30
Common (read & write)	50	50
Common (spoken)	70	n/a
Criminal Culture	40	40
First Aid	50	50
Folklore	09	n/a
Foraging	40	30
Hide	40	40
Longarm	10	10
Navigation	40	40
Persuasion	40	40
Pistol	40	40
Running	30	30
Sneak	30	30
Tactics	50	50
Unarmed Combat	40	40
Vehicular Weapons	50	50

Possessions

A few pennies in loose change

Small knife

Cheap Clothes

Average Boots

Fish Oil Stove

Mess Kit

Money: £0.0s.10p

driven lostfinder

History and Desription

Many people in The City have no one to look after them. Forsaken by justice and authority, they have few choices in their times of need. That's where you come in: serving your burgh for little more than a few scarps of fish, the odd hot meal or simply the goodwill of the community. People come to you with their problems, their missing possessions, pets, money or even family members. As a lostfinder, it's your duty to search for missing items and people as best you can. From your damp room in a cheap tenement, you gather scraps of information, wheedle people for intelligence and scour the streets and canals for clues. Sometimes it pays off, sometimes it doesn't. But that's the lot of the lostfinder. That's what you do: helping those who can't help themselves.

Origin:	Drudge
Upbringing:	Independent
Age:	30

Attributes

Physical	Level	Cost
Agility	40	40
Dexterity	35	35
Health	45	45
Strength (bonus)	45	35

Mental		
Awareness	60	60
Intelligence	65	65
Personality	55	55
Willpower	45	45

Advantages & Disadvantages

Advantages	Level	+/-
Contact (local Politician)	Minor	-5SP
Contact (local shopkeeper)	Minor	-5SP
Contact (petty thief)	Minor	-5AP
Ment. ad. (memory)	/	-10AP

Disadvantages	Level	+/-
Poverty	Moderate	+10AP
Enemy (street gang)	Minor	+5AP
Eneny (law enforcement)	Minor	+5AP
Ment. disad. (nightmares)	Moderate	+10AP
Enemy	Minor	+5AP

Skills

Skill	Level	Cost
Bureaucracy	20	20
Commerce (spoken)	40	40
Commerce (read & write)	40	40
Common (read & write)	60	60
Common (Spoken)	97	/
Culture (spoken)	30	30
Criminal Culture	40	40
Diplomacy	10	10
Economics	10	10
Folklore	28	15
Forensics	20	20
Hide	30	20
Investigation	65	65
Lockpick	30	30
Mechanics	20	20
Negotiation	20	20
Persuasion	45	45
Pistol	40	40
Shadow	55	55
Sneak	50	50
Unarmed Combat	30	30

Possessions

Sparklock Pepperbox
Magnifying Glass
Notebook & Pencil
Dogskin Greatcoat
Money: £1.5s

ruthless ghostfighter

History and Desription

Anyone can aim a gun and pull a trigger. Guns are for idiots, cowards and amateurs. It takes someone different to look an opponent in the eye and slice their life out from under them. A relatively comfortable upbringing in the Three Canals Metropolitan Area was stultifyingly dull, an endless succession of boredom and triviality. A juvenile gang fight brought out talents you never knew you had: speed, hand/eye coordination and utter ruthlessness. From then on, you knew you could make your living from this, like the fabled ghostfighters. Now, many years later, you've established a reputation for yourself and become one of those selfsame ghostfighters you so admired.

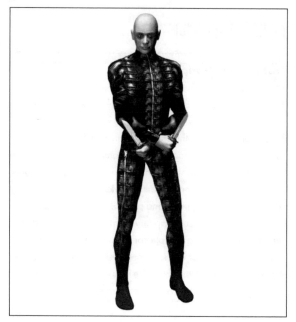

Origin:	Middle-class (Lower)
Upbringing:	Dangerous
Age:	29

Attributes

Physical	Level	Cost
Agility	60	60
Dexterity	60	60
Health	40	40
Strength	40	40

Mental		
Awareness	59	59
Intelligence	45	45
Personality	35	35
Willpower (bonus)	60	50

Advantages & Disadvantages

Advantages	Level	+/-
Contact (Booker)	Min	-5SP
Physical Adv (Ambidextrous)	Mod	-8AP

Disadvantages	Level	+/-
Enemy (Ex-client)	Min	+5SP
Enemy (Streetgang)	Min	+5SP
Enemy (3rd Syndicate)	Mod	+10AP
Enemy (Law enforcement)	Mod	+10AP
Mental Disad (Flashbacks)	Mod	+10AP
Physical Disad (Scarring)	Mod	+10AP

Skills

Skill	Level	Cost
Armed Combat	60	60
Improvised	+20	10
Knife	+20	10
Climb	45	45
Commerce (Spoken)	40	40
Common (Read & Write)	45	/
Common (Spoken)	68	/
Economics	20	20
First Aid	50	50
Hide	65	65
Mechanical Computing	20	20
Shadow	60	60
Sneak	65	65
Tactics	40	40
Thrown Weapons	40	40
Knife	+20	10
Unarmed Combat	60	60

Possessions

Ceramic blade
2 steel knives
Padded armour
Climbing kit (lotech)
Money: £30

Cocky young flowghost

History and Desription

The Dataflow is just a big pool of information, waiting to be tapped. All these old-timer who prattle on about hidden mysteries, deep code and strange encounters don't have a clue what they're on about. Information is power, and you've got access to the biggest source of information in The City. You keeping your dingin spinning, your codes fresh and your cryptological skills up to date. Those that think you're just a geeky wastrel can take a hike as well. Ghosting involves far more than that: breaking in to place to steal code to get through the infernal mechanical codelocks that seem to be everywhere, intimidating information out of people, running for your life before the Provosts catch you. It's a tough life, but you wouldn't trade it in for anything.

Origin:	Middle-class (Lower)
Upbringing:	Independent
Age:	20

Attributes

Physical	Level	Cost
Agility	35	35
Dexterity	50	50
Health	40	40
Strength	35	35

Mental		
Awareness	60	60
Intelligence	75	80
Personality	40	40
Willpower (bonus)	65	55

Advantages & Disadvantages

Advantages	Level	+/-
Contact (Thug)	Min	-5AP
Contact (Streetgang)	Min	-5AP

Disadvantages	Level	+/-
Enemy (Other flowghost)	Min	+5AP
Enemy (Macrocorp)	Min	+5SP
Enemy (Law enforcement)	Mod	+10SP
Physical disad (Bad sleeper)	Mod	+10SP
Poverty	Min	+5SP

Skills

Skill	Level	Cost
Bureaucracy	10	10
Common (Read & Write)	75	/
Common (Spoken)	99	/
Criminal Culture	50	50
Cryptology	50	50
Cryptography	+20	10
Dataflow Perception	60	60
Dinginsmith	50	50
Macroscale	+20	10
Economics	30	30
Electrician	30	30
Fast Talk	40	40
Lockpick	30	30
Mechanical Computing	70	70
Mechanics	30	30
Negotiation	30	30
Sneak	40	40
Unarmed Combat	20	20

Possessions

120 cubic inch macroscale dingin
Dataflow splice (lotech)
Keyboard (lotech)
Money:£15

embittered transit militia officer

History and Desription

Twenty years on the job. Twenty sodding years! And what do you have to show for it? Well, calluses on your feet, a permanent squint from gazing into the wind all the time and a permanently sore back from the knife wound all those years ago. Still, it keeps the wife and kids warm, there's food on the table and the Militia will look after you in your old age. It's better than what a lot of people got. Still, your neighbours don't like you much, tend to stop talking and act shifty whenever you appear round the corner, just coming home from a hard twelve hours on the lines. Nutter, fare dodgers, muggers, cutpurses, dollymops, jackers and murderers, it's all part of a long days work in the Transit Militia. Still, mustn't grumble.

Origin:	Drudge
Upbringing:	Apprenticed
Age:	38

Attributes

Physical	Level	Cost
Agility	35	35
Dexterity	30	30
Health	35	35
Strength (bonus)	65	55

Mental		
Awareness	52	52
Intelligence	40	40
Personality	35	35
Willpower	45	45

Advantages & Disadvantages

Advantages	Level	+/-
Contact (Homeless person)	Min	-5AP
Contact (Provost)	Min	-5AP
Contact (Train driver)	Min	-5AP
Physical Adv (Strong grip)	Min	-3AP

Disadvantages	Level	+/-
Enemy (Petty criminal)	Min	+5AP
Enemy (Petty criminal)	Min	+5AP
Enemy (Hohler gang)	Mod	+10AP
Physical Disad (Old wound)	Min	+5AP

Skills

Skill	Level	Cost
Armed Combat	55	55
Club	+20	10
Bureaucracy	50	50
Commerce (Spoken)	30	30
Electrospeak	+10	5
Common (Read & Write)	50	50
Common (Spoken)	60	/
Criminal Culture	60	60
Economics	15	15
First Aid	30	30
Folklore	33	25
Investigation	50	50
Machinist	20	20
Mechanical Computing	10	10
Mechanics	20	20
Negotiation	50	50
Pistol	50	50
Single Shot	+20	10
Shadow	30	30
Unarmed Combat	60	60

Possessions

Heavy sparklock pistol
Billy club
Uniform
Money: £60

hardline rccr peoples representative

History and Desription

Truly, the Republic is the only bastion of light and hope in this sea of strife. The Republic is the one place where men can be equal to strive for a better future, where children are taught true morals, values and ethics. Yes, the RCCR is the only hope. Imbued with a fervent respect for the Republic from an early age, you live only to serve the people, your komrades. A two year stint in the infantry, guarding the borders and shooting spies, insurgents and insurrectionists taught you that the Republic is assailed on all side by those who wish to drag her down into a pit of their own making. Now, you represent the people of the Republic, making decisions based on komradely agreement and fraternal discussion.

Origin:	Drudge
Upbringing:	Militaristic
Age:	35

Attributes

Physical	Level	Cost
Agility	40	40
Dexterity	44	44
Health	40	40
Strength (bonus)	60	50

Mental		
Awareness	45	45
Intelligence	55	55
Personality	42	42
Willpower	60	60

Advantages & Disadvantages

Advantages	Level	+/-
Contact (Special Department)	Min	-5AP
Mental Adv (Concentration)	/	-10AP
Physical Adv (Good speech)	Mod	-8AP

Disadvantages	Level	+/-
Enemy (Insurgents)	Min	+5AP
Enemy (Other representative)	Mod	+10AP
Infamy (RCCR only)	Mod	+5AP
Mental Disad (Fanaticism)	Maj	+15AP
Mental Disad (Paranoia)	Min	+5AP

Skills

Skill	Level	Cost
Armed Combat	10	10
Bureaucracy	55	55
Common (Read & Write)	50	50
Common (Spoken)	77	/
Electrician	20	20
Fast Talk	50	50
Folklore	10	n/a
Investigation	30	30
Longarm	25	25
Machinist	10	10
Mechanics	20	20
Negotiation	50	50
Oration	60	60
Persuasion	50	50
Pistol	30	30
Politics	60	60
Tactics	20	20
Unarmed Combat	40	40

Possessions

All possessions are shared equally amongst the people.

independently minded scientist

History and Desription

Whole chunks of the population may choose to lose themselves in religion, superstition and folklore, but only science offers a way out of this trap in which we live. Tired of the strictures and rules of the macrocorps and educational establishments, you struck out on your own to pursue pure research into the very nature of...things. What things exactly, you're still not sure, but important things nonetheless. You speak to flowghosts who trawl the Dataflow for information on The Shifted. You speak to chemists and apothecaries about toxins and poisons. You converse with half-mad antiquities hunters who have delved deep into the bowels of The City. You're not sure what it all points to, but it all points to something. Something meaningful. Something important.

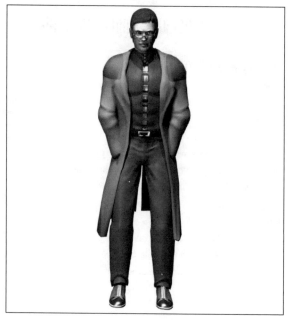

Origin:	Median corporate
Upbringing:	Sheltered
Age:	42

Attributes

Physical	Level	Cost
Agility	40	40
Dexterity	60	60
Health (bonus)	35	25
Strength	30	30

Mental		
Awareness	40	40
Intelligence	75	80
Personality	30	30
Willpower	35	35

Advantages & Disadvantages

Advantages	Level	+/-
Fame (Scientific community)	Mod	-10SP
Mental Adv (Concentration)	n/a	-10AP
Mental Adv (Natural scientist)	n/a	-10AP
Mental Adv (Quick learner)	n/a	-10AP
Wealth	Mod	-15SP

Disadvantages	Level	+/-
Mental Disad (Shy)	Min	+5AP
Mental Disad (Impatient)	Mod	+10AP
Physical Disad (Withered arm)	Mod	+10SP

Skills

Skill	Level	Cost
Common (Read & Write)	75	n/a
Common (Spoken)	99	n/a
Electrical Systems	35	35
Electronics	45	45
Hide	25	25
History	30	30
Investigation	30	30
Man-management	40	40
Mathematics	60	60
Mechanical Computing	30	30
Persuasion	60	60
Philosophy	25	25
Physics	90	120
Politics	17	17
Sneak	40	40
Writing	20	20

Possessions

Small, but well-equipped laboratory

Macroscale dingin

Lab assistant

Money: £200

ladylike thief

History and Desription

So, those boys in the gang all those years ago said you'd never amount to nothing. Father and mother said the same, screamed the place down after you got kicked out of that expensive school. Went made when you just upped and left without so much as a by-your-leave. Has to be said though, that expensive schooling helps in your chosen professions. The enunciated vowels and ladylike manner really fool some folks. Makes getting in to some places easy. Then again, when charm and persuasion don't work, there's always the lockpick set and the pry bar. Whatever needs to be stolen, you're just the young lady to do the job. If only your parents could see you now. Why, they'd probably have heart attacks!

Origin:	Middle-class (Upper)
Upbringing:	Sheltered
Age:	25

Attributes

Physical	Level	Cost
Agility	63	63
Dexterity	50	50
Health	40	40
Strength	30	30

Mental		
Awareness	65	65
Intelligence	51	51
Personality	65	65
Willpower (bonus)	60	50

Advantages & Disadvantages

Advantages	Level	+/-
Contact (Fence)	Min	-5SP
Contact (old gang friend)	Min	-5SP
Physical Adv (Attractive)	Mod	-8AP
Physical Adv (Good hearing)	Mod	-8AP

Disadvantages	Level	+/-
Enemy (Parents)	Min	+5SP
Enemy (Jilted lover)	Mod	+10AP
Enemy (Law enforcement)	Mod	+10AP
Mental Disad(Haughty)	Mod	+10AP

Skills

Skill	Level	Cost
Common (Read & Write)	51	/
Common (Spoken)	76	/
Criminal Culture	40	40
Culture (Spoken)	40	40
Diplomacy	20	20
Disguise	30	30
Economics	20	20
Fast Talk	60	60
Hide	40	40
Lockpick	50	50
Negotiation	20	20
Persuasion	50	50
Psychology	20	20
Shadow	40	40
Sneak	55	55
Unarmed Combat	40	40

Possessions

Lockpick set
Utility knife
Disguise kit
Rope (lotech) - 20 metres
Money: £50

doubting third church priest

History and Desription

Faith in a dark place. Faith in God and His Heavenly City. That's what your mother and father brought you up to believe. That's why you joined the priesthood as soon as you were eligible, driven on by a fierce, burning devotion to God. However, over these past months, doubts have been creeping in. As you travel about The City and see the suffering, cruelty and hatred, you wonder. Wonder if this really is all part of Gods great plan, part of His great scheme for man. And you faith in the Church is beginning to crumble as you see the thoughtlessness, the lack of compassion for the weakest members of society, the blind devotion to scripture and tradition. For so long, these were the things at the very core of your being, but now, like so much of The City, they are beginning to crumble.

Origin:	Middle-class (Lower)
Upbringing:	Religious
Age:	34

Attributes

Physical	Level	Cost
Agility	40	40
Dexterity	40	40
Health	50	50
Strength	35	35

Mental		
Awareness	40	40
Intelligence	65	65
Personality	65	65
Willpower (bonus)	70	60

Advantages & Disadvantages

Advantages	Level	+/-
Mental Adv (Compassionate)	n/a	-10AP

Disadvantages	Level	+/-
Enemy (Disgruntled parishoner)	Min	+5SP
Enemy (Deacon)	Mod	+10SP
Mental Disad (Phobia)	Mod	+10AP
Mental Disad (Crisis of faith)	Maj	+15AP
Physical Disad (Bad sleeper)	Mod	+10AP

Skills

Skill	Level	Cost
Act	40	40
Bureaucracy	40	40
Common (Read & Write)	65	n/a
Common (Spoken)	99	n/a
Culture (Read & Write)	40	40
Cant	+20	10
Culture (Spoken)	50	50
Cant	+20	10
Diplomacy	50	50
First Aid	40	40
Negotiation	50	50
Oration	60	60
Persuasion	50	50
Philosophy	30	30
Theology	60	60
Writing	50	50

Possessions

Priestly garb
Religious and philosophical books
Symbols of the Church
Small room in Church living quarters
Money: The Church provides all, but a few shillings here and there for 'personal expenses'.

"Uh huh, I want a big set of sparklocks just like One Eye Frank. Me mum says that guns isn't nice, that there's too many bad people wiv them. Nah, me mum talk shit. Guns is what folks respect you for. Got no guns, got no respect. Bankside here, you got no gun, people don't care 'bout you. I want a big gun. Then I can jack a macro and get his gun. Shiny, quick, slick. Guns are good."

Oleevia Harkness, age 9, Bankside

the product

Access Level: 16.7
Refer To: Brigade, VdH (Gen)

    From: Stahlecker, F J
    To: Borrowstoun, L N

    Subject: Testing, testing and more testing!

Lucy,

It's the old problem again. The projectile stabilisation just isn't working at these longer ranges. Can we not just be satisfied with the range we've got? I mean, who wants a weapon that fires that far anyway? I've had a look over the stats from the Hundred Block and over 90% of engagements were fought at aggregate ranges of less than 50 meters! Where is the justification for this system coming from?

And another thing! At any range less than 500 meters (and you show me where we can obtain a line of sight greater than that in this place!) the blow-through is going to be terrific. Yeah, it'll tear the target a new arse, but with something like this, we'll be delivering horrific collateral damage.

Just thought I'd express my concerns. Look after yourself.

Frank.

Access Level: 16.7
Refer To: Brigade, VdH (Gen)

    From: Borrowstoun, L N
    To: Stahlecker, F J

    Subject: Re: Testing, testing and more testing!

Frank,

I appreciate your concerns, but this comes from the highest level. I realise you feel the need to speak your mind, but just concentrate on the matter in hand, OK?

Stabilisation at the ranges we require is vital, even if you have to sacrifice short range accuracy. Get this right and it could be a big feather in your cap, even more so than project 1010L. This could be big for all of us.

Lucy

Access Level: 16.9
Refer To: Brigade, VdH (Gen)

    From: van den Haas, K (General)
    To: Stahlecker, F J
    Copy: Borrowstoun, L N

    Subject: Re: Testing, testing and more testing!

Mr Stahlecker,

I'd like to take the time to express my profound thanks to you for your commitment to this project. You've carried out exemplary work for us in the past and I'm sure your skill and devotion will prove the decisive factors in this particular development programme.

However, I would like to caution you against expressing your doubts in transmittable form again, just for the safety of the project and your own personal protection.

van den Haas

Access Level: 15.0
Refer To: N/A

    From: Borrowstoun, L N
    To: Stahlecker, F J

    Subject: ??????

See what I mean? A direct communication from the General herself! Shit Frank, you must really have stirred something up, even I didn't realise she was directly involved! I'd watch your step if I were you.

Lucy

Money in the city

Currency in The City consists of Pounds, Shillings and Pence. While all of the macrocorps, several banks, some local governments and a few churches produce their own scrip, all are denominated in the same manner and are generally given equal value, as money circulates around The City at a fairly rapid rate. That having been said, most people prefer to deal with macrocorp pounds, as they are backed by the power and resources of the largest institutions in The City. Local governments, such as the TCMAA issue money through banks which they control, as is the case with the TCMAA and the Canals Trading Bank.

One pound contains twenty shillings, with each shilling being made up of five pence. A good baseline for working out the value of items can be found by looking at the average weekly wage, which amounts to £5.0s.0p. Admittedly, this is an average, many earn far less than this and a few earn vastly more.

Pricing & scarcity of resources

When browsing through The Product, you'll notice that each item has a cost and availability. The cost indicates an average price for the item if it were freely available on the open market, whereas the availability indicates the scarcity or otherwise of the item. Cost and availability have a direct relationship, as scarcity will tend to increase the perceived value of an item.

There are six levels of availability, as show below:

Very common: The item can be purchased anywhere and commands no premium on the listed price

Common: The item can be purchased in most places and if it does command a premium, this will only be a matter of a few percent.

Uncommon: The item is available in specialised retailers or through underground contacts. It may command a premium of up to 100% more than the listed price.

Rare: The item is hard to come by, requiring a bit of work to obtain. It may command a premium of 100 to 200% more than the listed price.

Very rare: The item is very hard to come by and will require a lot of tracking down or considerable influence or money to purchase. It can command a premium of from 200 to 400% more than the listed price.

Scarce: The item is almost impossible to find. If available, it will command a premium of 500% more than the listed price. And that's just for a start, it could be a lot more.

technology levels in the city

Broadly speaking, technology in The City can be divided into two areas: hitech and lotech. Hitech equipment is generally compact, highly designed, reliable and most of all, expensive. Hitech gear is generally produced by the macrocorps or by smaller companies with ties to the macrocorps. At the opposite end of the scale is lotech equipment. Lotech items are often crude, clunky and large but can be astonishingly well made and reliable. Lotech technology does not imply a lack of skill on the part of manufacturers. Indeed, the skill required to produce a lotech microscale dingin may exceed that required to produce a hitech nanoscale dingin.

armament technology in the city
sparklocks

The most common and the most primitive firearms in The City, sparklocks range from crudely lashed together specimens made from old iron pipe to cunningly fashioned devices made by skilled artisans. The weapons function by using an electric spark to ignite a propellant charge of loose powder. The powder is poured down the barrel, tamped down, then a ball or bullet forced down the barrel on top of the powder. When the trigger is pulled, a spark is provided by scavenged capacitors or superconductors. The spark causes the propellant to ignite and propel the bullet down the barrel. After firing, the capacitors or superconductors need to be recharged, usually accomplished by connecting them to a small clockwork generator/dynamo mechanism. In order to allow more rapid fire, many sparklocks mount more than one power source.

Ammunition for a sparklock is usually a ball or elongated bullet made from compressed brick dust bound with resin, carved stone or cast iron. The weapons can come in a variety of forms, including pistols, carbines, rifles and small cannon. They can also come in single or double barrel variants, or even in rare revolver or repeater configurations.

Sparklocks are, in the main, unreliable at best and tremendously dangerous at worst.

cartridge guns

Offering superior reliability with good power and accuracy, cartridge guns are highly favoured by most of the militant organisations in The City. The guns themselves are fairly easy to manufacture but it is the ammunition which poses problems. Intricate primers, precision made bullets and high-tolerance casings are required to make the weapons function effectively. Hence, they tend to be made by the macrocorps or companies affiliated with them. This having been said, a cartridge revolver is possibly the most inherently reliable weapon in The City, and find much favour with soldiers, police officers and criminals. Cartridge guns can be found in single shot, semi-automatic, revolver and fully automatic versions, Depending on your needs, you can acquire the weapons as pistols, rifles, sub-machineguns, machineguns, shotguns and a whole plethora of weapons types.

magnetic repeaters

The highest of hitech weapons, magnetic repeaters are almost exclusively used by macrocorporate forces and a few favoured allies. Magnetic repeaters use no propellant, but instead use a series of stepped magnets arranged down the barrel to propel an iron flechette up to very high velocity. Although very small, the projectiles are fired at such a speed as to ensure great armour penetration and reasonable tissue damage. Another feature of these weapons is the rate at which they can fire. They can, if required, spew out flechettes at an astounding rate, allowing them to literally 'hose' a target. If striking power is the issue, then magnetic repeaters can also be made very powerful. Long barrels can endow such weapons as sniper rifles with extreme rage, accuracy and firepower. They can also be used in lower-velocity applications such as mortars and grenade launchers, where their adjustability allows for a variety of range settings.

reliability

In the harsh world of The City, having a reliable weapon by your side is often an important issue. Some types of weapon are more reliable than others, some manufacturers make weapons which are inherently of better quality, some systems are just more prone to breakage by their very nature. In a game context, each weapon is rated according to its reliability. In simple terms, this rating tells you how often the weapon needs to be cleaned/maintained in order to stop it malfunctioning

There are five classes of reliability. They are:

Very Unreliable

Needs maintenance and cleaning every 10 shots.

Unreliable

Needs maintenance and cleaning every 20 shot.

Average

Needs maintenance and cleaning every 100 shots.

Reliable

Needs maintenance and cleaning every 1000 shots.

Very Reliable

Only needs maintenance and cleaning about once per year.

Weapons

Pistols (lotech)

Sparklock Pistol

Most primitive of firearms found in The City, sparklocks use batteries or clockwork to charge scavenged capacitors or superconductors to spark-ignite powdered propellants. They are single shot weapons, mostly of dubious reliability. When fired, they create voluminous clouds of smoke which can often impair the vision of the firer. Repeating pepperbox and double barrelled versions are available at an increased cost (roughly 75% more than their single barrelled cousins).

Light
Cost: £20
Availability: Common

Medium
Cost: £30
Availability: Common

Heavy
Cost: £40
Availability: Common

Pepperbox
Cost: £50
Availability: Uncommon

Cartridge Pistol

Representative of the thousands of sidearms manufactured by back street shops and microcorps, the Cartridge Pistol is a regular, cased ammunition weapon with no special ad-ons. The cartridge pistol is available in Light, Medium and Heavy versions as well as in semi-automatic and revolver styles.

Light
Cost: £65
Availability: Uncommon

Medium
Cost: £85
Availability: Common

Heavy
Cost: £110
Availability: Uncommon

PISTOLS (hitech)

Furien 'Jacketcracker' Heavy Pistol

Currently holding the title of 'most powerful handgun ever produced' the 'Jacketcracker' was designed specifically to defeat Hirplakkers FLAKK line of armour jackets. Hirplakker launched the line claiming they were proof against any handgun in The City. Via Furien, Arclight responded by designing the 'Jacketcracker', a handgun of sizeable proportions but which can punch holes in the Hirplakker armour.
Cost: £900
Availability: Very rare

Furien 'Linetrooper' Medium Revolver

A bizarre but successful weapon, the 'Linetrooper' is one of the few magnetic repeater revolvers ever produced. The 'cylinder' of the weapon is essentially six small magazines arranged in a star shape, with strengthening material in between to provide the traditional revolver look. Each separate slot in the cylinder can hold 4 5mm flechettes, giving the user a choice of ammunition types. The gun can fire all four rounds in a slot in succession or can switch between slots by rotating the cylinder. An onboard nanoscale dingin provides the computing power to co-ordinate the firing of this complex but useful weapon.
Cost: £850
Availability: Very rare

Gorunna 'Sling' Heavy Pistol

A bulky, ugly weapon, the Sling is a semi-automatic heavy gauss pistol used by Gorunna corporate forces. Due to Gorunna's liberal sales of arms and equipment, untold numbers of these weapons have found their way on to the streets. Many toughs find the size and bore of the weapon appealing and intimidating, that is until the recoil breaks their arm. They are limited in ammunition capacity but have massive stopping power.

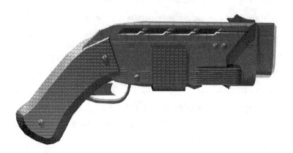

Cost: £300
Availability: Rare

Hirplakker 'Pantera' Heavy Revolver

A massive double-action revolver of menacing appearance, the 'Pantera' is widely marketed by Hirplakker and its subsidiary sales concerns. Of very simple design, the 'Pantera' offers ultimate reliability and strength.

Cost: £250
Availability: Uncommon

Micintyre 'Kicker' Medium Pistol

A militant model magnetic repeater pistol, the abilities of the weapon have been tailored for the widest possible acceptance. The penetrative abilities are high enough to discourage lightly armoured attackers but the compact barrel and the use of ferrous coated light alloy flechettes reduces the long range capabilities of the weapon.
Cost: £300
Availability: Rare

PPIM E35 Hideout Pistol
A very high quality, very small magnetic repeater pistol, manufactured by the production arm of the Personal Protection Inc militant corporation. Long for a pocket pistol, it compensates by being exceptionally slim. An integral laser dot projector assists aiming.
Cost: £350
Availability: Scarce

Souken Vent-450 Heavy Pistol
Manufactured in plants across The City, the Vent-450 has become the symbol of a mercenary for hire, and as such has become something of an institution. Its popularity is mainly due to its reliability and solid hitting power.

Cost: £230
Availability: Rare

Trilhoeven GP-013 Heavy Pistol
The more modern replacement for the centuries-old GP-010, the GP-013 uses a magnetic repeater action rather than the liquid propellant system of the older weapon. The ammunition is the same, but with a ferrous coating to allow the magnetic accelerators to 'grip' the round.
Cost: £750
Availability: Very rare

Submachineguns and Machine Pistols (lotech)

Cartridge SMG
Like the Cartridge Pistol, the Street SMG is a typical, cheap weapon found on the streets. While variants may differ slightly, they all share broadly the same characteristics.

Cost: £120
Availability: Uncommon

Submachineguns and Machine Pistols (hitech)

Mitushi 'Whistler'
A lightweight but somewhat bulky SMG, the 'Whistler' is one of the lower tech gauss weapons available. Mitushi are not wealthy or powerful enough to have access to the latest superconductor technology, hence the fact that the gun is at least two generations behind the times. The weapon's major flaw, however, is the extreme susceptibility of its onboard electronics to any form of interference. Indeed, if pushed too hard the magnetic field created by firing the weapon can scramble the processor and burn out circuits. It is, however, still a popular and effective weapon, mainly due to the large numbers manufactured over the past sixty years.
Cost: £350
Availability: Rare

Trilhoeven KM-067R
Trilhoeven's latest SMG produced for its front line troops and security operatives, the KM-067R is well ahead of anything produced by other corporations, perhaps with the exception of Arclight. Each round consists of a projectile bonded to a superconducting power cell. On discharge, the cell is ejected from the bottom of the weapon, just ahead of the trigger guard. Integral to the weapon is a din-gin moderated sensor array which scans for human silhouettes and highlights them for the user. An additional back-up din-gin unit makes the gun effectively invulnerable to any kind of interference and very resistant to battlefield damage.
Cost: £900
Availability: Very rare

Rifles (lotech)

Sparklock Carbine
A short, easily wielded weapon designed to provide the power of a rifle in a compact package. Most carbines simply look like large sparklock pistols with stocks added on to the back.

Cost: £75
Availability: Common

Sparklock Rifle

Other than sparklock cannon, these are the largest and most powerful sparklock weapons in The City. Generally between three and four feet in length, they provide good firepower but are pretty unwieldy for use in tight spaces.

Cost: £100
Availability: Common

Cartridge Rifle

Using fixed metallic cartridges, these weapons are available in a multiplicity of forms. Second only to the sparklock in popularity, they can be found in heavy and light versions, as well as single shot, semi-automatic and fully automatic versions.

Single Shot
Cost: £150
Availability: Common

Semi-Auto
Cost: £200
Availability: Uncommon

Full-auto
Cost: £250
Availability: Uncommon

rifles (hitech)

Hakken IR0018r Assault Laser

A special purpose infantry weapon designed by Hakken Industrie AG. As a result of lessons learned during the Hundred Block War (during which Hirplakker irregular troops used the IR0018), the IR0018r version was made available for sale, boasting improved sighting aids and further power splitting systems.

Cost: £1900
Availability: Scarce

Tenlier Assault-100

For decades, successive models of the Assault-100 have been best sellers in the militant market.

Cost: £1000
Availability: Uncommon

Trilhoeven KSK-G30

Rarely available in the commercial markets, the KSK-G30 equips large numbers of Trilhoeven militia troops. The weapons main advantage is its massive ammunition supply, which allows troopers to literally hose targets with flechettes.

Cost: £1500
Availability: Very rare

sniper weapons

Arclight 'Redeye' Laser Rifle

One of Arclight's most advanced pieces of technology, the 'Redeye' equips some elite Brigade of Light recon troops. While none have been sold on the open market, it is known that the rifle is frequency agile, allowing it to cut through some atmospheric obscuration. Sighting aids fitted as standard include a multimode laser sight, target predicting HUD and datapaths for connection into powered armour systems.

Cost: £2300
Availability: Scarce

Furien 'Shellbreaker' Gauss Rifle

A devastatingly accurate and powerful weapon, the 'Shellbreaker' has enabled Furien to virtually corner the market in gauss sniper weapons. Fully 50% of this type sold to militant organisations are Furien 'Shellbreakers'. Expensive, they are seldom seen outside militant or macrocorporate hands.

Cost: £2000 (including basic sight)
Availability: Scarce

shotguns (lotech)

Sparklock Blunderbuss

Using a design common to most other sparklocks, the sparklock blunderbuss looks like nothing more than a sparklock carbine with a grossly over-sized barrel. While inaccurate in the extreme and possessing a hopelessly short range, few toughs will argue with someone toting one of these vicious weapons.

Cost: £70
Availability: Common

Cartridge Shotgun

A step up from the common sparklock, cartridge shotguns use cased ammunition, either manufactured by one of the many small companies across The City or laboriously produced by hand in back alley workshops. Versions vary from simple break action breechloaders right up to semi-auto weapons.

Cost: £150 (single shot), £200 (pump)
Availability: Uncommon

Shotguns (hitech)

Hirplakker 'Lacerator' Gauss Shotgun

This versatile 15mm weapon can fire clusters of needles, HEAP shells, APDS rounds or all manner of specialised ammunition. Examples captured by Arclight during the Hundred Block War were studied and Arclight have since produced their own weapon, the 16mm 'Thorn'.

Cost: £600
Availability: Scarce

Micintyre L16B

A high tech conventional weapon, the L16B is the longarm of choice for militant units engaged in house clearing operations. A helical magazine slung under the barrel gives prodigious ammo capacity and a wide range of rounds including HEAP, HE, flechette and APDS are available.

Cost: £500
Availability: Very rare

Heavy Weapons

Arclight 'Boomer' A1 Pack-cannon

Fearsome in its power, the 'Boomer' is the prime armamnet of Arclight's legendary Tentenal troops. This 0.75 inch, semi-auto, magnetic repeater cannon provides immense striking power, as well as the capability to launch a wide variety of different projectiles.

Cost: £5000
Availability: No way.

Makei Assault Gun

A ruggedly simple but nonetheless hard-hitting weapon, the Makei AG is a highly effective light anti-armour weapon. Firing a variety of low-pressure 19mm rounds, it has often proved the bane of APA equipped units.

Cost: £500
Availability: Rare

Trilhoeven Microhowitzer

Part way between a grenade launcher and a hand-held cannon, the Microhowitzer serves Trilhoeven troops as an anti-armour, anti-building and indirect fire weapon. Its 45mm shell gives it enough velocity to be reasonably accurate at short ranges and provides good indirect fire range. The magnetic propulsion system also eases the felt recoil of the weapon, which is also managed by a fully integrated system of buffers and compensators.

Cost: £1000
Availability: Very rare

Vehicular Weapons

Sparklock Cannon

Ranging from the man-portable jezails (essentially a very, very large sparklock rifle) right up to substantial breechloading cannon, these are the ultimate evolution of the sparklock. Divided into light, medium and heavy classes, only the light variants are man-portable.

Light	Medium
Cost: £200	**Cost:** £600
Availability: Uncommon	Availability: Rare

Heavy
Cost: £1000
Availability: Very rare

Cartridge Cannon

Available in light (roughly 15 to 25mm), medium (roughly 30 to 45mm) and heavy (anything above 45mm) versions, cartridge cannon use the same technology as other cartridge weapons, only on a much larger scale. Single shot, semi-auto and automatic (light a medium only) versions are available for fitment to vehicles and fixed emplacements.

Light
Cost: £1500
Availability: Rare

Medium
Cost: £4000
Availability: Rare

Heavy
Cost: £10,000+
Availability: Very rare

Magnetic Repeater Cannon

Powerful, accurate weapons with an alarming tendency to go right through their intended target and blast through intervening walls, buildings and people, magnetic repeater cannons are undoubtedly the most powerful direct-fire weapons in The City. As with other vehicular class weapons, they are available in light, medium and heavy versions. Only the very largest vehicles can mount the heavy versions, as the power requirements and recoil are immense.

Light
Cost: £3,500
Availability: Very rare

Medium
Cost: £6,000
Availability: Scarce

Heavy
Cost: If you have to ask, you can't afford it.
Availability: Scarce

Rockets

Perhaps even more frowned upon than magnetic repeater cannons, rockets can cause widespread destruction due to their explosive warheads. Light variants can be carried and fired by a single man, while the medium and heavy versions require vehicles.

Light
Cost: £200
Availability: Very rare

Medium
Cost: £600
Availability: Very rare

Heavy
Cost: Anything the seller wants to ask.
Availability: Scarce

ammunition types & costs

Solid shot

The standard projectile for sparklocks, cartridge weapons and magnetic repeaters, solid shot is a basic solid ball, bullet or (in the case of magnetic repeaters) flechette. The listed DAM and PEN values for all projectile weapons (other than those firing explosive rounds, such as the Microhowitzer) are for solid shot.
Cost multiple: None (see table below for costs)
Availability: Same as weapon

Safety Rounds

Something of a misnomer, as they are anything but safe for the target. Safety round are designed to increase the damage done to a target at the expense of penetrating power. They can be frangible, soft-nosed, hollowpoint, crosshead or any number of similarly nasty ways to do more damage to living tissue. Safety rounds have their PEN reduced by 50% but any damage that gets through is increased by 50%.
Cost Multiple: x2
Availability: Same as weapon

Armour Piercing Rounds

The exact opposite of safety round, armour piercing (AP) rounds have increased penetration at the expense of delivered damage. AP rounds have their PEN increased by 50% but penetrating DAM is reduced by 50%.
Cost Multiple: x3
Availability: One level higher than weapon

Ammunition Cost is per clip, or 20 rounds if the weapon uses loose ammo.

Type of Weapon	Ammunition Cost
Sparklock Pistol (any)	£1
Cartridge Pistol or SMG (any)	5% of weapon cost
Magnetic Repeater Pistol or SMG (any)	10% of weapon cost
Sparklock Carbine, Rifle or Blunderbuss (any)	£1.10s
Cartridge Rifle or Shotgun (any)	5% of weapon cost
Magnetic Repeater Rifle or Sniper Weapon (any)	10% of weapon cost
Heavy Weapon (lotech)	5% of weapon cost
Heavy Weapon (hitech)	15% of weapon cost

weapon accessories

Adaptive Laser Sight

A useful and effective variation on the standard laser sight. An ultrasonic device measures the distance to the target and adjusts the depression or elevation of the laser beam to account for the drop. The sight also contains a tiny gyrostabiliser which detects rapid gun movement and adjusts the laser beam to compensate for angular barrel movement during snap shots. The sight must be keyed in to the specific weapon it is being used with upon purchase. If this is not done, it merely functions as a normal laser sight. The ALS is only really effective at ranges of under 100 metres, beyond this the time lag for the ultrasound pulse becomes too great for use in a combat situation.

Game effects are to give +1 round to aim time, -10% off firer movement penalties and the benefits of a laser rangefinder. The -10% to movement penalties does not have the deleterious effects of a gyrostabiliser.

Cost: £300
Availability: Rare

Gyrostabilisers

Hand weapon gyrostabilisation operates on six gyros (all controlled by an onboard dingin), with two contrarotating gyros on each axis, near the weapon's centre of gravity. Pressure switches speed up or brake certain gyros depending on how the weapon is moved, helping the user to change it from facing to facing. If the weapon is not being pivoted, the gyros tend to keep the weapon pointed in the same direction, regardless of firer motion. A gyro system will halve negative movement modifiers on firing but automatically makes the reaction modifier of the weapon 10% worse.

Cost: £250
Availability: Rare

Laser Dot

A simple red dot projecting system for weapons, only really useful over short distances due to the obscurative properties of the air in The City. Most versions are designed for close-range use, under 100m, and are very small and light. IR laser sights are also available, where the beam can only be seen through IR or lowlight sights or goggles.

Cost: £250
Availability: Uncommon

Holsters

Available in a wide variety of styles and materials and available to carry any handgun or machine-pistol.
Cost: 5s to £200
Availability: Common

Optical Sights

Ranging from simple versions using hand ground lenses, right up to dingin-moderated versions used by macrocorp snipers, optical sights are a common weapon accessory. They can only be used in aimed fire. Sights are available in three forms: x2, x3 and x4. These are used to multiply the aiming range of the weapon for the purposes of negating range penalties. For example: A rifle with a range of 50 using a x2 sight would have range bands of 100/200/400/800 for the purposes of aiming modifiers, although the maximum range would still only be 400 metres.
Cost: **x2:** £50 **x3:** £150 **x4:** £300
Availability: Uncommon

Silencers and Suppressors

True "silencers" are extremely difficult to construct because, although the sound of the cartridge firing can be muffled, the bullet itself cannot, and it is this supersonic crack which usually alerts the target. Sound suppressors effectively muffle the sound of the weapon firing while leaving the supersonic crack of the bullet unmodified. This will have no effect on the ability of target personnel to realise that they are being fired at but it does make it more difficult for persons who are not taking part in the firefight to realise what is happening.

Firefights conducted with suppressed weapons will seldom be heard beyond 100 metres. Truly silenced weapons not only muffle the sound of the cartridge firing but also slow the bullet (usually by bleeding off propellant gas) to sub-sonic speeds. This reduces the noise of firing but also considerably reduces muzzle energy. Silenced weapons will not be heard beyond 20 metres in open areas or beyond 5 metres in urban areas.
Silencer Cost: £20 per DAM point of weapon, plus 25% of original weapon cost to modify firearm for silent operating.
Availability: Very rare

Suppressor Cost: £10 per DAM point of weapon, plus 25% of original weapon cost to modify firearm for supressed operating.
Availability: Very rare

melee weapons

Ceramic Blade (hitech)

Constructed from composite ceramic materials, the blade of this knife has unrivalled sharpness and strength.

Cost: £25
Availability: Rare

Ceramic Long Knife (hitech)

A longer, larger version of the ceramic blade, offering slightly greater reach and a more intimidating appearance than its smaller cousin.

Cost: £40
Availability: Very rare

Llife (hitech)

Incredibly sharp weapons, llives are made up of extremely thin layers of diamond sheet, ceramic and high quality steel bonded together on the molecular level. Not designed at all as stabbing weapons, in a slashing attack they can cut through armour, bone, muscle, metal and just about anything else. They are very much in favour with ghostfighters and others who rely on quality edged weapons for their livelihoods.

Cost: £200
Availability: Very rare

Billy Club

As used by the Provosts and numerous other police agencies across The City. The billy club is constructed from high-impact materials and is carefully weighted to allow maximum energy transfer upon impact. In trained hands this can be an exceptionally effective weapon and gives superior punch when compared to a regular cosh or club.

Cost: £35
Availability: Rare

armour

Armoured Clothing (hitech)

Regular clothing with a layer of ballistic fibres.

Cost: £7 per item
Availability: Uncommon

Armour Vest (hitech)

Covers the torso, shoulders and groin with a layer of hardened plastics, ballistic fibre and other materials which the manufacturer chooses to include.

Cost: £20
Availability: Common

Integrated Armour Suit (hitech)

Fully sealed, semi-powered, used by some macrocorporate troops for assault duties

Cost: £500
Availability: Rare

Mail Vest (lotech)

Painstakingly made of tiny metal links, mail vests are generally the highest quality lotech armour.

Cost: £5
Availability: Common

Makeshift Armour (lotech)

Constructed from a hodge-podge of materials, most makeshift armour looks and is home-made.

Cost: Homemade
Availability: Very common

Padded Armour (lotech)

Really nothing more than very heavy clothing, perhaps reinforced with hardened dogskin at vital points. Useful against knives and suchlike, but pretty much useless against guns.

Cost: 10s per item
Availability: Common

Helmet (hitech)

Protects the head and features attachment points for sensor systems.

Cost: £20
Availability: Rare

Helmet (lotech)

Still protects the head, but not very well.

Cost: £1
Availability: Common

Roadarmour

Ideal for the powerbikers who wants that little edge in protection. Made from the same light but strong materials as light bullet proof vests, Roadarmour is a tight fitting, full body suit of powerbike/ekranoplan clothing. With padded joint sections and improved ballistic fabrics, it offers impressive protection in a potential roadrash situation.

Cost: £40
Availability: Rare

son to the clunky powered suits utilised by other macrocorps) and extensive sensory apparatus make it superior in almost every respect to any other similar item in The City. It is, however, very (very, very) expensive to produce, hence the rather small numbers which the Brigade of Light can field at any one time.

Cost: £35,000
Availability: Not a hope
Bonuses: +40 to all weapons fire, STR becomes 120 when using suit, 'Viridian' system has a 75% chance of hitting any missile, rocket or thrown item directed at the suit. It fires once the item is within 25m of the suit. A single hit will usually disable or destroy the target.

Trilhoeven 'Mad Dog' Battle Armour

A fearsome piece of combat equipment from Trilhoeven, this suit skirts the very edge of technological advancement. Incorporating mimetic stealth systems, self-repair nanoware and powerful artificial musculature, the 'Mad Dog' is the ultimate in lightweight personal armour.

Cost: £25,000
Availability: Scarce
Bonuses: +20 to weapons fire, STR becomes 150 when using suit. Mimetic systems offer the equivalent of Hide skill at 90%.

Trilhoeven 'Running Dog' Scout Armour

A counterpart to the heavier 'Mad Dog' system, the 'Running Dog' dispenses with much of the armour layers and self-repair systems of its brother and instead relies on speed, stealth and its amazing sensory systems to keep out of trouble. Most Trilhoeven infantry companies have at least one trooper outfitted with the system, acting as an advance scout and recon asset. Some units have even been know to equip their snipers with these suits, allowing the sniper to use the long range sensors and superior carrying capacity to achieve remarkable long-range kills.

Cost: £20,000
Availability: Scarce
Bonuses: +40 to weapons fire, STR is 100 when using suit. The mimetic capabilities of the suit give +50% to any Hide or Sneak rolls made while wearing the suit.

powered armour

Arclight 'Tentenel' Battle Armour

Tentenel armour provides Arclight heavy infantry with an environmentally sealed, power-assisted protective suit ideally suited to urban warfare. Its compact dimensions (in compari-

Living costs & upkeep

Even the most basic accommodation and sustenance costs money, often money that many of the poor unfortunates who live in The City don't have. The table below give a selection of costs for accommodation, food and a variety of services.

Services

Service	Cost (per week)
Sideband TV service	£2
Additional factual channels	£1
Telephone service	£3
Electricity for a home	£1 - £20
Gas for a home	£1 - £15
Healthcare	Extremely variable
e.g: TCMAA Health Service	10s (basic)
Macrocorp Health Care	£25 (basic)
Local taxes (depends on area)	From 5s to £50
e.g.: TCMAA Council Tax	10s (basic)
TCMAA Higher Band	£5
TCMAA Premier Band	£35
Servant (depending on status)	£3 to £20
e.g: Cleaner	£3 - 5
Bodyguard	£5 - 20
Butler	£10 - 20

Sustenance

Foodstuff	Cost
Poor quality fish (the kind of stuff produced in Bankside)	1s per fish
Good quality fish (macrocorp reared)	£2 per fillet
Bread (fishmeal and plant fibres)	1s per loaf
Dog (whole)	£1 - £10
Dog (leg)	4s to £5
Dog (steak)	2s to £3
Fruit	5s to £10 per item
Vegetables	3s to £10 per item
Spices	2s to £20 per small bag
Herbs	2s to £20 per small bag
Clean drinking water	1s per cup
Tea leaves	1s per small bag
Spirits, rough, 1 litre bottle	£1
Spirits, quality, 1 litre bottle	£10

Eating Out	Cost
Meatballs in sauce from street stall	2s
Fried fish & troot from street stall	3s
Cup of tea in cafe or street stall	1s
Meal for 1 at poor quality eatery	4s
Meal for 1 at mid-level eatery	£2
Meal for 1 at high-class eatery	Anything from £10 upwards

Accommodation

Standard	Cost (per week)
Squat or totally uncontrolled area (e.g.: Dreamingspires)	Nothing, although sometimes gangs may charge 'protection'
Slum hovel, very poor quality tenement or towerblock room (e.g.: Mire End)	Between 10s and £1, again, sometimes 'protection' may be charged in addition to this.
Low-grade tenemental rooms (e.g.: Folly Hills, Fogwarren, etc)	Between £1 and £2.
Mid-grade tenemental or towerblock rooms (eg: east Folly Hills)	Between £2 and £5
Best-quality (relatively speaking) tenemental rooms (eg: better areas of Fogwarren)	Between £5 and £10
Low-quality apartment in good area (eg: cheapest, least desireable parts of Clearwater Break)	Between £10 and £40
Mid-quality apartment in good area (eg: 'bottom of hill' properties in Lucent Heights)	Between £30 and £60
High-quality apartment in good area (the best properties in Lucent Heights and Clearwater Break)	Between £50 and £200
3 bedroomed house in poor area	Between £5 and £10
3 bedroomed house in reasonable area	Between £10 and £50
3 bedroomed house in good area	Between £70 and £300

dingins

Dingins are the fundamental building blocks upon which almost all the computing power of The City is based. Rod logic provides the power for businesses to operate and for the Dataflow to function. The dingin is both ubiquitous and vital, in all its many forms and variations. From the creaking, clanking macroscale engines still used by the Three Canals Metropolitan Area Provosts to store their crime information, to the compressed efficiency of single cubic inch nanoscale units (and all the sizes in between), dingins are everywhere you look, calculating, storing, processing and analysing.

All dingins are rated according to their volume, the more volume, the greater the power. However, this is relative within the different classes of dingin. A two cubic inch nanoscale unit is far more powerful than a two cubic foot macroscale unit. For reference, one cubic foot equals 1728 cubic inches.

The previously mentioned Provost dingins run to hundreds of cubic feet of rods, gears and cranks and can analyse and store vast amounts of data. For this type of engine, the data is stored on punched cards, tapes or optically read sheets. Data is fed into the machine in a similar manner, using laboriously prepared cards or punched in manually at enormous input desks. Output is generally in the form of typed sheets, fed out from automatic electric typewriters. Some macroscale engines can be linked to screens, but this is relatively rare.

Unlike macroscale dingins, microscale versions are far more portable. However, their increased compactness is somewhat tempered by the need for cooling devices such as heatsinks in order to bleed away the enormous amounts of heat produced by the unit. Microscales are rated according to the cubic inch, although there are some very large microscale units which are rated by the cubic foot. Very small microscale dingins are also rare, the smallest versions being about four or five cubic inches in size and of relatively limited capacity. The average size is about that of a large book, perhaps eight inches wide, eleven inches high and three inches deep, giving a total cubic capacity of 264 inches.

However, the main problem is that each cubic inch of macroscale dingin requires a similar cubic capacity of heat dispersal systems. So, our previously mentioned book-sized microscale dingin with a volume of 264 cubic inches would require another 264 cubic inches of heatsinks, fans and other cooling items. Microscales can be programmed via minia-turised metallic tapes or, like macroscale dingins, by labori-ously hand programming them. Again, they can also give similar output but they are also commonly linked into screens for ease of use. Some users go as far as to buy active gel-screens at great expense in order to obtain clear, full colour readouts from their dingins.

Nanoscale dingins are the ultimate in miniaturised computing systems. Compared even to microscale systems, they are tiny. Some can be built down to tenth of a cubic inch in size, suit-able for installation into weapons and other portable sys-tems. They do, however, require cooling systems equal to five times their own cubic capacity. So, a one cubic inch nanoscale dingin will require five cubic inches of heatsinks and coolants. A twenty one cubic inch nanoscale dingin (a cube measuring just three inches on a side) plus it's associat-ed one hundred and five cubic inches of cooling gear, would provide an immense amount of computing power, power far in excess of any macroscale dingin and vastly more powerful than all but the very largest microscale units.

In terms of processing power, a cubic foot of microscale din-gin is ten times more powerful than a cubic foot of macroscale engine. As a rough rule of thumb, a microscale engine will be a tenth the size of a macroscale unit of equiv-alent power (not taking into account the associated cooling systems, these would double the size of the unit, making it one fifth of the size of an equivalent macroscale unit). Nanoscale dingins are even more powerful by several orders of magnitude. A one cubic inch nanoscale dingin will have the processing power of several cubic feet of macroscale unit, depending on the techniques used to make the nanoscale unit.

Macroscale

Slow, clunky and requiring constant maintenance, macroscale dingins can perform basic arithmetical and math-ematical tasks. Provided you keep them oiled. They are gen-erally programmed by means of punched cards, punched tapes or manual programming inputs.
Cost: £30 to £1000
Availability: Common

Microscale

Faster and more powerful than macroscale dingins, microscale variants can run more sophisticated programmes and carry out far more complex tasks. However, they are high maintenance items requiring specialist skills and tools. They are programmed via tiny metallic tapes.
Cost: £50 to £2000
Availability: Common

Nanoscale

Packing immense processing power into the same space as a microscale unit, nanoscale dingins can also be made extremely small to fit into a variety of other devices. Exclusively produced by the macrocorps, they are programmed by molecular 'tapes' or 'chains'.

Cost: £80 to £5000
Availability: Very rare

dingin accessories

Code Lock

A popular system for defending against unwanted dingin intrusion, the code lock is available in all shapes and sizes. Regardless of size and cost, all work on the same principles. The code lock is spliced into a line leading to a dingin or memory system. Once in place, the user manually inputs a six figure code (changeable at any time), setting a series of six mechanical wheels, activated by combs or gears (each wheel corresponds to an individual numeral in the code). Anyone attempting to access the system must input the right six figure code through the Dataflow or the mechanical system will lock down, preventing any access to the system until the owner manually resets the lock. Essentially, this give an intruder a one-in-a-million chance of successfully entering a system without having the proper code.

Hitech Cost: £100
Availability: Rare

Lotech Cost: £10
Availability: Common

Dataflow Splice

Splices come in many shapes and size, but in essence they are the means by which a dingin can connect to the Dataflow. They convert the mechanical output of the dingin into an electronic signal and vice versa. Some are simple arrangements of components which can be clamped to bare telephone wires, others are complex little boxes of tricks with microscale switching systems and integral firewalls.

Hitech Cost: £100
Availability: Rare

Lotech Cost: £2
Availability: Common

Keyboard

Vital in order to make inputs into a dingin, keyboards can range from massive lotech static arrangements of iron keys, rods and levers to wafer-thin hitech foldable arrays of pressure switches using tiny flexible rods and levers to transmit instructions. Most portable lotech keyboards are fashioned from metal and are about the size of a typewriter.

Hitech Cost: £100
Availability: Rare

Lotech Cost: £20
Availability: Common

Memory

External memory which can be used to store information abstracted from the Dataflow, programmes, records or anything the user chooses to input. Hitech systems employ complex means of storing information such as laser-manipulated optical cores, whilst lotech mechanisms are simply dumb collections of gears, rods and switches, much like the dingins themselves.

Memory is rated according to 'Page Equivalents' (Pe), ie: the memory that would be required to store the information held on a single, standard sized sheet of paper. Lotech mechanical storage systems often use actual cards with information printed on them which are stored, then optically read when the information is required. The capacity of storage systems can vary from a few hundred Pe for macroscale mechanical memory to many billions of Pe for the optical cores or nanoscale substrates used by the macrocorps.

Hitech Cost: £100 per million Pe
Availability: Very rare

Lotech Cost: £20 per 100 Pe
Availability: Common

Output Devices

All dingins require some form of output. Some use ticker tape mechanisms, others printed cards and still others used a variety of screening systems. Screens themselves can range from mechanically actuated arrays of tiny flipping squares which arrange themselves to form words or pictures, through crude cathode tubes, right up to flat liquid displays which can be rolled up and stored in a pocket.

Hitech Flat Display: £100
Availability: Very rare

Hitech Hard Display: £70
Availability: Rare

Hitech Printer Output: £60
Availability: Rare

Lotech Cathode Tube: £30
Availability: Rare

Lotech Mechanical Display: £50
Availability: Rare

Lotech Tickertape Output: £15
Availability: Common

General equipment

Clothing

The following lists give costs for various common items of clothing.

ITEM	COST
Hat	2s to £50
Work Trousers	10s
Cheap set of clothes	15s
(trousers, shirt, jacket)	
Average Suit	£2.15s
Tie	1s to £100
Waterproof Jacket	£1.5s
Military Trousers	£1.2s
Jumpsuit	£2
Greatcoat	£2
Dogskin Coat	£10 to £500
Cheap Shoes	7s.2p
Average Shoes	£1.10s
Quality Shoes	Up to £200
Quality Boots	Up to £250
Powerbike Boots	£10 to £400
Belt	1s upwards

Navigation devices

Automapper (hitech)

A handy device for those who just can't find their way about. Simply tell the unit where you are currently and where you wish to go to, plug it in to a public phone and it will link in to the local Dataflow and access map databases to give you the best route to your destination. It can, however, take a very long time to access the information through the chaos of the Dataflow.
Cost: £10
Availability: Rare

Inertial Compass (hitech)

Must be calibrated at the starting point of each journey. The small dingin computes distance travelled and gives direction back to the starting point. Not hugely effective in a three-dimensional environment.
Cost: £7
Availability: Rare

Medical equipment

First Aid Kit (hitech)

Contains hypospray with a variety of drugs, self-hardening casts, second skin spray and a small dingin with diagnostic programming.
Cost: £5
Availability: Rare

First Aid Kit (lotech)

Contains some antiseptic, bandages and tourniquets.
Cost: 10s
Availability: Very common

Medical Kit (hitech)

A larger and better equipped version of the First Aid Kit, the medical kit contains three times the amount of disposables that the first aid kit contains, as well as more advanced tools for minor field surgery. Also included is a small biomonitor which will give readouts on respiration, blood pressure, blood type, respiration, heart rate etc. Two pints of artificial blood substitute are included in the pack.
Cost: £20
Availability: Rare

survival gear

Blanket
A simple doghair or plant fibre blanket.
Cost: 2s
Availability: Very common

Gas Mask (Lotech)
A lowtech solution to airborne gases and toxins, the gas mask is a simple, flexible mask with two glass covered eyeholes. Air is filtered through a bulky box attached to the users belt and makes its way to the mask via flexible hose.
Cost: £5
Availability: Uncommon

Respirator (hitech)
This is a small (10x20cm) oxygen cylinder attached through a hose to a light facemask. It provides enough air for five hours of moderate exertion.
Cost: £25
Availability: Rare

Rucksack
Multipurpose bag, ideal for all manner of outdoor activities. Available in a variety of sizes.
Cost: 5s to £50
Availability: Very common

Survival Kit (hitech)
This rugged box contains a useful assortment of stuff: flares, small utility knife, lighter, compass, lightweight thermal blanket, emergency rations, water purification tablets, a filter mask and many other items. Commonly issued to macrocorp operatives in the field.
Cost: £200
Availability: Rare

Utility Knife
The cheapest models come with three or four features while the most expensive versions can have up to twenty useful items. either on the knife or in the carrying pouch. Hitech versions will generally be of better quality materials, while lotech versions have a rugged simplicity about them.
Cost: £40 to £250
Availability: Common

tools

Basic Tool Kit
This kit includes small hand tools, suitable for a variety purposes, including wrenches, pliers, screwdrivers etc.
Cost: £10 to £100
Availability: Very common

Electrics Tools
A standard set of tools for working on electrical equipment.
Cost: £15 to £200
Availability: Very common

Electronic Security Circumvention Kit (hitech)
A useful (and sometimes highly illegal) little box of tricks used to bypass and override electronic security systems. Possession of such an item is punishable by a very heavy fine or a prison sentence.
Cost: £50
Availability: Very rare

Mechanics Tool Kit
All the tools needed for basic vehicle maintenance.
Cost: £30 to £500,
Availability: Common

Weapon Maintenance Kit (hitech)
Comes with a diagnostic dingin and a variety of cleaning, lubrication and general maintenance items.
Cost: £10
Availability: Rare

Weapon Maintenance Kit (lotech)
A can of oil, a rag and a rod for pushing the oily rag down a weapon's barrel.
Cost: £1
Availability: Very common

scientific equipment

Dissecting Kit
Kit containing a few small glass jars, forceps, scalpels and a selection of other tools for the dissection of flora and fauna.
Cost: 15s
Availability: Rare

Lab Apparatus, Chemical (lotech)

A whole assortment of glassware (flasks, pipettes, test tubes and suchlike) for the conducting of chemical tests and experiments. Also comes with a thermometer and a small burner which uses fish oil.

Cost: £15
Availability: Rare

Lab Apparatus, Electrical (lotech)

A multitude of bits of wire, insulation, coils, dynamos, meters and connections for the study of electrical phenomenon.

Cost: £20
Availability: Rare

Photographic Lab Apparatus (lotech)

Required to develop photographs produced by lotech cameras, the lab apparatus contains an assortment of chemicals, tweezers, trays and even a black blanket to serve as an extemporised darkroom.

Cost: £15
Availability: Common

vision enhancers

Binoculars

Either flat, compact digital imagers or bulky, easily damaged lotech optical versions. Hitech models can have lowlight, IR, gyrostabilisation and rangefinder facilities. Hand made optical binoculars can also be purchased, but only from specialised manufacturers at considerable (not to say extortionate) prices.

Cost: £4 to £200
Availability: Rare

Camera (hitech)

Compact, rugged and easily used, the hitech camera stores images on an optical storage medium and contains a tiny nanoscale dingin to run the various light meters, zooms and enhancement functions.

Cost: £50
Availability: Rare

Camera (lotech)

A single shot, bulky device which creates photographs on an emulsion plate or treated paper. Requires a photographic lab and some form of darkroom to develop the images.

Cost: £5
Availability: Common

Electric Torch (hitech)

Compact, reliable, tough and powered by high-capacity batteries. Once the batteries run down, it is almost impossible to buy spares unless you are in some way connected with the manufacturers of such things or have access to nomenklatura shopping areas.

Cost: £3
Availability: Rare

Electric Torch (lotech)

Powered from either a hand crank or clockwork mechanism connected to a dynamo or by very bulky, short-duration batteries.

Cost: £1
Availability: Common

Fish Oil Lamp (lotech)

Hand carried lamp which burns refined fish oil in a glass enclosed chamber in order to produce light. More than a little smelly in operation.

Cost: 5s (enough oil for an hour of operation costs 10p)
Availability: Very common

Magnifying Glass

Pocket sized, hand held glass which makes small things appear larger. Useful for examining fingerprints and the like. Much beloved of lostfinders, Provosts and assorted scientists.

Cost: 10s
Availability: Common

Spectacles

The simplest and most common way of resolving vision defects. They can range from cheap, fragile constructions which do little to correct problems to finely wrought items of great expense.

Cost: Ranging from 4s to £100
Availability: Very common

miscellaneous equipment

Climbing Kit

Contains 50 yards rope, pitons, hammer and slings.

Cost: £3 (lotech), £35 (hitech)
Availability: Common

Clockwork Generator

Wind-up dynamo used to recharge sparklocks, power dingins or similar activities.

Cost: £5
Availability: Very common

Fishoil Stove

A small stove, constructed of metal, burning fish oil contained in a hand pressurised tank.

Cost: £1
Availability: Very common

Disguise Kit

Contains a wide variety of make up, hair tints, artificial hair and padding to alter the appearance of an individual.

Cost: £6
Availability: Rare

Goggles

In hitech or lotech form, both feature flat lenses of glass plastic to prevent harmful objects reaching the eyes.

Cost: 7s (lotech), £3 (hitech)
Availability: Very common

Grappling Hook

A heavy, three pronged grapple designed for scaling walls.

Cost: £2
Availability: Common

Lockpick Set

As used by burglars, spies and persons of ill repute throughout the ages. A lockpick set contains around twenty different sizes of picks. It is very illegal in most areas with any kind of law to own such an item.

Cost: £25
Availability: Rare

Mess Kit

An assortment of dixies, forks and knives for outdoor cooking and eating. Some kits also include a small, solid fuel burning stove for heating food.

Cost: Basic: £1   **With Stove:** £3
Availability: Common

Rope, 10 Yards (hitech)

Artificial fibre rope with a breaking strain of 1000 kilos.

Cost: £5
Availability: Rare

Rope, 10 Yards (lotech)

Made from huyzel vine fibres, lotech rope has a breaking strain of 200 kilos.

Cost: 15s
Availability: Very common

Watch

Ranging from slimline, elegant models crafted from precious metals to bulky, clunky pocket watches which require winding several times a day. Watches are only really owned by those to whom a knowledge of time is vital. All watches are powered by traditional clockwork mechanisms of varying degrees of quality.

Cost: £5 to £500
Availability: Common

bioscience

A misunderstood, rare part of life in The City, the biological modification of the human body is only truly understood by the scientists working for the eight macrocorps. It is they who use it to its fullest extent, modifying their spies and soldiers to make them faster, stronger or many other, more subtle improvements. This does not mean to say that ordinary citizens do not come into contact with biosci. The fish breeders who tend their herds in the canals utilise primitive bioscience and selective breeding to improve their stocks. However most people do not recognise this as bioscience, merely an integral part of their everyday lives. Modifying the human system is both difficult and dangerous (not to say expensive).

Although rare in the general populace (only about 0.6% of the population of The City have some form of bio or nano implants), in the higher levels of macrocorporate and upper class existence, it is rare to find an individual who is not modified in some way. Senior executives, researchers, wealthy scions, all are integrated into a pervasive and at times invasive network of data, communications, analysis and observation. The most common form of implant is some form of biotech or nanotech headware, designed to optimise or increase the intelligence, analytical abilities and access to knowledge of a given individual. Within the secure, virus proofed, domains of the macrocorps, wireless links allow users to access remote databases, interface with machinery or communicate with colleagues at the speed of thought. Out of necessity, these systems integrate some electronic components (such as the transmitters and receivers for the links), but these are heavily shielded and are specifically programmed to shut down and totally seal the link when the user is not within a shielded area. However, the vast majority of modifications rely on 'soft' technology, cultured or force-grown biological implants. Individuals outfitted with a suite of implants can appear positively superhuman when compared with the average undernourished, sickly inhabitant of The City. As the decades roll by, the elite of The City are becoming further and further separated from the commonality. Hitech medical care, implants, anti-agathics and nanotech are taking them further and further from the human baseline towards the next stage of human evolution.

For a normal person, interaction with a heavily modified member of The Leet (as these individuals are commonly known) can be difficult. Vastly expanded sensoria and the ability to communicate by a range of different means can cause real problems. The ability to hear in a far wider range of sound than a normal human, coupled with the ability to communicate across a far broader range means that two Leet will often seem to be speaking noiselessly to each other, when in fact they are having an animated and intense discussion. Sociologists have commented that all the signs are pointing to a 'divergence singularity', where the two streams of humanity will separate, no longer having any form of common ground on which to communicate. In the eyes of many, this would lead to the increased isolation of The Leet, who would find it necessary to communicate with the general populace through less heavily modded intermediaries.

Problems also emerge from the bottom up. For example, in Bankside there are a number of 'clinics' offering simple bio modifications to those mad enough to go under the surgeon's knife. These modifications have grown out of the knowledge acquired from the breeding and genetic modification of the fish which provide Bankside with its livelihood. Primitive modifications are available in backstreet clinics, but these are highly dangerous and can often have horrible consequences (cancer being the least unpleasant of many side effects).

However, a more threatening aspect of the Leet cycle of modification is its application in warfare and espionage. The wealth of the macrocorps and their access to extreme hitech allows them to extensively modify certain operatives and soldiers in order to make them effectively unbeatable against those not suitably modified and trained. The prime example of this is the Hirplakker Gene Pool Troopers (GPTs). The result of a centuries long programme (possibly predating The Shift) to produce a soldier who was demonstrably tougher, faster, stronger and smarter than every other warrior out there resulted in the GPTs. In one on one combat, there has never been a case (in common knowledge) of a 'normal' individual get-

ting the best of a Trooper. Even the best ghostfighters The City has to offer would run a mile at the very thought of taking on a Trooper in single combat. This seeming invincibility of the modified forces possessed by the macrocorps instils a sense of fear in the populace, a sense of fear which is tapped into and used by the macrocorps whenever their workers begin grumbling about working conditions, pay or benefits.

However, some of the macrocorps do not go down this route. Arclight are notable for being very parsimonious in their use of soft technologies, preferring extremely well developed hard technology to counter soft technology applications. The Hundred Block War demonstrated the benefits of a more flexible approach when applied to the hard/soft technology approach. The inherent flexibility of the Arclight Tentenel troops proved too much for the Gene Pool Troopers, who were roundly defeated by the Arclight forces at almost every turn.

It should not, however, be assumed that hard technology orientated organisations such as Arclight do not use soft technology. The upper levels of Arclight are just as dominated by the heavily modified as any other macrocorps and certain elite forces, such as the Spyvers, receive just as much modification and training as the forces of other macros.

Modifications

Anti-toxin

A broad-spectrum filtering and neutralisation system, anti-toxin helps the body combat a wide variety of toxic compounds, including many commonly used poisons.

Effects: Triples the characters RES for the purposes of resisting toxins and poisons.
Cost: £1000
Availability: Very rare

Bleeder

Surprisingly (or not, as the case may be) another military bioware development that has found its way on to the civilian market. Initially developed to reduce the number of battlefield deaths from bleeding, this system implants two bioengineered glands which store the blood clotting compounds fibrin and fibrinogen. One gland is attached to the mesenteric artery where it branches in to the femoral arteries leading to the legs, while the other is located at the aortic arch where it branches in to the auxiliary arteries to the arms and the carotid arteries to the head. Wounds that cause a drop in blood pressure or massively elevated levels of histamine cause the glands to release their contents an quickly seal off the wound site with a fibrous scab.

Effects: Multiplies the time for eventually fatal wounds to lose HLT points by bleeding by five.
Cost: £3500
Availability: Scarce

Disease Defiance

Heavily boosting the base human immune system, Disease Defiance increases the body's efficiency when it comes to fighting viruses, infections and disease. It also has the pleasing side effect of slightly slowing the aging process. There is, however, one major drawback. Due to the nature of the system, the body is far more likely to reject further modifications or transplants. While not always a given, this can, and does, happen with alarming frequency.

Effects: +30% of recipients base Health for the purposes of fighting disease etc.
Cost: £2000
Availability: Very rare

Hirplakker Gene Pool Trooper mod

Most famous and infamous modification is that used by Hirplakker to create their Gene Pool Troopers. Selected volunteers are subjected to a battery of treatments and implants which serve to dramatically increase their fighting potential. Reflexes are speeded up, muscles are enhanced and resistance to damage is drastically improved. It can take up to six months for this sequence to be fully carried out and a full thirty-percent of subjects do not survive the process.

Effects

Agility:	+25% of recipient's base level
Strength:	+50% of recipient's base level
Health:	+40% of recipient's base level

Cost: £10,000
Availability: Scarce

Muscle Boost

A combination of tailored viruses and food supplements cause the body to increase the volume and density of muscle fibre. This gives the recipient increased strength and considerable additional bulk. The recipient must continue to take either the food supplements or have good diet and a strenuous exercise regime in order to maintain the muscle growth.

Effects: Strength: +20% of the recipients base level
Cost: £1000
Availability: Very rare

Nerve Streaming

Utilised by many macrocorporate soldiers and covert ops, nerve streaming serves to dramatically increase the speed with which the subject can react to stimulus. The side effect of this treatment is that users can appear to be extremely edgy and nervous at all times. Guffers, scops and mikefighter pilots who can afford the treatment also use it to enhance their fighting potential.

Effects

Agility:	+20% of recipient's base level
Dexterity:	-10% of recipient's base level
Reaction:	+10% of recipient's base level

Cost: £5000
Availability: Very rare

Next Step

Immensely popular with upper level macrocorporates and the extremely wealthy, Next Step represents a true evolution of the basic human genotype. Health, strength and co-ordination are all improved. The recipient also looks far younger than their true age, making a fifty year old look no more than thirty. The modification incorporates the effects found in Disease Defiance (as well as all the disadvantages). Parents who have chosen to have this modification can also choose to have it 'hardwired' into their DNA, which results in their children automatically being born with all the advantages of Next Step. With macrocorporate medical care and the advantages of Next Step, recipients can potentially live to an extremely old age.

Effects

Strength:	+10% of recipient's base level
Dexterity:	+15% of recipient's base level
Agility:	+10% of recipient's base level
Health:	+20% of recipient's base level

Cost: £10,000
Availability: Scarce

Night Eyes

A relatively simple modification (in relation to many of the others described here) which improves night vision by increasing the eyes' sensitivity to light.

Effects: User can see well in all but total darkness.
Cost: £2500
Availability: Very rare

Pain Deflector

Intending primarily for military applications, the Pain Deflector hooks in to the nervous system and releases a variety of blocking chemicals upon injury to the user. This has the effect of delaying the onset of shock and allowing the user to continue functioning. Recipients feel pain as a far away sensation; something which they are aware of but which has little effect on them.

Effects: Halves the skill penalty when the character is injured.
Cost: £3500
Availability: Very rare

Sleepless

A curious, rare (even by the standards of bio modification) alteration which counters the body's need for sleep. By sequentially shutting down parts of the brain and artificially enhancing the flushing of fatigue toxins, the users needs little, if any, sleep. However, going without sleep seems to do something to the recipients, turning them slightly...odd. It seems that there is a basic desire at times to close ones eyes and fall into a peaceful slumber. With Sleepless, this can't happen, leading to some unusual mental side effects.

Effects: Recipient need never sleep.
Cost: £8,000
Availability: Scarce

Tight Rope

By adapting the balancing systems of the human inner ear, partially adjusting its connection to the brain and modifying its systems, the Tight Rope modification gives the recipient a much finer sense of balance, thereby increasing agility.

Effects

Agility: +20% to recipient's base level
Cost: £2000
Availability: Very rare

Vehicles

boats

Of all types of vehicle in The City, boats are by far the most widely used. From tiny, one man, skiffs for punting about the capillary canals to massive ore barges used by the macrocorps to transport precious natural resources, all sizes and classes of vessel can be found on the watery network of canals. Almost as wide as the variety in size is the variety of construction materials used. Wood, harvested by the macrocorps from long dead forests in the Outlands, is used to construct rude rowing boats. Metal sheeting makes the hulls of barges. A melange of different materials goes towards making some vehicles, constructed from the scrap and detritus of life in The City.

Power sources also display wide degrees of variation. The smallest craft are powered by oars or punts, relying on the strength of their users to propel them along. Others use primitive electric engines, sparking and shuddering, driven by bulky, badly sealed, dangerously toxic batteries. Hitech watercraft use hydrogen-fuelled turbines and fuel cells, technology unavailable to the common citizen.

The examples below illustrate only a few of the myriad of designs available in The City

Gunskiff

Ranging from primitive versions mounting heavy sparklock rifles and using plates of iron for armour, right up to macro-corporate support variants carrying micro-howitzers and magnetic repeater machineguns, gunskiffs are the warships of the canals. Most are small, carrying no more than three or four crew, but all have substantial armament and good armour protection. The vast majority of the examples afloat on the canals are built from scavenged parts and stolen weapons.
Cost: Anything from £200 for a lotech versions, to well over £10,000 for a well-armed hitech version.
Availability: Common for lotech versions, rare for hitech.

Small Skiff

A small, flat-bottomed boat, ideal for swift, stealthy movement along the canals. Typical skiffs can seat up to four people in relative comfort, overloading the boat gives an increased chance of being dumped unceremoniously in the canals. Oar-driven versions are extremely common, with electric driven being slightly less common. For long journeys, some travellers mount sails on crude masts, taking advantage of the winds that whistle down the canals.

Cost: A new, oar powered skiff will cost between £25 and £100, depending on quality. Add another £30 to £70 for an electric engine.

Availability: Very common

Canal Taxi

Essentially large skiffs, canal taxis range from simple, oar driven craft (similar to the small skiffs mentioned above), to elegant, luxurious waterborne limousines, plying the waterways in the more respectable parts of The City. The hitech versions tend to be fully sealed against the worst The City can throw them, while in the lowest form, you'd be lucky to get a tarpaulin to cower under. Journey prices also vary widely, depending on quality of the vehicle, where you're going from, where you're going to and how much the driver thinks he or she can scam from you. A typical fare per mile is about 1 to 5s for an average quality ride.

Cost: For the lotech versions, same as a small skiff. For the hitech versions, anything from £500 for a second hand turbiner right up to £3,000 for a top-line, brand new limousine.

Availability: Common

Medium Cargo Barge

By far the most common form of cargo transport in The City, medium barges can range from 10 to 25 metres in length and 4 to 10 metres in width. If you can think of a cargo, there will be a barge carrying it somewhere in The City. Some citizens, disdaining a life fixed to one place, use barges as their homes, floating about The City in search of work, food or salvage. Macrocorporate barges tend to be swift, solid and well armed, typically with reinforced bows to allow them to breach right through obstacles (robbery on the canals being a regular occurrence).

Cost: £600 on average.

Availability: Common

Large Cargo Barge

Only really used by the macrocorporates, these are the largest vessels on the canals, huge hulls which spend their entire working lives going in straight lines up and down one canal. Generally, there are between 30 and 70 metres long and between 12 and 20 metres wide. In the main,

they are used for the transportation of resource materials from the Outlands to the manufactories and production areas within The City. Always heavily guarded, they present a tempting but deadly prospect to would be hijackers.

Cost: Unavailable to non-macrocorporates.

Availability: Rare

ekranoplans

Certainly the swiftest, if not the safest, way to move about the canals, ekranoplans come in all shapes and sizes, from home-built racers to macrocorporate attack craft.

An ekranoplan is a ground effect aircraft, a vehicle which flies along at a height of between two and five metres, taking advantage of the ground effect (a low drag, high efficiency method of flight). They are fast, (relatively) economical and versatile. Flying an ekranoplan at speed down a canal is a hair raising experience.

'Red Top' Limited class ekranoplan racer

Designed and built by eccentric mechanic Murray Hanson, 'Red Top' competes in Limited class races at the Straits Raceway. Driven by a twin prop set up (one front, one rear) and powered by two markedly different alcohol burning piston engines, the craft has been tracked exceeding speeds of 250mph, not bad by anyone's standards.

Cost: Hanson isn't saying.

Availability: Unique

Hirplakker YEG/0003 Class A ekranoplan racer

At the completely opposite end of the spectrum from 'Red Top', the YEG/0003 is Hirplakker's design for the current Class A season. A massive craft, fifteen metres in length and eight metres wide, it is powered by a highly secret fusion powerplant. Hirplakker are confident that this craft will win them the Class A crown this season.

Cost: Unknown, but rumours circulate that the five craft team (three racers and two back-ups) cost in excess of six million pounds to design, develop and build. If this is true, then Hirplakker must be really serious about winning the title.

Availability: Not a hope.

'Red Top' Limited class ekranoplan racer

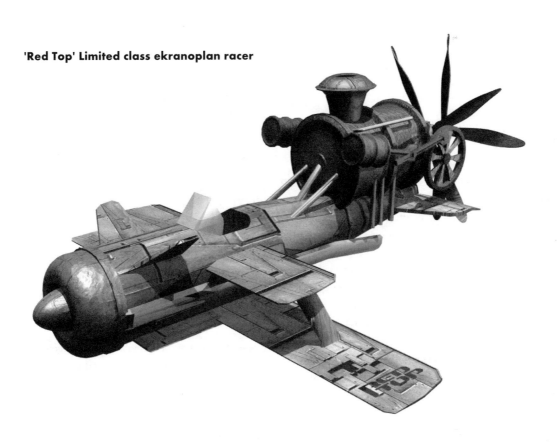

Hirplakker YEG/0003 Class A ekranoplan racer

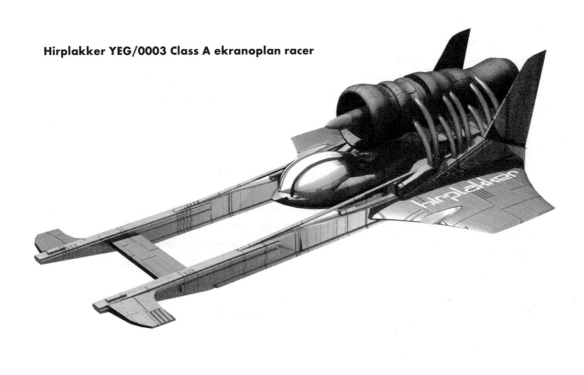

aircraft

As discussed in 'The Precepts', aircraft in The City can be divided into three broad categories: the heavy, lumbering aerostats, the flimsy, agile mikefighters and the wallowing, slow dirgibles.

aerostats

Gorunna Logistics 'Megalifter' Heavy Cargo Aerostat

Workhorse of aerostat fleets across The City, the 'Megalifter' is the most common large aerostat in The City. Used by all of the macrocorporations and a few smaller organisations, this disc shaped craft can lift up to five tons of anything you care to load inside it. Modified 'Megalifters' have been given massive underside doors and used as rubbish dumpers over Smokey Mountain whilst others are used by macrocorp forces as troop transports. Their wallowing, disc-shaped bodies can been seen everywhere in The City, yet very few citizens will ever see one close at hand or from the inside.

Cost: £150,000
Availability: Rare

Hirplakker Aerial Gun Platform

AGPs are nothing more than airborne weapons carriers, designed to pound ground targets into submission through overwhelming firepower. The Hirplakker AGP mounts its main weapons in two turrets, one above and one below the main body of the craft. Each turret contains two 88mm medium magnetic repeater cannons, able to fire an astonishing range of projectiles, from canister flechette rounds to high explosives. To back up the power of cannons, the AGP carries six rockets in internal bays and can also mount rocket pods, sensor pods or gun pods externally.

For such a complex vehicle, the AGP has a small crew of only two (pilot and gunner). However, they are amply aided by banks of dedicated dingin processors and expert systems.

Cost: £200,000
Availability: Very rare

Nakamura-Yebisu 'Pollen' Personal Aerostat

If you can afford it (and very few can), the ultimate form of individual transport in The City is the personal aerostat. This rare breed of aircraft is typified by the Nakamura-Yebisu 'Pollen', a svelte, streamlined craft, somewhat at odds with the bulky, oid cargo and military aerostats. Accodating the pilot in luxurious comfort, the 'Pollen' is the preserve of the super-wealthy nomenklatura or very high level macrocorp executives. Powered by a single, highly compact, turbine, this is a vehicle which makes the ultimate statement about the owner's status.

Cost: £75,000
Availability: Scarce

mikefighters

Nakamura-Yebishu 'Wave'

Mainstay of the Nakamura-Yebisu Group Weapons Division airborne forces, the 'Wave' is a slender, elegant aircraft with sweeping crescent wings and a tail which narrows to a single slim spar topped by an angled twin tail section.

Powered by a single lightweight hydrogen burning turbofan, it can take off and land vertically and carry a reasonable weapons load. Its normal load is a .40 calibre light magnetic repeater cannon for dogfighting purposes and two small rockets for attacking ground targets.

Cost: £37,000
Availability: Rare

Gorunna Logistics 'Invalidator'

Brutally simple and hard-hitting, the 'Invalidator' is a dedicated attack mikefighter, optimised for taking out heavy ground targets such as warcrawls and armoured personnel carriers. Slung underneath the craft is a long 35mm medium anti-armour cartridge cannon which runs the entire length of the mikefighter. The punch from this weapon is incredible and when fired, it actually slows the aircraft down by quite a considerable margin.

Gorunna only keep a limited stock of these vehicles in operation, as its size and status have so far prevented it being attacked by the other macrocorporations. They have, however, sold a few to other organisations such as Iron Hand Security.

Cost: £35,000
Availability: Rare

Hirplakker Aerial Gun Platform

Nakamura-Yebisu 'Pollen' Personal Aerostat

Nakamura-Yebishu 'Wave'

Gorunna Logistics 'Invalidator'

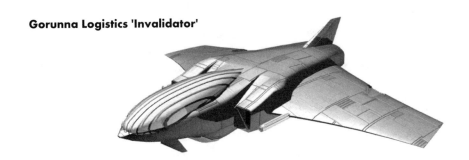

powerbikes

Toys of the rich and shameless, gleaming new powerbikes are a common site in the well-to-do areas such as Lucent Heights and Clearwater Break. Sleek and streamlined, they are the fastest ground vehicles in The City. Most are powered by advanced electric motors powered by superconducting battery blocks.

GSV SGM5000D

Most popular among Gorunnas wide range of powerbikes, the SGM5000D is a large, rugged affair, easily able to cope with anything The City can throw at it.
Cost: £1000
Availability: Rare

GSV VBS9000R

Latest entry into the powerbike market from Gorunna Special Vehicles is the astonishing VBS9000R. Displaying a phenomenal amount of technological advancement for what is, essentially, an expensive toy, it can run rings round anything else currently available. Powered by a compact fuel cell (with a small superconductor block as back up), it uses a nano-dingin monitored shaft drive to take power to both wheels. The drive train also provides the braking mechanism for the bike. When the accelerator is released, the natural braking effect of the electric motor takes over, slowing the bike down and also using the power from the shaft to charge the superconductor block. If the brake lever is applied, a resistance is created which slows the bike down even faster and, if REALLY swift braking is required, the dingin will increase the power to the electromagnets in the motor, making it come to a halt very, very quickly. Only the richest of rich kids can afford one of these bikes, it is the ultimate status symbol for the rebellious macrocorporate youngster.
Cost: £3,000. That's 600 times the average weekly wage, by the way.
Availability: Scarce

Nakamura 'Chainsaw' Bis3

Third incarnation of the famous 'Chainsaw', this is without doubt the most common powerbike in The City. So many have been manufactured, stolen, copied, stolen again, dumped and trashed that even the non-wealthy can sometimes be seen on one. The superconductor block can give three hours flat out endurance, but under braking the motor will recharge the superconductors to give extended range.
Cost: A new Bis3 will cost about £1,200. Some older, slightly trashed models are available for as little as £250.
Availability: Common

military vehicles

Arclight Cube36 medium warcrawl

Small and quick, with devastating armament, the Cube36 is the standard medium warcrawl used by the Brigade of Light. Initially produced four years ago (just in time, coincidentally, for the Hundred Block War) the vehicle is used in large numbers in the Contested Grounds, where its size gives it a considerable edge over the larger, older Hirplakker AFVs. Mounting a 45mm medium magnetic repeater cannon as its main armament, backed up by a 65mm mortar and two heavy magnetic repeater machineguns, the Cube36 has the firepower to handle almost any threat. The two man crew are ably assisted by an outstanding computer suite, centred around a phenomenally fast and powerful nanoscale dingin unit. Power is derived from a compact turbine, based on a design purchased several decades ago from Gorunna Logistics. There are quite a number of variants of the Cube36, including the AirClaw anti-aircraft version which mounts two 15mm rotary cannon.
Cost: Current production cost for a latest generation Cube36 runs to £178,000.
Availability: Very rare

Gorunna 'Lancer' APC

Designed for the militant market, this is an effective and common light AFV. Able to carry ten soldiers in relative comfort and mounting a simple 27mm light cartridge cannon, the 'Lancer' has gained wide acceptance amongst the more wealthy militant organisations. Eight powered wheels give it good traction on almost any surface and its sturdy, rugged fuel cell give good endurance and bomb-proof reliability.
Cost: £23,000
Availability: Rare

groundcars and other vehicles

Haulage Wagon

Commonly used in the more outlying areas of The City, where the canal network becomes more sparse, these behemoths are normally powered by pantograph systems, massive battery trailers or (rarely) by compressed gas burning internal combustion engines. Most of the space on the wagon is normally taken up by the engine which in most versions transmits power to the massive rear driving wheels. Cargo is carried on a trailer or series of trailers strung behind the wagon. Constructed of iron and brass and often very, very old, these vehicles are most usually owned by small private haulage companies.
Cost: £500 to £20000
Availability: Common

GSV Imperator Automobile

Wide, low, sleek, menacing and always black, the Gorunna Special Vehicles Imperator is the vehicle of choice for those who wish to make a serious impression. Rising on wide HyGrip tires and clamped to the road by DynaGlyde suspension, the Imperator carries it passengers smoothly and comfortable from one high-powered appointment to another. Its powerful hydrogen burning engine gives impressive acceleration combined with quiet running. Gorunna's latest Glyphread driving aids, running off of a powerful nanoscale dingin unit, give the driver every possible assistance. The sinister, dark Imperators are rarely seen outside of macrocorp controlled areas or the domains of the supremely wealthy. If they do venture out of such areas, they do have discreet armour to protect themselves from the occasional stone or garbage throwing mob.

Cost: £35,000
Availability: Scarce

GSV SGM5000D

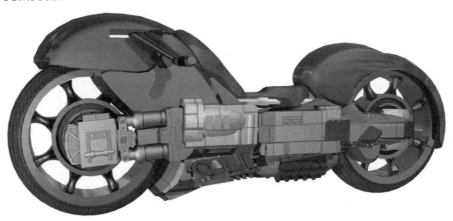

Arclight Cube36 medium warcrawl

GSV Imperator Automobile

	DAM	PEN	RNG	ROF	REM	CLIP	MSS	Rel.	Cost	Avail.
Pistols										
Sparklock Pistol, Light	5	4	5	1	+10	n/a	0.5kg	UR	20	Common
Sparklock Pistol, Medium	7	5	10	1	+10	n/a	1.0kg	UR	30	Common
Sparklock Pistol, Heavy	9	5	10	1	+5	n/a	1.5kg	UR	40	Common
Sparklock Pistol, Pepperbox	5	4	5	3	+10	10	1.0kg	VUR	50	Uncommon
Cartridge Revolver, Light	6	4	10	3	+10	6	0.8kg	VR	65	Uncommon
Cartridge Revolver, Medium	9	7	15	3	+5	6	1.3kg	VR	85	Common
Cartridge Revolver, Heavy	11	9	15	2	+5	5	1.7kg	VR	110	Common
Cartridge Auto, Light	6	4	10	4	+10	10	0.5kg	AR	80	Uncommon
Cartridge Auto, Medium	9	7	15	4	+5	10	1.0kg	AR	120	Common
Cartridge Auto, Heavy	11	9	15	4	+5	8	1.5kg	AR	150	Common
Furien 'Linetrooper'	10	15	15	4	+5	24	1.5kg	R	850	V. rare
Furien 'Jacketcracker'	13	21	20	4	+5	20	1.8kg	VR	900	V. rare
Gorunna 'Sling'	16	13	10	4	+5	4	2.3kg	VR	300	V. rare
Hirplakker 'Pantera'	15	11	10	2	+5	6	2.0kg	VR	250	Uncommon
Micintyre 'Kicker'	7	12	15	4	+5	20	1.6kg	AR	300	Rare
PPIM E35	5	6	5	4	+15	10	0.3kg	AR	350	Scarce
Souken vent-450	13	11	15	4	+5	12	1.2kg	VR	230	Rare
Trilhoeven GP-013	12	20	20	4	+5	30	1.6kg	VR	750	V. rare
Sub-machineguns										
Cartridge SMG	9	7	15	3(5)	+5	25	3.5kg	UR	120	Uncommon
Mitsushi 'Whistler'	7	12	15	4(3)	+5	50	2.5kg	UR	350	Rare
Trilhoeven KM-067R	12	17	20	4(5)	+5	100	2.5kg	VR	900	V. rare
Rifles										
Sparklock Carbine	11	10	15	1	+5	n/a	3.5kg	UR	75	Common
Sparklock Rifle	13	12	20	1	+0	n/a	4.5kg	UR	100	Common
Cartridge Rifle, Single Shot	19	22	60	1	-5	5	4.0kg	R	150	Common
Cartridge Rifle, Semi-auto	19	22	60	4	-5	10	4.5kg	AV	200	Uncommon
Cartridge Rifle, Full-auto	19	22	60	4(3)	-5	20	5.0kg	UR	250	Uncommon
Hakken IR0018r	15	40	30	10	+0	20	6.0kg	R	1900	Scarce
Tenlier Assault-100	15	17	40	4(5)	+0	30	3.6kg	R	1000	Uncommon
Trilhoeven KSK-G30	16	24	50	4(10)	+0	100	3.5kg	VR	1500	V. rare
Sniper Weapons										
Arclight 'Redeye'	17	42	50	10	-5	20	3.0kg	R	2300	Scarce
Furien 'Shellbreaker'	19	47	100	10	-10	10	6.0kg	R	2000	Scarce
Shotguns										
Sparklock Blunderbuss	15	4	5	1	+5	n/a	2.5kg	UR	70	Common
Cartridge Shotgun, Single Shot	25	5	10	1	+0	n/a	3.5kg	R	150	Uncommon
Cartridge Shotgun, Pump	25	5	10	2	+0	5	4.0kg	AR	200	Rare
Hirplakker 'Lacerator'	30	10	15	4(5)	+0	40	3.0kg	R	600	Scarce
Micintyre L16B	30	7	15	4(3)	+0	50	3.5kg	VR	500	V. rare
Heavy Weapons										
Arclight 'Boomer' A1	77	63	90	4	-20	12	35.0kg	R	5000	No way
Makei Assault Gun	30	40	60	4	-10	5	15.0kg	R	500	Rare
Trilhoeven Microhowitzer (BR:2m)	32	16	70	4	-10	6	15.0kg	VR	1000	V. rare

	DAM	PEN	RNG	ROF	REM	CLIP	Rel.	Cost	Avail.
Sparklock Cannon									
Light	20	14	30	1	-10	n/a	UR	£200	Uncommon
Medium	45	25	60	1	-20	n/a	UR	£600	Rare
Heavy	100	45	80	1	-30	n/a	UR	£1000	V. Rare
Cartridge Cannon									
Light	85	60	70	4	-10	50	AV	£1500	Rare
Medium	100	100	80	4	-20	10	AV	£4000	Rare
Heavy	200	150	100	1	-30	1	R	£10,000+	V. Rare
Magnetic Repeater Cannon									
Light	70	60	80	4(3)	-10	200	R	£3500	V. Rare
Medium	90	120	100	4	-15	100	R	£6000	Scarce
Heavy	150	220	120	4	-20	30	VR	Haha ha	Scarce
Rockets									
Light (BR: 3m)	32	16	120	1	-10	n/a	UR	£200	V. Rare
Medium (BR: 5m)	48	24	120	1	-20	n/a	UR	£600	V. Rare
Heavy (BR: 8m)	64	32	150	1	-30	n/a	UR	£1000+	V. Rare

	RES	AV	MAN	SPD	ACC	DEC	CRW	PSS	CRG
Boats									
Gunskiff (lotech)	30	40	4	6	1	2	3-4	2-4	100kg
Gunskiff (hitech)	40	60	4	10	1	2	3-4	2-4	100kg
Small Skiff (Oar powered)	10	00	5	4	0.5	2	1	3	100kg
Small Skiff (Engine powered)	10	00	5	8	1	3	1	4	150kg
Canal Taxi (lotech)	10	00	5	10	1	3	1	6	200kg
Canal Taxi (hitech)	20	10	6	12	2	3	1	6	200kg
Medium Cargo Barge	40	30	3	8	0.5	1	2	n/a	10,000kg
Large Cargo Barge	60	30	1	6	0.5	1	4	n/a	25,000kg
Ekranoplans									
'Red Top' Ltd. Class Racer	30	10	6	100	5	20	1	0	0kg
Hirplakker YEG/0003 Class A Racer	80	60	7	200	10	25	1	0	0kg
Aerostats									
Gorunna Logistics 'Megalifter' Heavy Cargo Aerostat	100	30	3	70	4	20	3	30	5,000kg
Hirplakker Aerial Gun Platform	90	100	4	80	4	25	2	0	0kg
Nakamura-Yebisu 'Pollen' Personal Aerostat	20	10	6	80	6	25	1	0	50kg
Mikefighters									
Nakamura-Yebishu 'Wave'	25	20	7	180	12	20	1	0	500kg
Gorunna Logistics 'Invalidator'	30	30	6	150	10	20	1	0	700kg
Powerbikes									
GSV SGM5000D	10	0	6	50	7	12	1	1	50kg
GSV VBS9000R	10	0	7	65	8	15	1	0	40kg
Nakamura 'Chainsaw' Bis3	12	2	6	45	6	12	1	1	60kg
Military Vehicles									
Arclight Cube36 medium warcrawl	100	120	6	14	1	7	2	0	100kg
Gorunna 'Lancer' APC	40	60	5	20	2	5	2	10	500kg
Ground Cars & Other Vehicles									
Haulage Wagon	20	0	4	9	1	5	1	2	2,000kg
GSV 'Imperator' Automobile	40	15	6	60	5	15	1	5	500kg

Weapons Accessories

	Weight	Cost	Avail.
Adaptive Laser Sight	0.3kg	£200	Rare
Gyrostabilisers	1.0kg	£250	Rare
Laser Dot	0.2kg	£250	Uncommon
Holster	n/a	5s-£200	Common
Optical Sights x2	0.5kg	£50	Uncommon
Optical Sights x3	0.7kg	£150	Uncommon
Optical Sights x4	1.0kg	£300	Uncommon
Silencer	0.4kg	£20 +	V. rare
Supressor	0.3kg	£10 +	V. rare

Dingins

	Weight	Cost	Avail.
Macroscale	Varies	£30-£1000	Common
Microscale	0.5-50kg	£50-£2000	Common
Nanoscale	0.1-20kg	£80-£5000	V. rare

Dingin Accessories

	Weight	Cost	Avail.
Cathode Tube (lotech)	10kg	£30	Rare
Code Lock (hitech)	n/a	£100	Rare
Code Lock (lotech)	0.5kg	£10	Common
Dataflow Splice (hitech)	n/a	£100	Rare
Dataflow Splice (lotech)	0.2kg	£2	Common
Keyboard (hitech)	0.5kg	£100	Rare
Keyboard (lotech)	5.0kg	£20	Common
Memory (hitech)	0.1kg+	£100+	V. rare
Memory (lotech)	2.0kg+	£20+	Common
Flat Display (hitech)	0.5kg	£100	V. rare
Hard Display (hitech)	1.0kg	£70	Rare
Mechanical Display (lotech)	20kg	£50	Rare
Printer (hitech)	1.0kg	£60	Rare
Tickertape Output (lotech)	4.0kg	£15	Common

Navigation Devices

	Weight	Cost	Avail.
Automapper (hitech)	0.5kg	£10	Rare
Inertial Compass (hitech)	0.5kg	£7	Rare

Medical Equipment

	Weight	Cost	Avail.
First Aid Kit (hitech)	0.5kg	£5	Rare
First Aid Kit (lotech)	1.0kg	10s	V. common
Medical Kit (hitech)	5.0kg	£20	Rare

Survival Gear

	Weight	Cost	Avail.
Blanket	2.0kg	2s	V. common
Gas Mask (lotech)	2.0kg	£5	Uncommon
Respirator (hitech)	0.5kg	£25	Rare
Rucksack	1.0kg	5s-£50	V. Common
Survival Kit (hitech)	0.5kg	£200	Rare
Utility Knife	0.2kg	£40-£250	Common

Tools

	Weight	Cost	Avail.
Basic Tool Kit	5.0kg	£10-£100	V. common
Electrics Tools	2.0kg	£15-£200	V. common
Electronic Security			
Circumvention Kit (hitech)	1.0kg	£50	V. rare
Mechanics Tool Kit	25kg	£30-£500	V. common
Weapon Maintenance			
Kit (hitech)	0.5kg	£10	Rare
Weapon Maintenance			
Kit (lotech)	0.5kg	£1	V. common

Scientific Equipment

	Weight	Cost	Avail.
Dissecting Kit	2.0kg	15s	Rare
Lab Apparatus,			
Chemical (lotech)	30kg	£15	Rare
Lab Apparatus,			
Electrical (lotech)	30kg	£20	Rare
Lab Apparatus,			
Photographic (lotech)	30kg	£15	Common

Vision Enhancers

	Weight	Cost	Avail.
Binoculars	1.0kg	£4-£200	Rare
Camera (hitech)	0.3kg	£50	Rare
Camera (lotech)	5.0kg	£5	Common
Electric Torch (hitech)	0.5kg	£3	Rare
Electric Torch (lotech)	2.0kg	£1	Common
Fish Oil Lamp (lotech)	1.0kg	5s	V. common
Magnifying Glass	0.3kg	10s	Common
Spectacles	n/a	4s-£100	V. common

Misc. Equipment

	Weight	Cost	Avail.
Climbing Kit (hitech)	5.0kg	£35	Common
Climbing Kit (lotech)	10.0kg	£3	Common
Clockwork			
Generator (lotech)	1.0kg	£5	V. common
Disguise Kit	1.5kg	£6	Rare
Fish Oil Stove (lotech)	1.0kg	£1	V. common
Goggles (hitech)	n/a	£3	V. common
Goggles (lotech)	0.5kg	7s	V. common
Grappling Hook	2.0kg	£2	Common
Lockpick Set	0.5kg	£25	Rare
Mess Kit (Basic)	0.5kg	£1	Common
Mess Kit (with Stove)	1.5kg	£3	Common
Rope (hitech)	2.0kg	£5	Rare
Rope (lotech)	3.0kg	15s	V. common
Watch	n/a	£5-£500	Common

	AV	Weight	Cost	Avail.
Armour				
Armoured Clothing (hitech)	5	1.5kg	£7	Uncommon
Armour Vest (hitech)	20	3.0kg	£20	Common
Integrated Armour Suit (hitech)	50	35kg	£500	Rare
Mail Vest (lotech)	10	5.0kg	£5	Common
Makeshift Armour (lotech)	8	5 - 15kg	n/a	V. common
Padded Armour (lotech)	3	2.0kg	10s	Common
Helmet (hitech)	30	1.5kg	£20	Rare
Helmet (lotech)	15	2.0kg	£1	Common
Powered Armour				
Arclight 'Tentenel' Battle Armour	90	100kg	£35,000	Not a hope
Trilhoeven 'Mad Dog' Battle Armour	100	130kg	£25,000	Scarce
Trilhoeven 'Running Dog' Scout Armour	70	90kg	£20,000	Scarce

	DAM	PEN	RCH	REM	Weight	Cost	Avail.
Ceramic Blade	5	10/12	+0	+10	0.3kg	£25	Common
Ceramic Long Knife	7	10/12	+0	+10	0.5kg	£40	V. rare
Cosh	6	0	+0	+5	1.0kg	10s	V. common
Hatchet/Axe	6	8	+0	+0	1.5kg	£5	Common
Knife	5	7/8	+0	+10	0.5kg	£2	V. common
Llife	6	5/20	+0	+5	1.0kg	£200	V. rare
Polearm/Spear	8	12/7	+2	-10	2.0kg	£20	Uncommon
Sword	8	7/8	+1	-5	3.0kg	£40	Uncommon
Billy Club	6	0	+1	+0	2.0kg	£35	V. rare

"Though we walk in the shadow of death, we fear no evil. For we are the guardians of all that it sacred, protectors of order. Though the ravening hordes may assail us from all sides, we shall endure. For, if nothing else, we must endure. The great purpose at the heart of our being drives us on. In the end, it's them or us. And it's not going to be us."

Hauptmann Niederlage, Grauschjager, Trilhoeven

the prescription

a few guidelines for running a/state

Create an atmosphere and be descriptive

a/state is a game which thrives on atmosphere. Whether it's the grimy, reeking backstreets of Mire End or the hallowed hallways and pristine offices of Luminosity Tower, each place, person and organisation has a character of its own. Give vivid descriptions of the places the PCs are visiting, covering all the senses, not just what they can see.

Sight: What does the place look like, what stands out, who is there?

Sound: Whether it's a person or a place, sound is everywhere. How does an individual talk, what noises are they making when they move, are there dogs barking in an alley, fishmongers yelling by a canal?

Smell: Smells are an oft overlooked part of gaming description, yet The City is alive with a myriad of different smells. A labourer hauling crates from a canal barge may smell of oil, sweat and mildewed clothes while the apartment of a wealthy executive in Lucent Heights may smell faintly floral, overlaid with subtle odours of nebelweed smoke and rich foods.

Taste: An adjunct to smell, tastes can often linger in the air, either attracting or repelling a character. With someone sweating nervously, you can almost taste their fear.

Touch: The roughness and sliminess of a crumbling brick wall, the smoothness and softness of a well-manicured hand. Touch can offer a whole world of descriptive possibilities. A trustworthy figure may seem slightly more sinister when he offers a clammy, cold handshake.

Emphasise the differences between rich and poor and the many layers in between

There are many layers in the society of The City, not all of which have an easy time of it. Emphasise and detail the shabbiness of poor workers' clothing, the run-down nature of their houses. Yet, also emphasise a sense of community, sometimes even the clannishness prevalent in their communities. After all, the PCs themselves may come from such an environment. There can be, at times, something of an insularity about certain areas, a wariness of outsiders which may at first appear like outside hostility. All the above having been said, being wealthier doesn't imply that the people are any more approachable or pleasant. Frequently ,the more comfortably off will want little or nothing to do with the vast majority of the population. Even further removed are those who live and work in the higher echelons of the macrocorps, whose outlook and mindset may be radically different to the average man in the street.

Horror stems from the unknown, juxtaposition and the strangeness of the familiar

Slashed corpses, horrific discoveries and awful creatures are but one aspect of horror. Horror can also come from the fear of unknown, the juxtaposition of totally dissimilar things or a strange twist on familiar people, places or objects.

The unknown: That which is unknown inspires dread and fear. PCs are more likely to be scared of a mysterious, quiet sound in a tunnel, a voice on the wind in an abandoned alley or a darkened figure seen at the end of long corridor.

Juxtaposition: An eight year old child is not normally scary. An eight year old child smiling faintly while holding a cut-throat razor is scary. A glass-fronted cabinet in the room of an old lady may appear to contain knick-knacks and junk, yet on closer inspection, may contain, hidden in the bottom right hand corner, a dried and shrunken human head. A clean hospital ward where the PCs briefly see a slab of what looks like animal meat being wheeled by on a rickety, rusty trolley is liable to set nerves on edge.

The familiar: Putting a twist of familiar objects, people and places links in to the other two. Two sinister men in high-collared grey greatcoats and peaked, military style caps may appear frightening and tough, yet why are they carrying brightly coloured carpet bags? A kitchen table may seem as ordinary and commonplace a thing as you could imagine, but look closely. Is that a film of dried, crusted blood round the edge of the table? Could be.

Horror is a vital part of the a/state setting. Make the most of it, induce some paranoia and anxiety into the players by subtle manipulation and sinister, insidious dread.

Don't overuse The Shifted and the macrocorps

The temptation is always there to use the two most misunderstood groups in The City as the major bogeymen in almost all adventures. A wise GM should avoid overusing them in his/her adventures, keeping them sinister, rare features. Not every dark happening should have a Shifted being behind it and not every dire conspiracy should have a macrocorps lurking in the background. There are plenty of ordinary organisations and people in The City who are just as cunning, calculating and capable of causing PCs grief.

Remember the technology level

Unlike our modern world, citizens of The City can't just pick up their mobile phone and call a friend. Nor can they radio for help at the drop of a hat. Instantaneous communication is very rare in the City, therefore the players need to be aware of this. Then there is the standard of living of the majority of population. Most people will live in rather horrid rooms, lit by flickering gas or electric lamps, damp spots visible on the walls and fungus growing in corners. Dominating the room will be a bulky black and white TV set plumbed in to Sideband's insidious cable network.

If PCs have a firearm, its most likely to be a sparklock or, maybe, a cartridge pistol. Clockwork mechanisms attached to computers, guns and electrical devices are more common than neat little batteries. The clicking of dingins and clockworks fill the air. Flowghosts spend days trawling the dataflow for significant bits of information, peering myopically into screen and intently listening through headphones for anything significant.

Reward role-playing and the creation of hope

When awarding Improvement Points to players, reward good role-playing, character interaction and that all important category of 'hope'. Players shouldn't be rewarded simply for completing an adventure, blowing away the bad guys or just surviving by the skin of their teeth. Now, that's not to say that players should explicitly be told "Do good and thou shalt be rewarded!" Gradually reveal the nature of Improvement Points and how the PCs actions in improving peoples lives can have a positive effect on the development of the character.

Remember the consequences of actions

Every action has its own reaction. Encourage your players to think about this, particularly when they are all set to indulge in violent gunplay or something similar. What if they miss their target? The City is densely populated and stray shots can easily hit an innocent bystander. A rifle round can quite easily punch through a rotting brick wall and kill or injured the child on the other side. If the PCs accidentally (or deliberately) kill or injure someone, what are consequences for his or her friends and family? Crippling someone may seem like a good idea at the time (to a certain, possibly deranged, mindset), but what if you cripple the only person in a poor family who brings in money? What happens to the rest of the family, how do they survive?

the prescription

'The Prescription' is an introductory adventure for a/state designed for 3 to 6 players and a GM. During the adventure, the players will be taken round various areas of The city, allowing them to explore and investigate The City and to find out about the political, personal, environmental and social tangles of this massive urban sprawl. If you are intending to play a character in 'The Prescription', please read no further, the following information is for GMs only.

SYNOPSIS

The adventure begins in Folly Hills, a burgh under the control of the Three Canals Metropolitan Area Authority (TCMAA). On a slum street, a young man is found dead, having been horribly wounded then apparently ejected from a third floor window. By hook or crook, the players find there have been similar murders within the Three Canals area over the past few weeks. Witnesses are few and far between, with only the vaguest recollections and descriptions. However, looking at the killings, they appear to run in a roughly straight line, as if someone is moving along this line killing as he (or she) goes. At this point, the players will be accosted by a group from the famed Longshore University, who claim that the killer is in fact one of their research assistants who has been exposed to psychoactive drugs whilst working in the chemistry department. Further investigation and use of contacts will reveal that there has been another murder and that this time a suspect has been arrested and incarcerated in Inferno, the huge, terrifying mental asylum. Visiting the suspect, the players become involved in a riot in the asylum and will only be able to escape with luck, skill and cunning. The suspect reveals that the Longshore group have not been entirely truthful with them, yet he remembers little of the killings apart from moments of clarity before fading back into amnesia.

The players are then encouraged to hotfoot it over to Longshore to confront the group which accosted them, who rather grudgingly admit that they aren't chemists, but in fact work for the mysterious Shift Studies Faculty. The players will be shown some of their experiments, where they are attempting to find out how Drache control their human possession targets. The experiments are carried out on live human targets, targets selected by the researchers from a pool of labour provided by Trilhoeven. Whilst viewing this highly secretive set-up, they will notice a couple of grey-clad, unobtrusive figures who always seem to be hanging around. These are representatives of Trilhoeven, who are sponsoring the research. In fact, Trilhoeven want to use Drache to control certain individuals, primarily senior figures in other macrocorps. Revealing this to the university authorities will result in the experiments being shut down. Revealing this to another macrocorp will result in a tactical strike against the university, attempting to take out the experimental building.

getting the players involved

One possibility is that the PCs are a group of Provosts who have been assigned to investigate the murders. The Provosts in Folly Hills are and under-resourced, under manned, poorly equipped division who have little motivation to carry out their gruesome task. A second possibility is a group of characters associated with a stringer or directly with Sideband Media. They may be covering the grisly happenings in Folly Hills in the hope that it will turn out to be a highly newsworthy story. The PCs can also be any other group of characters, from the totally random to the highly specific. One avenue that could be used is that they are hired by the distraught family of the dead young man to find out who killed him. Another avenue is that the murder victim could be a friend or relative of one of the PCs.

murder, murder polis!

The scene is Brookmyre Walk in Folly Hills, one of the less reputable streets in the burgh, close to the Green Canal and Mire End. The buildings along Brookmyre Walk are all ancient stone three storey tenement blocks, crammed with families. Walkways cross the street from all levels and down the centre of the street runs a collapsed sewer, taking rainwater and other, less mentionable liquids, to the Green Canal.

Rain falls lightly on the street as the working day draws to a close. Men and women are heading home to the comforting fug of their one room apartments. Hawkers and vendors shout their wares. Food sellers offer spiced meatballs in gravy only yards from the sewer, entrepreneurs offer scavenged machine parts, costermongers try to get rid of the last of their rapidly rotting stock of vegetables. In the midst of this scene, a small crowd has gathered round a body which appears to have fallen from an upper storey window, crashing through two walkways on his way down. Various gawpers are retching onto the street at the sight of the victim, who has been horribly mutilated. Provosts arrive on the scene and start to take notes, addresses and statements. The crowd dissipates with remarkable rapidity. If the players are playing Provosts or the Sideband team, then they should come into the adventure at this point.

the victim

Name: Owen Harpur
Age: 26
Residence: 256E Brookmyre Walk, Folly Hills, Three Canals Metropolitan Area (TCMA)
Physical Description: Harpur was of above average height, of wiry build. His skin was engrained with dust from the brickworks where he worked. He had dusty brown hair and dull blue eyes.

During the course of the attack, Harpur had his hands, feet, ears and nose removed, all apparently before he died. He was then eviscerated and his throat cut. The remains then appear to have been thrown from his third storey window.

The players may have to do a bit of asking about amongst the locals in order to find out Harpurs name and which flat he lived in. This would be an Easy roll against the Investigation skill.

the victims apartment

If the players are Provosts, then gaining access to the apartment is simply a matter of demanding to be let in. Other characters will have to deal with the self-styled warden of the apartment block, Mrs Genscher. Mrs Genscher is a well built woman in her middle thirties, dressed in old but clean working clothes. She is deeply, deeply suspicious of strangers, especially ones that want to go poking about in the apartments of recently deceased residents. In truth, she has no actual power, but she believes she does, which is what counts these days.

PCs will have to exercise the skills in diplomacy, negotiation and persuasion to the utmost in order to get past this formidable figure.

Harpur's apartment is a scene of devastation. Body parts are scattered about the room and blood lines the walls. The room itself is small, barely 14 feet long by ten feet wide. At one end of the room is the smashed window where the body was obviously thrown out. The whole place smells bad. A small gas stove in corner props up a single corroded pan which contains an unidentifiable mass covered in fungus. Above the stove, various sealed jars contain pickles, preserved fish and various other foodstuffs. Other than that, the walls (under the blood) are bare grey stone. One of the jars, however, contains ten small bags of scrape, all carefully sealed and ready for sale. Harpur carried out some small time drug dealing on behalf of the local Hohler Gang assembly.

Observant characters will notice a pile of old clothes, fragments of news papers, disused jars and suchlike which appear to have been shoved from under the bed. This is where the killer hid from sight when various local residents rushed into the rooms after the killing. The killer then fled once everyone had run out into the street. A Difficult Awareness will reveal a fragment of white cloth which has caught on a hanging spring under the bed. Although dirty, the cloth appears to be tough and of a quality not often found in these parts.

Whether the players are investigating the apartment immediately after the murder, or a short time later, they will be rudely interrupted by the victims mother, Mrs Harpur. She will be accompanied by the fearsome Mrs Gensche and will be in a state bordering on hysteria. At first, she makes raving accusations about the PCs being thieves, burglars, and other such forms of lowlife. When she calms down sufficiently (a Difficult Diplomacy skill roll will placate her enough to allow the PCs time to question her), she will be more amenable to giving information. She strongly suspects her sons girlfriend, one Therese Jung, of being complicit in the murder of her beloved son. Mrs Gensche claims she saw a young woman leaving the building shortly before the body came crashing out of the window.

reveal that she was aware of Harpurs criminal activities. She did visit Harpur shortly before he died, but he seemed in good humour and good health. Again, if pressed or if the PCs mention the scrap of white cloth, she will recall that she saw a man in a dirty white coat entering the building as she left. Other than that, there is precious little that she has to offer.

investigating the girlfriend

Judicious investigation will reveal that the girlfriend of the deceased lives in a young womans refuge on Grassick Way, about half a mile north of Brookmyre Walk. Therese is pretty much destitute and does not yet actually know that her boyfriend is dead. When the PCs arrive at the Hartenstein Memorial Fallen Womans Refuge (for that is where she lives), they will find her readying herself for work, gutting fish for a living in a small factory on the Green Canal. She will understandably be shocked when informed of Harpurs death, collapsing to the floor in a genuine display of grief. If questioned about the scrape found in Harpurs apartment, she will feign ignorance. Observant character will realise she is hiding something. The reason for this is that her sister is heavily involved with the local Hohler Gang assembly and is the one that supplied Harpur with the drugs to sell on. If pressed, she will

investigating the scrape

If analysed, the drug itself is of fairly low quality, cut with a variety of unpleasant and possibly toxic substances. The locals will remain silent on the subject, but tracking down some destitute scrape addicts is not too difficult. They can be bribed with pennies and will reveal nothing more than the fact that Harpur did deal drugs.

investigating the scrap of cloth

The scrap is made of high quality, machine manufactured artificial fibres. Other than that, there is precious little to go on.

broader investigations

Broader investigations, such as questioning criminal or Provost contacts or trawling through the archives of the Three Canals Observer (the local newspaper) will reveal a series of similar murders across the area over the past few weeks. Including Harpur, there have been four murders, the victims of which have all be mutilated in a particularly horrible fashion. The first reported killing of this type took place three weeks ago (Ursula Janes), the last just over four days ago (George Lupton).

the victims

Victim 1: Ursula Janes
Age: 17
Residence: Folly Hills, Three Canals Metropolitan Area
Occupation: Fishmongers assistant

Janes was found in the back room of the fish shop where she worked. She had been gutted with a filleting knife, her entrails strewn about the room. The body was discovered by Mrs Kotel, her employer.

Victim 2: Fedor Dankov
Age: 48
Residence: Folly Hills, Three Canals Metropolitan Area
Occupation: Bar owner

Dankovs body was found by a Provost patrol in the narrow, dank alley behind his bar. His injuries were almost identical to those suffered by Harpur.

Victim 3: George Lupton
Age: 31
Residence: Folly Hills, Three Canals Metropolitan Area
Occupation: Artisan

Found by a customer who had called by to pick up a completed dingin, Lupton's throat was cut almost to the spine, his ears removed and entrails twined around his neck. The customer, a Mr Faure, is currently being held by the Provosts in Folly Hills due to the fact he went a little mad after discovering the body. Rumour has it that he is now a prime candidate for transfer to the hell of Inferno.

George Lupton had a young family, with a wife and three children. In all likelihood, the party will encounter them if investigating his death. Making any kind of assurances to his wife and kids that they will do their best to hunt down the killer is worth an extra 5 improvement points to each character present at the time. Mrs Lupton will thank the party effusively and timidly ask if they could let her know the results of her investigations. If they do so at the end of the adventure, this will gain the characters another 5 additional improvement points and the eternal thanks of Mrs Lupton and her children. Mrs Lupton herself knows many people in the Folly Hills artisan community and could prove to be a useful contact in the future.

There are no connections between the victims, all were killed totally at random. However, don't let the players know this. Players love thinking up esoteric and complex reasons why people have been killed. So why spoil their enjoyment. Witnesses to the killings, local people and grieving relatives will start asking why there is so much interest in the deaths of these people. First the Provosts, then some well-spoken strangers, now this lot! This should prompt the players to wonder who the well-spoken strangers are and what they want.

an encounter in the dark

At some point during their investigations, the players will find themselves set upon by the group of "well spoken strangers" mentioned previously. They can either be the victims of an attempting mugging (which is what it initially appears to be) by the Longshore University group or they can run into them (perhaps literally) when visiting the site of previous murders, checking things out at the Folly Hills Central Provost bunker or some other situation they may find themselves in. The group consists of three academics and three Portreeves from Longshore University. Effective leader of the group is Dr Irina Clausewitze, a moderately senior figure in the Shift Studies Faculty. The other two academics are her research assistants, Sennett and Konev. They are backed up by three burly Portreeves seconded from the university staff (see NPC Details at the end of the adventure for further information on the group).

The academics will use the Portreeves to try and disable the PCs (even if they are Provosts). The Portreeves all carry snub-nosed cartridge shotguns loaded with extemporised sand-bag rounds (they also have a few more lethal rounds for dire situations) and their usual massive keys which they uses as coshes. They will attempt to subdue the PCs, allowing the academics to intervene and sedate the PCs with sedatives they have in massive hypodermic syringes. This can go either of two ways: the PCs get subdued and carted off to the groups rented rooms in Folly Hills or they defeat the Longshore group. If it is the latter case, you should be careful to ensure that at least two of the academics survives the encounter (with Dr Clausewitze being one of them). In either circumstance, the Longshore group will NOT reveal they are from the Shift Studies Faculty. They have developed a cover story to mask the fact that they are working on some pretty dodgy scientific ground. Clausewitze will do most of the talking in either situation and will explain that they are chemists from Longshore, tracking a poor unfortunate research assistant who came into contact with a very powerful psychoactive gas they were working with. This sent him a bit bonkers, he fled the university and has gone on the killing spree which the PCs have been investigating.

The above explanation is, of course, a total lie. Clausewitze is in charge of an experiment in the Shift Studies Faculty which seeks to find means of controlling and manipulating the Shifted entities known as Drache. They have been attempting to force Drache to 'possess' target subjects and are trying to measure the effects they have and any potential for controllability and (possible) communication. Unfortunately, the containment systems being used are not really very reliable and one contained Drache manage to escape and 'possess' a young research assistant named Foyle Langen. Operating according to its own impenetrable mental processes, the Drache took Langen on a killing spree across The TCMA to Folly Hills. Langen has been drifting in and out of lucidity, as the Drache relaxes, then tightens control over him. In the rare moments where he has control of himself, he has been wandering confusedly through the streets wondering exactly how he got here.

strength in numbers

After getting explanations from the Longshore group, there are a couple of possibilities:

1) The group will try and extract information on the PCs investigations from them, stopping short of actual torture. They have a wide range of drugs, including sedatives, truth serums and psychoactives (this will help reinforce the image of them as experimental chemists). Once they feel they have got enough info, they will offer the players the chance to work for them, in return for a small monetary consideration. Clausewitze will offer them £10 each (negotiable up to £15) to find, apprehend and return the missing research assistant. Alive. Most sensible PCs, faced with a bunch of tooled up scientists armed with a large cache of drugs will probably agree to this. If they don't, coercion can easily be used. If the characters are Provosts, Clausewitze could intimate that she has friends in high places and could have a noticeable effect on the PCs future careers (this is pretty much a bluff). Alternatively, the PCs could be offered future employment, the everlasting gratitude of Longshore University or a grisly death if they do not comply.

All of the above will take place in secluded garret (a floored and furnished attic) rooms in a relatively respectable part of Folly Hills. The garret is in a partially empty three storey tenement block, with no inhabitants on the floor immediately below. The walls are of bare brick, the floors worm eaten old boards covered with a selection of threadbare rugs. There are three rooms, arranged 'shotgun' style, all accessed through a narrow, dark stairwell from the third floor of the tenement. The first room is a sitting room, lit by two tiny skylight windows and a couple of sputtering gas lamps on the walls. Through the only door (other than the entrance) is a small,

rather dismal kitchen with a gas stove and a few cupboards containing little more than insects. The door from the kitchen leads into a shabby bedroom dominated by a substantial iron bedstead, upon which sits a foetid doghair mattress and some rather odorous blankets (which have obviously lain undisturbed for some time).

2) If the PCs have managed to subdue the Longshore group, Clausewitze and her lackeys will offer almost anything to the PCs in order to avoid torture, beatings or their investigations being compromised. Again, Clausewitze will do most of the talking and will offer substantial sums of money to the PCs if they let them go and assist with their investigations. She will appeal to their egos, praising their abilities, knowledge of the local terrain and their all-round wonderfulness as human beings. She'll also offer up to £100 each if they let them go and help with the investigation. This is a very substantial sum of money, a sum which should tempt all but the most financially independent of PCs.

Even Provost groups should be tempted by the offer of such a sum of money. Besides, having friends at Longshore may prove useful at some point in the future. And who knows what the blackmail opportunities might be?

incarceration

Shortly after their meeting with the Longshore team, the party will be sought out by one of their contacts (or, if they are a Provost team, they will be informed by one of their superiors). The contact/superior informs them that there has been a fifth murder and that the perpetrator has actually been apprehended on the scene. This quite handy set of circumstances is down to the fact that the Provosts received an anonymous tip off that the killer was going to strike in a certain area. How was this knowledge acquired? Well, the suspect is himself being stalked by two Grauschjager, part of Trilhoevens secret police/intelligence gathering force/assassins. These two individuals have been the go-betweens in the Trilhoeven/Clausewitze relationship and are adept at maintaining an extremely low profile.

Should the party follow this up, they will find that the suspect (as yet un-named) has been incarcerated in the maximum security basement at the main Provost Bunker in the heart of the TCMA. Bribing Provosts at the bunker or garnering information from contacts within the Provosts will reveal that orders have come down from on high that the suspect is to be transferred immediately to Inferno (the result of Trilhoeven putting pressure on the TCMAA). Oh dear. Bringing someone back alive from Inferno is not the most likely of prospects, but there are a few routes they might take to expedite the suspects release.

1) A Provost group could legally visit Inferno in order to question the suspect, others would need to find other ways of gaining entrance. One method would be to fake some sort of ID or possibly ask Clausewitze for Longshore staff identification. This might allow academic staff into the building to interview test subjects for their 'researches'. If the party visits the huge asylum, emphasise the massive scale of the place, the strange look of the tilted walls and floors, the charnel house stench which permeates the building. They will be confronted with a chaotic confusion of slanted corridors, constant noise, screams, moans, ravings, inmates wandering randomly through rooms, prone bodies being dragged around or shunted this way and that on rusted, bloodstained trolleys. Inferno is a place of absolute, soul-crushing horror, a seemingly limitless warren of rooms and passages.

Foyle Langen, the poor unfortunate at the centre of this entire sorry mess, is currently locked up in Transfer Wing 2 on the ground level of Inferno. This is where most new inmates are kept for the first few days prior to assignment to their permanent wing. Although perhaps the least horrifying of the areas of Inferno, Transfer Wing 2 still fits the description given above. Langen is trussed up in a straitjacket and manacles in a sloping cell with a level floor provided by rusted iron plates braced against the wall. If the party have got to Inferno in some haste, Langen will only have been here a couple of hours. By this point, the Drache has actually departed and he is in a state of some distress as to why he is locked up. He won't know anything about the murders, apart from the occasional horrible suppressed memory which surfaces to cause him even more distress. He will, however, be more than happy to

spill the beans to the party about what he thinks is going on at the SSF. Remember that the party still currently believe that Clausewitze is a chemist. Langen will talk about the Drache experiments at the SSF (thus revealing that Clausewitze was lying) and will mention his suspicions about what happened to him. He is completely unaware of the Trilhoeven involvement, although he will mention a couple of grey-clad, military looking types who occasionally visited the SSF and talked with Clausewitze.

Aside from his information about the experiment, Langen is also desperate to get out of Inferno. He will beg the characters to try and get him out any way they can, even offering everything he owns if they will free him. At this stage, he is a pitiable sight. In truth, he is effectively innocent of the crimes due to the influence of the Drache. The only problem with this being the Three Canals authorities who would not see things in such a considerate light. If the characters refuse to help him, he will then beg them to leave him something he can kill himself with as he would rather end it all that be forced to spend the rest of his (probably fairly short) life in the asylum. What the players do at this point is entirely up to them.

2) Players with contacts in the Provosts or if the players are Provosts themselves, they could try and gain access to the suspect in the few hours that he is held in the Central Bunker before being transferred to Inferno. If they do manage to meet Langen (promising favours to contacts and extensive negotiation will probably be needed to get anywhere near him), he will essentially tell them the same as noted in '1' above, but in a slightly less distressed state (he doesn't yet know he's going to Inferno).

3) Perhaps the most foolhardy option is to attack the boat which the Provosts use to transport Langen to Inferno. It's a clunky but fairly well armoured gunskiff, manned by five Provosts (one pilot, one gunner and three others). It will be travelling slowly up the Grand Canal towards Inferno.

Obviously, if the players are Provosts, then this isn't a viable option, as attacking their own colleagues would be tantamount to committing suicide. Killing a Provost is a bad move, so the best option would be to try and take the crew by surprise and incapacitate, rather than kill, them. Players should be encouraged to come up with as outlandish plans as they can for attacking the gunskiff and getting Langen out. The more madcap the scheme, the more fun it will be.

The Provosts on the gunskiff are not on the lookout for attack and everyone apart from the pilot is sitting in the rear compartment of the dim little craft drinking tea and playing cards. Langen is trussed up on the floor, his hands and feet bound and mouth gagged. All of the Provosts are family men and will most likely surrender if faced with superior numbers or the threat of violence. If captured, they will be at pains to point out that they have children, wives, pets, aged grandmothers and so on who rely on them for support. Players killing or badly mistreating any of the Provosts at this point should be penalised when IPs are totted up at the end of the game. Should the players do something really stupid (like an all out frontal attack on the gunskiff), the Provost gunner will immediately leap to his weapon and open fire. The skiff mounts a hand cranked heavy machinegun (use stats for an Automatic Cartridge Rifle) in a cramped one-person cupola. The other Provosts are armed with sparklock carbines and pistols.

If the players manage to release Langen, he will reveal information as noted in '1' above.

we don't like being lied to.

All in all, the characters have a good chance of being pretty pissed off at this point, having been lied to by Clausewitze and her colleagues and generally put upon by different groups. The most obvious next stop is Longshore University, to confront Clausewitze and friends with the evidence, hand Langen back over to them and find out what the hell has been going on!

During the daytime, it is fairly easy to slip into the sprawling, dark, looming edifice that is Longshore University. The massive main gates are wide open, allowing easy access through the twenty foot high black iron fence which surrounds the entire campus. Students wander in and out all day and the Portreeves on duty seldom pay attention to who is going in and out. The Shift Studies Faculty is located in a massive

building at the back of the university, its ancient stones black with age, its windows all bricked over or covered with thick plates of iron. There are only two entrances into the faculty: one is the small personnel entrance which connects with the rest of the university, the other is the service entrance.

The personnel entrance is a six foot high, foot thick iron door which is controlled by a small dingin mechanism built into an adjacent wall. The service entrance uses a similar mechanism, but the twin doors are both twelve feet high and six feet across. Those wishing to get in or out must use a punched copper card which fittings in to a slot by the door. The dingin reads the pattern of holes on the card and allows the user in if they fitted the allowed patterns (which change on a regular basis). Given time, a competent flowghost could probably lever the reading mechanism out of the wall and attempt to convince the dingin to open the door. This would be a Very Difficult Mechanical Computing task (requiring the use of the flowghosts own dingin) and take up to an hour to complete. During the daytime, there is a good chance of students and staff wandering by and asking what the players are doing. Alternatively, the could just press the large brass button on the door which rings a bell inside the faculty.

Ringing the bell will cause (after a suitably irritating delay), a small, barred hatch to be opened in the door and a voice to emanate from the hatch asking what the players business is here. They will be given the impression that they are not going to be allowed in under any circumstances. Mentioning Dr Clausewitze will result in a tetchy "Wait here." And then a period of about fifteen minutes hanging around. The same voice will then emanate once more from the hatch and announce that the Doctor does not have time to see them. This should suitably enrage the PCs. The GM should actively encourage any hare-brained schemes that the PCs might come up with in order to get in. After all, there's nothing players love more than coming up with hare-brained schemes to get into places where they have no right to be.

About a minute after the players have been told that they are not welcome, the hatch will open again and a slightly more pleasant voice will announce that Dr Clausewitze would actually now be happy to see them. If they are at the service entrance, they will now be directed round to the personnel entrance. The door will swing open with an audible thump and the group will be led into a small ante-room, with walls of damp, dark stone. The only exit is another iron door similar to the one they have just been brought through. A small, balding Portreeve will politely ask them if they would care to deposit any and all weapons they might be carrying into a steel box which is at his feet. His voice should indicate that should they choose not to do this, they will travel no further into the faculty.

inside the faculty

Once through the iron door, the scene could not be more different. The group will find themselves, led by the small Portreeve wheeling the steel box, in a hallway lined with old, but clean white tiles. The hallway is approximately square and contains a framework lift shaft around which curves a staircase. Looking up, they will see this extends up three stories. The roof appears to be made of iron plates. Leading them to the lift, the Portreeve will open the sliding door and usher them in. They find themselves transport up to the second floor and led out of the lift by a sliding door on the opposite side to the one they came in on. They will now be in a small hallway with a short corridor lined with doors extending in from of them. At the end of the corridor there appears to be some sort of glass walled viewing gallery. It is here that Dr Clausewitze greets them. Nervously. Extremely nervously, in fact.

The players will note that the viewing gallery extends round a large sunken area in which sit a variety of complex and somewhat sinister looking machines constructed of glass, iron, steel, brass and copper. Even through the glass, the clicking of dingins rapidly processing information fills the air with an irritating vibration. The viewing gallery extends right round the sunken area on all sides and various individuals in white coats can be seem monitoring dials and verniers, taking notes or tapping instructions into brass dingin keyboards. The centrepiece of the sunken area is a massive machine at least twenty feet tall. It consists of a thick glass tube surrounded by what look like black obelisks (they are in fact huge electromagnets) and a web of cables and wires. The entire construction appears to be connected to two massive macroscale dingins at one end of the sunken area which, at the moment, appear to be quiet and inoperative. Emphasise to players the disquiet that this room generates, noting that even though it is brightly lit, there always appear to be shadows lurking at the edges of their vision.

Clausewitze will be pleased to see Langen again, but be somewhat wary of him. She will nervously answer the players questions, admitting the involvement of Trilhoeven and the nature of the experiments. Observant characters might notice that sunk into the floor of the sunken area are a number of what appear to be thick windows, hinged at one side. Looking careful, a character might notice that these are in fact cells containing a single human being each. If questioned, Clausewitze will explain they are crimianls sentenced to death who volunteered for the experiment in return for their sentence being commuted. At this point, Sennett will appear round a corner and start yelling at Clausewitze to stop lying. Sennett, all the while being shouted at by Clausewitze, will claim that the people in the cells are innocent and were simply poor unfortunates grabbed by Trilhoeven and brought here to provide the faculty with experimental subjects. Once he has finished his declaimation, both Sennett and Clausewitze will fall silent.

showdown

At this point, a sharp cry, followed by silence will be heard from the lift shaft end of the corridor. If the PCs have any sense, they will notice that the Portreeve has left the box containing their weapons and gone back to his post. Particularly aware characters will hear the sound of booted footsteps coming from the stairs.

The Grauschjager have taken the decision to terminate the experiment and all those involved with it. The two sinister figures have entered the faculty determined to kill anyone they find in the experimental facility, including the characters (who they are already aware of). The Grauschjager are well armed, tough and supremely skilled. Such is there reputation, the mere knowledge that they are present should be enough to inspire fear in almost anyone. They will open fire on anyone with cool, calm precision, shooting to kill. The players will require a considerable amount of luck, skill and good judgement to defeat these two men.

consequences

If the players manage to defeat the Grauschjager and save the lives of SSF staff, they will have made valuable allies in Longshore University. If the Grauschjager attack turns in to a massacre, then there is a good chance they will need to flee pretty quickly.

On the other hand, Trilhoeven and the Grauschjager will be rather annoyed if they kill two of their officers. Although they won't have concrete details on who the players are, they will have suspicions and could prove to be a very serious menace at some point in the future.

appendix: improvement point awards

GM's should award points for role-playing as they see fit, according to the guidelines given in 'The Players' chapter. Further specific IP awards can also be made if the characters have done particular things during the adventure (note: only characters who were directly involved in the events listed below can get the IP awards):

5IP: Reassuring Mrs Lupton and her family.

5IP: Visiting Mrs Lupton and family after solving case.

5IP: Freeing Foyle Langen from Inferno.

5IP: Uncovering Trilhoevens plan, thereby forcing them to stop.

10IP: Freeing the test subjects held at Longshore.

10IP: Helping the test subjects to get back to their previous lives.

adventure nuggets

cabaret of horror

Deep beneath the northern edge of Bankside, something rotten lurks. In vaulted chambers deep in the earth, in brick cells which have never seen the light of day, unspeakable acts are performed for titillation and pleasure. This is the Cabaret of Horror, a sinister, exclusive entertainment which preys on the weak, dissolute and vulnerable.

The Cabaret is, approximately, a form of entertainment. Through hidden underground passages, wealthy residents from Clearwater Break come to indulge their basest fantasies. A brick arena allows the viewing of staged fights between, men, women, children and animals, all kidnapped from various places around The City and forced to fight for their very lives. Sometimes displays of torture or surgery without anaesthetic are carried out for the delectation of the audience. In more secluded chambers, private showings and displays can be arranged, ranging from simple whippings and beatings to slayings and worse. None who are dragged kicking and screaming into the holding cells of the Cabaret ever see The City again. The corpses are used to feed the fighting dogs and other, less identifiable animals.

This entire sick enterprise is run by Natalie Heron, only scion of the wealthy and somewhat frivolous Heron family. The family made its money from ironworks in Burningfell but has, in recent decades, had more than its fair share of philanderers, dilettantes and gadabouts spring from the family tree. Natalie is the last of the line and is, in her own specific and very directed way, quite, quite mad. In fact, she is an extreme sociopath, appearing quite pleasant and normal on the surface but being a writhing cesspool of insanity underneath. She initially began the Cabaret as an entertainment for a select group of friends, hiring some cripplecut fighters from Bankside to provide a private show. The entire thing snowballed from there, eventually becoming what it is today: a sick, twisted, depraved form of theatre. Invitations to the Cabaret are issued strictly on the basis of a personal recommendation. Invitees can only access the chambers of the Cabaret through a mile long tunnel leading from the basement floors of the Heron residence in Clearwater Break. The tunnel is, of course, booby trapped and rigged with explosives, should the horrible activities of the Cabaret be uncovered.

The players could be dragged into the Cabaret in any number of ways. A few suggestions are given below.

1) They notice someone being mugged and dragged away in a dark alley one night. What strikes them as odd is that the muggers, although dressed in shabby street clothes, appear to use some form of hitech stun weapon, a bit strange for impoverished cut-throats. Following the muggers will lead to the old, collapsed Crayker Rendering Works at the very northern edge of Bankside. The works have been abandoned for decades, left to fester and collapse in the their own pools of toxic waste. Even hardened Banksiders don't dare to come here. The abandoned brick worksheds are filled with tangled iron girders which used to hold up the roof. Corroded vats leak varicoloured liquids and pools of strange hue lie everywhere. If they watch carefully, they'll see the muggers disappear into a massive section of rusting pipe. Concealed in the pipe is a trapdoor (a very well secured trapdoor) which leads, via ancient passages, sewers and pipes, to the holding cells of the Cabaret. See below for a description of the Cabaret chambers.

2) A friend, colleague, relative or some other individual goes missing and it's up to the brave, resourceful PCs to investigate. Obviously, whoever it is who has gone missing has been lifted by the Cabaret and it's only a matter of time before they are dead. Or worse. Interviewing people who may have witnessed the disappearance will garner the facts that it was two (or possibly three) men (or maybe women) who accosted the poor unfortunate. However, one vital piece of evidence comes to light, either by interviewing people or by investigating the site of the disappearance. One of Herons strong-arm men is getting cocky and has started leaving cards at the site of muggings. They are plain, off-white pasteboard with a stylised skull on them (see picture below). However, what the mugger has not noticed is that each and every card has the address of the printers who made the cards in tiny grey letters on the bottom right hand corner on the reverse of the card. The printers is a high-class establishment in Clearwater Break which mainly makes exclusive greetings and business cards for the well-heeled residents of that area. How the adventure progresses from here is up to the GM.

3) Perhaps the most horrific way to involve the players is to have they themselves kidnapped and used in the Cabaret. They stand a greater chance of survival than most of the people brought into this awful underworld, as most of the subjects are homeless, drug addled or insane. To escape will require cunning, foresight and a good deal of brute force, as the Cabaret employs a large number of well-trained and single mindedly brutal guards. Most of them work undercover as hose servants for Heron but one, going by the name of Keeler Voronetz, is an undercover Provost. He's spent the last two years infiltrating the Cabaret and will quickly catch on if

it looks like the PCs are going to blow the whole thing wide open. Voronetz has become slightly unhinged by his work and more than a little desensitised to degradation but still retains a strong sense of honour and decency (Voronetx can also feature in situations 1 and 2 above). Should the PCs make an escape attempt, Voronetz is likely to try and persuade them to hold everyone up while he goes and phones for more Provosts. How the players react and where things go from here is up to individual groups.

In most situations, there will be a final showdown between the players and Heron, who is quite, quite mad and has several well-armed and loyal guards to hand. If cornered, she will attempt to wheedle her way out of the situation, offering money, drugs, sex or whatever in exchange for her freedom. If Heron escapes their clutches, they PCs will have made a powerful and very insane enemy. If they assist in bringing down the cabaret, they will have gained a Minor Provost Contact in the shape of Voronetz. There is, however, the problem of prosecuting upwards of one hundred wealthy and influential people. In all likelihood, almost all of them will be fined and given a warning (if that), while if Heron is caught, she will be packed off to Inferno for the rest of her life if the Provosts check out the thousands of hours of films in her residence: Scenes of rape, torture, killing and brutality are captured on grainy colour films and these are enough to convince even the most over-awed magistrate to send her to the nuthouse.

The Cabaret Chambers: A series of dripping brick tunnels centred around a massive vaulted chamber where the main entertainment's take place. The main chamber is tiered and can seat approximately 100 people. The tiers look down onto a central pit where fights, displays and demonstrations take place. Radiating from the upper tiers is a series of five passages, each lined with iron doored cells, cells which contain a mind-boggling variety of surgical, torture and sexual equipment. It is in these private rooms that the paying guests can satisfy their innermost desires. Below these rooms are the holding cells: tiny, damp rooms lit by flickering bulbs. Here the people and animals used for display are held until they are required. The entirety of the Cabaret rooms stinks of damp and corruption, mingled with sweat, blood and fear.

disengage the simulator

Firefinger Software Development has some strange operating practices. Idiosyncrasies, if you will. Some view these practices as downright dangerous or irresponsible, Firefinger just views them as alternative means to an end. However, today things have gone all wrong. One of their many external consultants, a flowghost named Krystyna Lowell, has created something of a problem for them. Lowell was hired to test detailed simulations for Project Verge, a fairly lucrative contract from Gorunna. Lowell locked herself away in one of her safe houses and proceeded to simulate like a woman possessed. Sadly, a day ago, she suffered a massive stroke. She's now an unconscious, slavering husk who will die very shortly of dehydration. Ordinarily, this wouldn't be too much of a problem. The problem is the simulations for Project Verge. Verge is designed to swamp targets in the dataflow with masses of simulated comms traffic, overloading the receiving stations until they have to shut down. And it doesn't just do it through one channel, oh no. Every conceivable way in to the target is swamped. It even goes so far as to simulate telegrams and phone calls to courier companies who then dispatch couriers to the address of the target. The simulation was running against a department of Firefinger itself and was going fairly successfully until Lowell had her stroke and couldn't switch off the simulation. The entirety of Firefinger is now being swamped with dataflow traffic, phone calls, telegrams, couriers knocking at the door every minute, even by random people who have been contacted and told to turn up for job interviews!

Through contacts, friends or random circumstance (perhaps receiving a job offer via telegram?), the players are contracted by an increasingly desperate Firefinger to find out where the hell Lowell lives and disconnect the simulation from the Dataflow. And bring Lowell back to explain what in the name of goodness she thought she was doing.

Finding Lowells home can be as difficult or as easy as the GM wishes. Contacts in the flowghost community would be helpful, as would trawling the Dataflow for some sort of information. Lowell actually lives in Fogwarren, just round the corner from the Firefinger building, something which should irritate players no end. However, when conducting business, Lowell is somewhat paranoid. Her basement rooms are under a seedy, decrepit old towerblock. The block itself is ten storeys of cracked, damp concrete patched with bricks and lath. A few gas lights show in windows and ragged, dirty children scuttle through the corridors and halls, attempting to good-natured pickpocketing on the PCs. Lowell has, however, hired members of a local turfgang, The Y-Mob to provide a little extra 'security' while she remains locked in her room. The gang have been told not to disturb her and they've done exactly that. They've also been told not to let anyone into her rooms. And they're the kind of people who take such a job seriously, especially as Lowell has given them a substantial amount of money in order to keep nosy parkers out of her business. The PCs can deal with the gang however they wish, be it negotiation, violence or more subtle means. The GM should tailor the number of gang members to suit the number of PCs. All are armed with sparklock pistols or blunderbusses.

However they manage to gain entrance to Lowell's rooms, they will find her slumped in her chair in front of a stripped out cathode tube screen linked into a whirring, clicking assembly of three dingins. All are processing information at a furious rate. More technically astute characters will be able to find the thick copper cable which links the dingins to the Dataflow. Cutting this will sever the link and stop the assault on Firefinger. Needless to say, Firefinger will be extremely grateful for this. However, Lowell is little more than a vegetable and Firefinger will not really want anything to do with her, essentially leaving the characters to deal with the aftermath.

the sculptor

Dominic Cuthatch is a struggling, hard-up artist. That in itself is not unusual, most artists in The City are struggling and hard-up. Unfortunately for Cuthatch, things have recently got a lot worse. He was found a couple of days ago curled up in his sparse room, half dead through shock and blood loss and gibbering madly about nothing in particular. The blood loss stems from the fact that someone has lopped off his fingers. If that wasn't enough, his ruined hands were bound in musty, damp cloth and the resultant infection means he will be lucky if he only loses his hands as a result. Scattered around the floor were the smashed remains of his latest work, a bizarre constellation of intertwined iron circles.

Players can be involved with Cuthatch in whatever way the GM chooses. If they are less than concerned about his well being, have a patron of the arts express an interest in finding who committed this crime, with a possible pecuniary advantage to be gained by those who get to the bottom of the mysteries to be uncovered here.

1) Cuthatch was very heavily in debt to a local iron merchant by the name of Brownstaple. He'd taken delivery of a quantity of iron rods from Brownstaple in order to begin his latest project, not realising that Brownstaple expected to be paid pretty damn quickly. Because of Cuthatches unbalanced mental state (see below for reasons), the normal variety of threats failed to have any effect, so Brownstaple sent round some of his 'boys' to give the hapless sculptor a 'bit of a going over'. Sadly for all concerned, they went a bit far and decided to teach the artist a lesson he wouldn't forget. Being a bunch of sadistic sods, Brownstaples men chopped his fingers off, their low IQ not allowing them to realise that by doing this they were preventing any chance of their boss ever getting paid.

2) Cuthatch has been teetering on the edge of madness for quite some time. Now, this isn't an unusual state of affairs for an artist, indeed many consider it part of their idiom to be slightly eccentric. However, Cuthatch was being driven deliberately and slowly insane by the attentions of a Lugner that has decided to derive some 'pleasure' (who really knows with The Shifted?) from whispering dark thoughts into Cuthatchs ear and lingering in the corners of his vision. The Lugner will continue to visit Cuthatch, driving him further into the abyss. If the PCs have made contacts in the Longshore University Shift Studies Faculty (see 'The Prescription' introductory adventure), this might be a good opportunity to give them a call and see exactly how far their goodwill extends.

Whatever happens, Cuthatch has been hopelessly unhinged by his experiences and has been left as little more than a burnt out shell of a man. How the players choose to treat him is a moral and ethical question that only they can answer.

you might go to the ball

"This is John Proudfoot reporting for Sideband Media outside the first Folly Hills charity ball. This major new event is the brain child of one of the local provosts, Derek Mikelson, who has used his connections within Trilhoeven and Arclight, to persuade the macrocorps into investing in the area. No one knows why the macrocorps have decided to invest in this area, but it seems that they have put aside some of their differences for one night of fun and frivolity in the upper Folly Hills area. A gigantic warehouse has been converted over the last few months, to hold this ball, and I have to say it is one of the most impressive buildings I have seen outside the domains of the macrocorps. Several hundred children, all related to the macrocorps in some way, will flock here to dance the night away, while the officers of the TMCA and the macrocorps own personal guard watch over them, with their customary enthusiasm for their job. From my vantage point, I can see Derek Mikelson waiting to...."

(sound of explosion in the distance)

"My god, what the hell was that?"

"John this is Katherine at the studio, is everything OK, what just happened, we saw the plume of flame from here"

"I'm OK Katherine, we'll have to disconnect our hardline for a few minutes as we move to the scene of the explosion."

(several minutes of desperate filling in and summarisation by the studios team before the feed from the field team comes back on line)

"We have arrived at the scene, it looks as if the front security car was hit from below and is now on its roof, there are several dead bodies nearby, some security guards, some people, possibly gangers, are lying dead along the sides of the street, there is blood and metal everywhere. It looks like the macrocorp transports were trapped by an explosion to the rear, and front of the caravan, and the aerostats that were above were simultaneously shot down. "

"What has happened to the children, are they dead?"

"No, there is no sign of the children, it looks as though this was a kidnapping attempt, though who would carry out such a scheme is as yet unidentified. One thing is sure this was a very professional job, achieved with great timing and precision. The security teams from the macrocorps have just arrived in aerostats, and are cordoning of the area, I'll get back to you as soon as I can. This is John Proudfoot for Sideband media."

There are many people who would like to get their hands on a bargaining chip as big as the children of the macrocorps. These are the nearest and dearest of some very powerful individuals, even though most of them are spoiled little brats, but there are the few amongst them that do give a fuck about what is happening in The City and are genuinely decent people in their own right. It is these very people that the macrocorps value most highly: their public face is good, while their minds are ruthless.

So who would have the audacity to kidnap the children, on the eve of a new era of investment for Folly Hills?.

It this scenario, PC's can be locals charged with finding the kids, gang members who have been involved in the kidnapping, security forces trying to find the children, or maybe even the children themselves.

1) It is just one of the local gangs out to make some serious money. Maybe it is the Third Syndicate, or maybe a conglomeration of the local gangs who saw an opportunity, took it but will now have no idea what to do.

2) The Mayor has set the whole thing up in order to capture the macrocorp kids in order to bargain with them and get investment for the Folly Hills region, better waterways etc. He could have either hired the local gangs to do this or used some off-duty Provosts as a handy source of muscle. The PCs could discover the conspiracy slowly, but may decide to help him if they are from the Folly Hills area and think the area should be regenerated.

3) One of the security chiefs got fed up carting arrogant little bastards around all the time, and decided to teach them a brief lesson about real life. He arranged the attack, either using his own men, or one of the local gangs, got the kids to dress up in rags and set them on their way down the boulevards and alleys of Folly Hills. They will be harder to find this way, and the PCs could stumble across one in order to get clues to the others.

4) The macrocorps have decided to get rid of their unwanted and squabbling offspring all at once. They couldn't quite go as

far as killing them directly so have merely discarded them in Folly Hills. Maybe the PCs come across one of these children and sympathise with their sob story, or maybe they are the children themselves suddenly ejected into a cold and hard world.

something fishy in the air

Fish farm owners in Bankside are being killed. And nobody has a clue who or what is doing it. Over the past few weeks, several prominent fish breeders have been found dead, killed in a variety of unsavoury ways. One was injected with home-brewed parasite repellent, one was fed through a fish food mincer and another was found suspended headfirst in a breeding tank, his face nibbled away by his own fish. Needless to say, even in the hardened, violent confines of Bankside, crimes like this are not exactly going unnoticed. The residents are getting restless, as this is something which strikes at the very heart of the way of life. The perpetrators of these crimes must be found and brought to justice. The killings are, in fact, part of a rather dubious and secretive TCMAA scheme to gradually bring Bankside to it's knees and bring it back into the fold. The killings are being carried out by a three person team made up of former Provosts. Their plan is to make the Banksiders believe that it is all internal, that one fish farmer is trying to wipe out the opposition. The TCMAA hopes to create such an atmosphere of paranoia a mistrust that Bankside will literally tear itself apart, thereby leaving the way open for the Provosts to march in and take control.

guns in the sky

A ripple of excitement is running through the scavengers who infest the peripheries of the Contested Grounds. Rumour has it that Arclight troops have very recently shot down a large Hirplakker Aerial Gun Platform. Even more exciting is the part of the rumour that states the Arclight troops were all killed when the AGP crashed. The race is on to find the AGP and strip as much as possible from it before Hirplakker get to it to claim what is rightfully theirs. The scuttlebutt seems to indicate that the crashed craft is located somewhere in the western end of the 'Grounds and large numbers of scavengers are loading up and heading out in that direction.

The rumour is true, an AGP has been shot down over the western end of the 'Grounds. However, in crashing, the aircraft has punched into the ground and cracked open ancient toxic waste tanks. The waste is already beginning to well up out of the ground, forming a shallow lake around the craft. Worse still, several injured members of the crew are still trapped inside. Hirplakker would no doubt be very grateful for the safe return of a highly skilled gun platform crew. Aside from this, parts stripped from the platform could prove to be very lucrative on the black market.

a grand day out

It's that time of year again, when the Grand Canal 2000 ekranoplan race takes place, to the delight of thousands of citizens. Unfortunately for the characters, their usual favourite viewing spot has been cordoned off by the Provosts and reserved for the use of invited guests only. Not only that, but they need to meet a contact inside the cordoned off area to get some money that she owes them in order to pay off another debt to some rather serious 3rd Syndicate hoods. There are several options for trying to get in: through the sewers and cellars, over the roofs via walkways and ziplines or simply trying to blag their way through the cordon. The race starts in forty five minutes, their contact is getting impatient and the 3rd Syndicate are sharpening their knives. Better think of a plan!.

stuck in a hole

Markus Gregor is a man on the way to the top. As one of the rising stars within Arclight, he's a man with a future. Unfortunately, that future could be very short if he doesn't watch out. After an assignation with a young lady of negotiable affection, his chauffeur failed to pick him up in his personal aerostat. Oh dear. But, being a young man of wit and ingenuity, he decides to make his way back to Luminosity Tower on his own. Attempting to dodge the fare on a train, he has been chased by the Transit Militia and has ended up in Bankside. Arse! At night. Desperately jamming cash into a public phone, he screams that he is in mortal danger (which is quite correct) and demands an assault team be sent to get him out. Because of the poor quality of the line, things get a bit garbled and the Brigade of Light over react. A little. Well, quite a lot actually. An aerostat is on it's way with a platoon of armoured Tentenel troopers, supported by a couple of gunships.

The characters could either be part of the Arclight rescue force or residents of Bankside who have found Gregor and figured that he could be worth a lot of money. The Tentenel troopers are amongst the best equipped warriors in The City, but are they ready for Bankside? And is Bankside ready for them? Let the showdown commence.

Most of the information contained within this timeline is not known to the bulk of the population in The City. Most people have a hazy (at best) knowledge of history and are more concerned with where the next meal is coming from than pondering the mysteries of the past. The only way for players to find out this information is to trawl through the archives of such places as Longshore University or the Cathedral or, if they wish, trawl the dataflow for years on end to dredge up snippets of information.

-999

The Shift and The Bombardment

-999 to -900

The Wasted Years. The first rumours of Shifted beings begin to circulate.

-950 to -940

Most of the macrocorps are assumed to have been founded at some period during this decade.

-940 to -600

The Rebuilding Time. Under the influence of the macrocorps, The City undergoes something of a revitalisation. The macrocorps allow the common populace access to very low levels of technology in return for their labour and loyalty. This represents the beginnings of the domination of the macrocorps. It is during this time that the appearance of the Simils is noted.

-650

First appearance of the sect which would eventually become the Mortal God Church.

-500

The Third Church of God the Architect grows out of the warfare between the First and Second Churches, both of which have radically different views on the nature of God, The City and the ultimate fate of man.

-350

Founding of Longshore University as a bastion of knowledge and learning.

-300 to -290

The Ancient and Honourable Guild of Fulgurators begins the construction of what would eventually become Dreamingspires. The massive cost of the project brings about the downfall of the original guild and creates the guild as it is recognised today. For fifty years after this time, the railway system falls into disuse and disrepair.

-284

Scientists at Longshore University confirm the existence of the Lost Places through trial, error and at times totally random and bizarre experimentation.

-270

With the railways no longer operable to any great degree, small transport companies and barge owners band together to form the Water Trade Guild. There follows an intense period of low level war between the guild and the macrocorps, who see the organisation as a major threat to their dominance over trade and the distribution of resources within The City.

-240

The revitalised Fulgurators Guild begins to rejuvenate the railways, challenging the might of the Water Trade Guild.

-235

Under pressure from the Fulgurators and the macrocorps, the Water Trade Guild finally collapses into tens of squabbling factions. Over the next few years, their influence dies away altogether as they succumb to factional infighting and internecine conflict.

-200

The Wasser Strasse Schism within the Mortal God Church. This splits the church into four groups, each claiming to be the arbiters of true faith.

-160

A number of local councils in the area of the Grand Canal unify to form the basis of the Three Canals Metropolitan Area Authority.

-130

The TCMAA formally adopts its current name and begins a five-decade period of expansion throughout the burghs bordering the Grand Canal.

-125

The TCMAA creates The Provosts as its police and security service.

-100

Appearance in Shore Ditch Warrens of the Shining Sky religion.

-80

Founding of Arclight as a small manufacturing company which grows over the decades into a sizeable economic entity.

-63

Macrocorporate, religious groups, business interests and civil authorities form The Council in an attempt to exert some control over the chaos of The City. It is regarded a failure almost from day one.

-20

Councillor Rhilfele takes control of The Council, a position he holds until the present day.

-3

The Hundred Block War between Hirplakker and a strong, emergent Arclight.

-2

The Hundred Block War ends, but a formal peace agreement is never signed between Hirplakker and Arclight. The war continues in the Contested Grounds.

0

The present.

3rd Syndicate, the
Largest, most powerful and influential criminal organisation in The City.

Ack-ack
Soldiers term for anti-aircraft fire.

Ack-am
Soldiers term for anti-armour fire.

Aerial Gun Platform
A heavily armed and armoured aerostat, generally used as an airborne artillery platform.

Aerostat
Originally, an aerostat referred to an object (normally some sort of balloon or fan powered observation platform) which remained static in the air above a point on the ground. It is now a general term which refers to the many disk or oval shaped VTOL platforms used in The City.

Appfel Plants
Common fruit bearing plants.

Arclight
One of the eight macrocorps. Specialises in very high technology items, including communications and laser systems.

Bleeders
Endemic, blood-sucking insects, feared for carrying disease and parasites.

Bombardment, the
Devastating event which stuck The City shortly after The Shift. Fire rained from the sky and large tracts of The City were devastated.

Brigade of Light, the
Military arm of Arclight.

Broken
A dialect of common, very compressed and difficult to understand.

Burgh
Any area of The City with a defined boundary and (generally) some sort of controlling authority (civil, military, economic, criminal or otherwise).

Cant
A dialect of culture, the official language of the Third Church of God The Architect.

CATCH Team
Heavily armed and armoured members of the elites Assault Division of the TCMAA Provosts.

Cathedral, the
Home of the Sideband Media macrocorp.

Commerce
One of the three main language groups of The City. Commerce is the language of trade and industry.

Common
One of the three main language groups of The City and the most commonly spoken tongue. Almost everyone in The City can speak common to a greater or lesser extent.

Community Service Board, the
Part of the Three Canals Metropolitan Area Authority. Deals with such things as tax, employment and social services.

Council, the
City-wide group made up of representatives from most major interest groups. Nominally in charge of lawmaking and suchlike within The City. In reality, it is little more than a glorified talking shop.

Cripplecut
A popular underground spectator sport, where armed participants attempt to cripple but not kill their opponent.

Crypt, the
A quasi-mythical organisation, reputed to covertly run everything in The City.

Culture
One of the three main language groups of The City. Culture is the language of art and high-society.

Dataflow
The computer and communications network which spreads through the entire city.

Daylight
Sinister and violent organised crime group.

Dingin

A mechanical computer. Can be macroscale (large, visible components), microscale (components can be seen with a powerful magnifying glass) or nanoscale (components can only be seen through the most powerful microscopes).

Dinginsmith

Someone who manufactures dingins.

Dirigible

A powered airship, usually made up of a gas bag (either rigid or soft) and a gondola slung beneath. Lifting power is provided by hydrogen gas and motive power by engines of varying types.

Dollymop

A prostitute, generally of the female variety.

Drache

Mysterious, ethereal Shifted beings who can manipulate electrical fields.

Edge

Drug. Heightens perception and increases creative ability.

Escape

Drug. Has hallucinogenic properties.

Ekranoplan

A ground effect plane which 'flies' 2 to 5 metres above the surface of a canal. Popular racing vehicles.

Electrospeak

The internal language of the Ancient and Honourable Guild of Fulgurators.

External Order Cadre, the

External security force of Gorunna Logistics macrocorp.

EyEwiRE Corps

The military arm of the GRID macrocorp.

Fighting Talk

A dialect of commerce, spoken very fast and favoured by those who earned their living through combat.

Flowghost

A data-retrieval and cryptological specialist who trawls the Dataflow for information.

Forbidden City, the

Home of the Nakamura-Yebisu macrocorp.

Fulgurator

A member of the Ancient & Honourable Guild of Fulgurators, a group who maintain decaying power networks and railway systems throughout The City.

Furies

Deformed, mutated, insane creatures that live under The City. They are not a single breed, but are a variety of creatures lumped into the one group.

Gadgie

A person (as in "That gadgie over there.")

Ghostfighter

Stealthy knife fighters, found to be popular as bodyguards.

Gorunna Logistics

One of the eight macrocorps.

Grauschjager, the

The secret police, internal security agency, intelligence gather arm and covert operations force operated by the Trilhoeven macrcorp.

Great Demolisher, the

Main demon-figure in the pantheon of the Third Church of God The Architect.

GRID

One of the eight macrocorps. GRID are primarily concerned with power production.

Gunskiff

Any small, flat-bottomed boat with mounted weapons.

Hager

Tall, pale, faceless Shifted beings.

Hirplakker

One of the eight macrocorps.

Hohler Gang, the

Second largest organised crim group in The City. Fierce rivals of the 3rd Syndicate.

Hundred Block War
Conflict between Hirplakker and Arclight, during which Arclight asserted its status as a macrocorp and subjected Hirplakker to a humiliating defeat.

Huyzel Vine
Tough plant which grows almost anywhere.

I-LOK
One of the eight macrocorps.

Internal Order Cadre, the
The internal security force of the Gorunna Logistics macrocorp.

Konkret
Home of the Trilhoeven macrocorp.

Iron Bastion, the
Home of the Hirplakker macrocorp.

Lay Reserves Martial
Military arm of the Third Church of God The Architect.

Lithograph
A primitive photograph.

Llive
Common name for knives and short swords made out of laminated layers of steel and diamond sheet. Very, very sharp.

Lostfinder
Community-based private investigator who works not for money, but for the goodwill and assistance of the people.

Lugner
A shifted being.

Luminosity Tower
Home of the Arclight macrocorp.

Macrocorps
A group of eight mercantile organisations who are in almost complete control of all resources within The City.

Magnetic Repeater
Hitech projectile weapon which uses stepped magnets to accelerate iron flechettes to very high velocities.

Media Break
The security arm of the Sideband Media macrocorp.

Menace
Dialect of common, full of hissing and low tones.

Mikefighter
Tiny, one-man aircraft used for combat in the skies above The City.

Minger
An unpleasant or ugly person.

Mortal God Church, the
Religion. Believes that God has died (for a variety of reasons).

Nakamura-Yebisu
One of the eight macrocorps.

Nebelweed
Common plant which can be dried and smoked, producing a mildly narcotic effect.

Outlands, the
Anywhere outside the limits of The City. Those within The City are prevented from reached the Outlands by unknown forces.

Parish
Any area of The City controlled by a religious group or the area that an individual priest, propagator or other religious figure is responsible for.

Portreeves, the
Porters and security guards who work ar Longshore University.

Powerbike
Any powered, two wheeled vehicle. Most often the toys of the rich.

Powerhouse, the
Home of the GRID macrocorp.

Provost
A member of the police force of the Three Canals Metropolitan Area.

Radstrip
Industrial area owned by Gorunna Logistics.

RCCR
The Red Canal Collectivist Republic, a group of burghs on the east bank of the Red canal controlled by a local government subscribing to the political ideology of collectivism.

Scrape

Drug. Invariable lethal narcotic with horrible side-effects.

Scurts

Endemic, six-legged vermin.

Shift, the

Event which occurred nearly one thousand years ago, cutting The City off from everywhere else and giving rise to The Shifted.

Shifted, the

Beings which rose out of the chaos of The Shift. Scientists are unsure of their exact origins; folk tales and speculation abound.

Shining Sky, the

Religious organisation that believes The City is an experiment in a crystal bubble, watched over by sinister Observers.

Simils

Humanoid Shifted creatures made of black iron, brass and glass. They are surmounted by a human head, twisted in untold agonies.

Skiff

A small, flat bottomed canal boat.

Skinners

Those who live on the outer 'skin' of Project 97, nearest to the light and air of the outside world.

Sparklock

A common, primitive muzzle-loading firearm using capacitors or superconductors scavenged from hitech sources or painstakingly built clockwork mechanisms to electrically ignite a charge of propellant.

Streethealer

Wandering doctors and apothecaries who tend the sick and injured.

Stringer

A gutter journalist, working freelance or for a variety of newspapers, publishers or even for Sideband Media.

Swedge

To hit someone (as in "I gave him a right good swedge!"), or the fight itself ("He's a mean guy in a swedge!").

TCMA

The Three Canals Metropolitan Area, a large aglomeration of burghs clustered between the Red and Green canals.

TCMAA

The Three Canals Metropolitan Area Authority, the local government which controls the TCMA.

Tentenel Armour

Powered armour used by Arclight's military arm, the Brigade of Light.

Third Church of God The Architect, the

Religious organisation. Believes The City is a testing ground for the souls of the faithful before they ascend into His Heavenly City.

Transit Militia

Paramilitary arm of the Ancient and Honourable Guild of Fulgurators. Responsible for policing on the railways.

Trenevier

Home of the Gorunna Logistics macrocorp.

Trilhoeven

One of the eight macrocorps. The premier manufacturer of armaments in The City.

Troot

Most common vegetable in The City.

Tyrants

Legendary, quasi-mythical creatures said to live deep under The City.

Ubel

Dangerous and deadly Shifted creatures, the psychopaths of the Shifted world. They walk creaking through The City on bones of wood, dragging rags behind them.

Warcrawl

A heavy armoured fighting vehicle, usually running on caterpillar tracks.

Weapons Division, the

Military arm of Nakamura-Yebisu.

Zipline

A cable or rope slung between buildings, over canals and suchlike. Used to go from place to place at speed by sliding down the cable using a length of dogskin or hoop of metal slung across the cable.

skill modifiers

Difficulty	Modifier
Absurdly Easy	+80
Very Easy	+60
Easy	+50
Simple	+40
Routine	+30
Complicated	+10
Challenging	0
Difficult	-10
Very Difficult	-30
Extremely Difficult	-50
Formidable	-70
Impossible	-90

melee combat area to-hit modifiers

Area	Penalty
Head	-20
Chest	-10
Abdomen	-10
Arm	-15
Upper Leg	-10
Lower Leg	-15

fire combat range modifier

Range	Penalty
Close	00%
Medium	-20%
Long	-50%
Extreme	-80%

fire combat situational modifiers

Situation	Modifier
Walking	-10
Jogging	-20
Running	-30
Sprinting	-40
Poor Light	-10
Bad Light	-30
Near Dark	-70
Mist	-20
Fog/Smog	-40
Light Rain	-10
Heavy Rain	-30
Poor Footing	-10
Restricted Movement	-10
Aiming (1 second)	+10
Aiming (2 seconds)	+20
Aiming (4 seconds)	+30
Aiming (8 seconds)	+40
Laser Targeting	+20

fire combat called shot modifiers

Area	Penalty
Head	-40
Chest	-20
Abdomen	-20
Arm	-30
Upper Leg	-20
Lower Leg	-30

sample armour values

Cover Type	AV
Brick Wall	10
Plasterboard Wall	03
Reinforced Concrete	40
Table	02
Wooden Door	03

hit location table

D10 Role	Location
1	Head
2,3	Chest
4	Abdomen
5	Right Arm
6	Left Arm
7	Upper Right Leg
8	Upper Left Leg
9	Lower Right Leg
10	Lower Left Leg

damage table

	Light	Moderate	Serious
Head	1S	4S	Dead
Chest	2S	4S	Dead
Abdomen	1S	2S	4S
Upper Leg	1S	2S	3S
Lower Leg	Bleeding	1S	2S
Arm	Bleeding	1S	2S

first aid situational modifiers

Situation	Modifier
Light Wound	+0%
Moderate Wound	-20%
Serious Wound	-40%
Using Extemporised Materials	-20%
Working Under Poor Conditions (e.g.: in a rain-soaked alley)	-20%
Working Under Terrible Conditions (e.g.: in a combat zone with mortar shells falling all around)	-40%

shock point accumulation

Most Severe Wound Is	Additional Shock Points
Light	+1 per hour
Moderate	+1 per 30 mins
Serious	+1 per 10 mins

recovery from injuries modifiers/effects of care

Level Of Care	Mod	Recovery
Intensive hospital care	+20%	1 shock point regained per day
Hospital care	+0%	1 shock point regained per 2 days
In-home care	-20%	1 shock point regained per 4 days

falling damage

Height	Damage Value
0 - 2m	06
3 - 4m	10
5 - 7m	14
8 - 10m	18
10m+	20

vehicle maneuver stat modifiers

MAN	Modifier
1	-40
2	-30
3	-20
4	-10
5	+0
6	+10
7	+20
8	+30
9	+40
10	+50

vehicle maneuver task modifiers

Task	Modifier
Drive/pilot in a straight line	0
Shallow turn	-10
Medium turn	-20
Sharp turn	-40
Gentle weaving	-20
Violent dodging	-50
Sharp braking	-30
Bootlegger turn (ground vehicles only)	-60
Power dive (aircraft only)	-40

vehicle fire combat range modifiers

Range	Modifier
Close	00%
Medium	-20%
Long	-50%
Extreme	-80%

vehicle hit location table

D10	Location
1	Superstructure
2	Superstructure
3	Powerplant
4	Powerplant
5	Drivetrain
6	Controls
7	Sensors
8	Weapons
9	Passengers
10	Crew

	Light	Medium	Heavy
Controls	MAN reduced by 2 levels.	MAN reduced by 5 levels.	Vehicle is uncontrollable.
Crew	1 crew member takes hit at 50% of penetrating damage.	All crew take hit at 50% of penetrating damage.	Crew killed.
Passengers	1 passenger takes hit at 50% of penetrating damage.	All passengers take hits at 50% of penetrating damage.	Passengers killed.
Weapons	1 weapon out of action. Repairable.	1 weapon destroyed.	All weapons destroyed.
Superstructure	Holes in superstructure, minor damage, RES reduced by 10% (round up)	Noticeable damage to superstructure, RES reduced by 30%.	Catastrophic damage.
Powerplant	ACC and SPD reduced by 25%	ACC and SPD reduced by 50%.	Catastrophic damage.
Drivetrain	ACC, DEC and SPD reduced by 25%	ACC, DEC and SPD reduced by 50%.	Destroyed.
Sensors	1 sensor put out of action. Repairable.	1 sensor destroyed.	All sensors destroyed.

Catastrophic damage: The vehicle is totally destroyed. All passengers and crew take damage equivalent 50% of that which penetrated the vehicle.

Destroyed: The component in question is rendered useless and unrepairable.

character sheet

name :	height :
occupation :	weight :
origin :	eye colour :
upbringing :	hair colour :
age :	complexion :

attributes | level

agility :
dexterity :
health :
strength :

awareness :
intelligence :
personality :
willpower :

skills | mod | level

advantages | level

disadvantages | level

location | injury

head	(1)
chest	(2,3)
abdomen	(4)
r. arm	(5)
l. arm	(6)
upper r. leg	(7)
upper l. leg	(8)
lower r. leg	(9)
lower l. leg	(10)

Character Sheet

Derived Attributes

reaction :
encumbrance :
resiliance :
punch damage :
kick damage :

Physical Appearance

Character Background

Character History

Possessions

	Weight

Possessions

	Weight

Projectile Weapons

weapon	dam	pen	rng	rof	rem	clp

Melee Weapons

weapon	dam	pen	rch	rem

forthcoming supplements for a/state

The Lostfinders Guide To Mire End

First in a series of profiles of individual areas of The City, this guide looks at the downtrodden, bedraggled burgh of Mire End. Featuring new locations, NPCs, maps, adventures and artwork, The Lostfinders Guide To Mire End will be an invaluable guide for players and GMs looking to further explore the mysteries of Mire End. 32 pages.

Avenues & Alleyways

The first full-length supplement for a/state, Avenues & Alleyways details new burghs, parishes, significant locations and notable buildings. From the claustrophobic confines of Crouch Lanes to the black horror of Soulsgate Debtors Prison, from the chaos of Dark Cross Railway Yards to the sinister silence of Lunatic Bend, Avenues & Alleyways allows GMs and players to explore new, vibrant and at times horrifying areas of The City. 96 pages.

Captive Market

The macrocorps dominate life in The City. But what is it like to work for them? How do they operate? How do they view each other? And, what exactly do they do? Captive Market offers an insight into the world of the macrocorps, expanding on and enriching the information given in the main a/state book. 96 pages.

The Lostfinders Guide To The TCMAA

Largest, most fiendishly bureaucratic and unfathomably complex of the local governments in The City, the Three Canals Metropolitan Area Authority controls the lives of hundred of thousands of citizens, from the slum-dwelling unfortunates of Folly Hills, to the high-living nomenklatura of Lucent Heights. Take a walk down the corridors of power, a stroll through previously unseen boulevards and witness the machinery of government at work. 64 pages.

The Once Before

There was a time before, a time before the legends of The Shift and The Bombardment. These are nothing but myths and folklore, old wives tales whispered to wide-eyed children. Tales occasionally surface, only to be buried beneath layers of confusion, fear and apathy. Some tales, however, refuse to die. The Once Before is a major campaign pack for a/state, taking players into the heart of the mystery, fear and horror of The City. 96 pages.

Other future supplements

The Lostfinders Guide To Bankside

The Lostfinders Guide To Clearwater Break

Fallen By (adventure pack)

The Insiders Guide To The Red Canal Collectivist Republic

The Lostfinders Guide to Mire End

The first supplement for **a/state**, 'The Lostfinders Guide To Mire End' delves into the sodden, degraded burgh of Mire End and comes up with choice nuggets of information about this most despised of places.

New locations, NPCs, organisations and adventure possibilities unfold in this 32 page guide. Trawl through the pawnshop of Emmanuel Detseted, recoil from the barrios of Redberry Park or wonder at the child-like violence of Wastrels Lot.

'The Lostfinders Guide To Mire End' is the first in a series of 'Lostfinders Guides', each focusing on a specific area of The City.

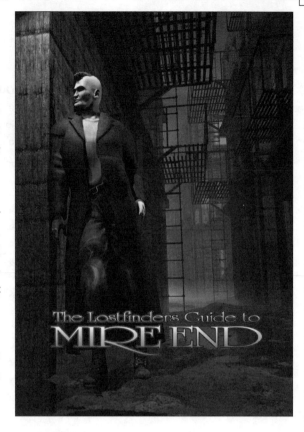

The Lostfinders Guide to
MIRE END

Avenues & Alleyways

With 30 new city areas, background essays on health, education and whole host of other topics, 'Avenues & Alleyways' opens up whole new regions of The City for adventure and exploration.

From the downtrodden miners of Sullen Cut to the frenetic free market of Ringtown, from the glittering opulence of The Grand Emporium to the looming horror of Soulsgate Debtors Prison, 'Avenues & Alleyways' details more of the highs and lows of city life.